SIGNPOST

Selected Premier Hotels in Great Britain & Ireland

2007

ii

Get up to 10% off your bill at many of the 230+ top class hotels in this book. Simply present the card to receive your discount or room upgrade. See inside back cover for full details.

SIGNPOST
ADVANTAGE CARD
2007
EDITION

1. CITY OF DUNDEE
2. CLACKMANNANSHIRE
3. FALKIRK
4. EAST DUNBARTONSHIRE
5. WEST DUNBARTONSHIRE
6. INVERCLYDE
7. RENFREWSHIRE
8. CITY OF GLASGOW
9. NORTH LANARKSHIRE
10. WEST LOTHIAN
11. CITY OF EDINBURGH
12. MIDLOTHIAN
13. EAST RENFREWSHIRE
14. NORTH TYNESIDE
15. NEWCASTLE UPON TYNE
16. GATESHEAD
17. SOUTH TYNESIDE
18. SUNDERLAND
19. DARLINGTON
20. STOCKTON-ON-TEES
21. MIDDLESBROUGH
22. HARTLEPOOL
23. REDCAR & CLEVELAND
24. BRADFORD
25. CALDERDALE
26. KIRKLEES
27. WAKEFIELD
28. BARNSLEY
29. SHEFFIELD
30. ROTHERHAM
31. DONCASTER
32. CITY OF KINGSTON UPON HULL
33. NORTH LINCOLNSHIRE
34. NORTH EAST LINCOLNSHIRE
35. CONWY
36. DENBIGHSHIRE
37. FLINTSHIRE
38. WREXHAM
39. CITY OF STOKE-ON-TRENT
40. CITY OF DERBY
41. CITY OF NOTTINGHAM
42. TELFORD & WREKIN
43. CITY OF LEICESTER
44. CITY OF PETERBOROUGH
45. LUTON
46. SWANSEA
47. NEATH & PORT TALBOT
48. RHONDDA CYNON TAFF
49. MERTHYR TYDFIL
50. BLAENAU GWENT
51. TORFAEN
52. MONMOUTHSHIRE
53. VALE OF GLAMORGAN
54. CARDIFF
55. CAERPHILLY
56. NEWPORT
57. NORTH SOMERSET
58. CITY OF BRISTOL
59. SOUTH GLOUCESTERSHIRE
60. BATH & NORTH EAST SOMERSET
61. SWINDON
62. READING
63. WOKINGHAM
64. BRACKNELL FOREST
65. WINDSOR & MAIDENHEAD
66. SLOUGH
67. THURROCK
68. SOUTHEND-ON-SEA
69. MEDWAY
70. CITY OF PLYMOUTH
71. TORBAY
72. POOLE
73. BOURNEMOUTH
74. CITY OF SOUTHAMPTON
75. CITY OF PORTSMOUTH
76. CITY OF BRIGHTON & HOVE

Internet

Reservations and enquiries can be made directly via our INTERNET site on **http://www.signpost.co.uk.** Watch this site also for special offers from individual hotels throughout the year.

Contents

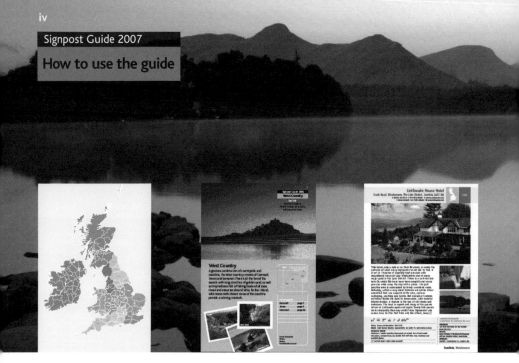

CHOOSE A REGION

There is a map of the regions at the beginning of the guide. If you want to look up the hotels in a particular region, simply turn to the relevant regional colour-coded section.

Alternatively, turn to the colour maps starting on page 303. The numbers on the maps refer to the pages in this guide on which **Signpost** approved hotels are described.

FACT FILE

Each regional section is prefaced by an illustrated guide to places of interest, walks, historic houses, museums and local entertainment venues. All designed to give you a feel for the area.

SIGNPOST member hotels make an annual contribution towards the costs of our inspections and a range of member services we provide.

SELECT A HOTEL

The hotel entries for each region follow and all hotels have a page to themselves. There are colour photographs of each hotel and a description of its situation, local attractions and general ambience to give you an idea of its character.
This is followed by a list of the hotel's facilities, number of bedrooms, dining options, leisure/sporting opportunities and opening times.

Rates Room and Breakfast £99–£135
Meals Light lounge lunches, Special diets, no under 7s.
Romantic breaks
Minimum 2 nights including champagne on arrival, bo...

Check the room rates
Room rates are clearly shown as well as details of any special offers for weekend breaks etc.

light weekday lunches
able. My room was spa
benign ghost who is re
well situated for wedd
the AA has nominated

🛏 14 (inc 1 ♿) ✂ ♋ 1...

Rates Single room with br
Meals Tdh dinner £26 (3-c
orders 2100.
Leisure Breaks Two-day br
Awards AA ★★★ ◎ 79%.
Other activities Fishing w

HOTEL FACILITIES

Unless stated otherwise
ALL Signpost hotels have:

- **direct dial telephones**
- **colour TV**
- **tea/coffee making**
- **en-suite bathrooms**
- **hairdryers**
- **laundry service**

SYMBOLS are printed >
where there are other
unique facilities at hotels.

Whenever **golf, fishing,
shooting** or **riding** symbols
are used, these can be
arranged **near** to the hotel.
When they are not adjacent
to, or part of a hotel's
grounds, details are shown
under 'OTHER FACILITIES.'

Key to symbols

Ad	Advantage Card accepted
◎	archery
➙	baby listening service
⍉	badminton court
⚓	beach
//	beauty salon
⚐	billiards/snooker
⚑	birdwatching
⚓	boating
•○	boules, pétanque
❀	civil wedding licence
⚠	childrens play area
❧	children welcome
🧗	climbing
⋮⋮⋮	conferences/meeting rms (no
⚖	croquet
♿	disabled rooms available
⚏	family room
⊙	fax/modem points
✎	fishing
⚐	fitness centre/gym
▥	four poster
✿	gardens
⚑/⚑	golf course
⛬	helicopter landing pad
●	indoor games room
⚑	indoor swimming pool
⚏	jacuzzi
⊡	lift
⊟	minibar
✂	non-smoker rooms avail.
⚘	outdoor swimming pool
P	parking (no)
♋	parkland setting
🐾	pets welcome (+ fee)
✕	pets not allowed
⚏	private cinema
⚑	putting green/pitch n putt
U	riding
⚑	running track
⚑	safety deposit box
⚓	sailing
⚑	sauna
⚑	shooting
⚑	shower only
⚑	solarium
⚑	squash
⚑	stalking
⚏	stately home/hotel
⚑	tennis
⚑	24-hr room service
⚑	walks
⚑	waterski-ing
⚑	watersports

How to book a hotel

By phone or fax

You can book your hotel
by phoning the number
given in the guide or
alternatively you could
fax a reservation request.

Internet

Reservations and enquiries
can be made directly via
our INTERNET site on :

www.signpost.co.uk

Watch this site also
for special offers from
individual hotels
throughout the year.

SIGNPOST
ADVANTAGE CARD
2007
EDITION

Get up to 10% off your
bill at many of the 230+
top class hotels in this
book. Simply present
the card to receive your
discount or room upgrade
See inside back cover for
full details.

SIGNPOST 2007

Signpost is the oldest established colour accommodation guide - now in its 68th year of publication!

Carrying on the work of the original founders, our inspectors check hotels every year personally, trying to stay or eat at each one to make sure that the highest standards are maintained and that the Signpost criteria continue to be met:

**individual style,
good value, friendly service
and a personal welcome**

We are looking for fine cuisine, using the best fresh produce. Bedrooms should be furnished with style and have all the comforts you need away from home. The hotel should be located in an interesting area, with plenty of opportunity for sport and leisure.

Above all hotels should be welcoming, places you want to return to again and again.

The Signpost sign
Your guarantee of
a top quality hotel

Signpost hotel inspector **Dan Walker** (left) with **James Hiley-Jones**, General Manager of **Carey's Manor Hotel** in the New Forest.

Signpost Guide 2007
West Country

Fact File
Illustrated Guide to
Historic Houses and Gardens,
Attractions and Walks

West Country

A glorious combination of countryside and
coastline, the West Country consists of Cornwall,
Devon and Somerset. There's all the fun of the
seaside with long stretches of golden sand, as well
as tiny harbours full of fishing boats of all sizes.
Coves and estuaries abound while further inland,
wild moors with distant views of the coastline
provide a calming interlude.

Hotels guide

Cornwall	page 5
Devon	page 17
Somerset	page 29

Further information:
South West Tourism
Woodwater Park, Exeter,
Devon EX2 5WT
Tel: 01392 360050

www.swtourism.co.uk

Eden Project

Tintagel

Bedruthan Steps

Cornwall and The Scilly Isles

Polperro

The Scilly Isles form Britain's south-westerly bulwark against the potential invader and indeed the island's waters are littered with World War and earlier wrecks. Puffin and seal viewing trips can be arranged. The gardens on **Tresco** are sub-tropical and boast plants which are not seen in the rest of Europe. Access to the Scillies is either by boat from Penzance or by helicopter.

If imposing scenery, surfing and bracing cliff walks are for you, then make for **Cornwall's** rugged **North coast**. If the weather is fine, you can play golf. If it is overcast, that is normally a sign that the surf will be good. But be careful to observe the Red Flag limits that are put up by beach guards as currents can be strong.

Cornwall is now within one hour of London, thanks to regular flights from London City Airport to Newquay. The **South coast**, by contrast, has palm trees and the picturesque **Helford** estuary and its tributary **Gillian Creek**. There are over 30 golf courses in the county and glorious little fishing ports to explore.

Above all Cornwall is an area steeped in history and legend, with tales of shipwrecks, smugglers and strange happenings in the tin mines. **Bodmin Moor**, with its hut circles, sacred sites and giant tors, has the county's highest hill, Brown Willy, at 315m, and was the setting for the atmospheric Jamaica Inn by Daphne du Maurier.

Cornwall's largest visitor attraction since 2001 has been the **Eden Project**, near St Austell, consisting of two huge biodomes, one Tropical and one Temperate.

Near Boscastle

Devon

Exmoor

Devon is England's most visited county, largely due to its enduring beauty and improved road, rail and air connections.

Plymouth, its largest city, is a happy blend of holiday resort, historic centre and modern city. The famous Hoe has its associations with Francis Drake and the Barbican with the Pilgrim Fathers.

Brixham Harbour

Exeter is the cultural capital of the county, with its university, theatre, medieval cathedral and Maritime Museum. The Quay House Interpretation Centre tells the story of the city from Roman times (there are remnants of Roman walls) until the present day. 19th-century dramatist Richard Ford wrote "This Exeter is quite a capital, abounding in all that London has, except the fog and smoke."

Inland are the two magnificent National Parks of Dartmoor and Exmoor. Dartmoor, in the South, has 365 square miles of great natural beauty and rugged grandeur with wild heather moorland and deep wooded valleys. From the sparkling streams of the lowlands to the starker granite tors of the 'high moor', new pleasures unfold. The wild heather moorland and deep, wooded valleys are the home of red deer and the legendary Doones of RD Blackmore's novel. Exmoor, in the North, famous for its ponies, is a great place for walking or relaxation in one of its sleepy villages.

The North Coast has the resorts of Ilfracombe, Woolacombe and Bideford, whereas the South has little inlets, harbours and fjords and is known as The English Riviera. Torquay is the 'capital' of this area and has palm trees and a Mediterranean atmosphere.

TOP 10 Historic Houses Gardens and Parks

Arlington Court, near Barnstaple,
Bicton Park Botanical Gardens,
 near Budleigh Salterton
Buckfast Abbey, Buckfastleigh.
Buckland Abbey, near Yelverton.
Castle Drogo, Drewsteignton
Killerton, near Broadclyst, Exeter
Knightshayes, near Tiverton,
Overbecks Museum & Garden,
 Salcombe.
Powderham Castle near Exeter.
Saltram House, Plympton

TOP 10 Attractions

Combe Martin Wildlife &
 Dinosaur Park
Dartmoor Wildlife Park &
 West Country Falconry Centre,
 Plymouth
Dartmouth Castle & Museum
Exeter Cathedral
Kents Cavern Showcases,
 Torquay
Paignton & Dartmouth Steam
 Railway
Paignton Zoological & Botanical
 Gardens
Plymouth City Museum & Art
 Gallery,
Plymouth Dome
Royal Albert Memorial Museum,
 Exeter

TOP 10 Walks and Nature Trails

Brixham > Man Sands
Chagford > Castle Drogo >
 Fingle Bridge
Dartmoor National Park
 Guided Walks
Eggesford Forest Walk
Scabbacombe Bay >
 Two Bays Walk
South West Coast Path (South)
 Plymouth > Budleigh Salterton
South West Coast Path (North)
 Bideford > Combe Martin
The Tarka Trail
Two Moors Way:
 Lynmouth (Som) to Ivybridge
Widecombe in the Moor >
 Grimspound >Hound Tor

4

Somerset, Bristol and Bath

Somerset is a county of contrasts, with rocky **Exmoor** to the west, together with the gentler **Quantocks**, **Brendon** and **Blackdown Hills** and the limestone **Mendip Hills** and **Cheddar Gorge** to the North-East. In between are the wetlands around **Glastonbury**, ideal for apple growing, the resorts of **Burnham** and **Weston-super-Mare**, and the county town of **Taunton**, scene of bitter Civil War struggles.

Bristol, the largest city in the West Country and a former capital of England, is steeped in history. You can stroll down King Street, famous for its Theatre Royal, Almshouses and sup in the Llandoger Trow. The city docks are of great interest, providing a home for the SS Great Britain, Brunel's famous iron ship, the Industrial Museum and the Watershed shopping area.

Bath

A few miles up the river **Avon** is Britain's only World Heritage City - **Bath**, whose Roman Baths have just been re-opened. Bath's second great era was the Regency period, characterised by the Assembly Rooms and Royal Crescent. Tea in the Pump Room, with a string quartet playing, should not be missed.

Nearby **Wells** is England's smallest cathedral city. Its cathedral's west wall dates from 1230 and the Bishop's Palace is one of England's oldest inhabited houses.

A village cricket match is a traditional summer sight

Bedruthan Steps Hotel

Bedruthan, Mawgan Porth, Cornwall TR8 4BU

T (0870) 860 8472 F (01637) 860714 E office@bedruthan.com
T (International) +44 [0] (1637) 860860 W www.bedruthan.com

The Sixties exterior of this unique hotel contrasts quite surprisingly with the veritable oasis within. High levels of comfort, good taste, hospitality and wonderful facilities welcome you and make leaving difficult. There are expansive views across the wild and rugged Cornish coast down to sandy coves and long coastal walks. Family holiays are a speciality. Children can be permanently occupied in the crèche, nursery, swimming pool, gym and adventure room. There are designated 'adult areas' in the hotel and families come from far and wide to enjoy the child friendly yet child not-on-top-of you atmosphere. The spa offers a variety of Elemis treatments, hair and make-up stylists, indoor and outdoor heated pools, saunas and aromatic steam room. Bedrooms are simple and contemporary, reflecting the hotel's architecture and beachside setting. Most have sitting areas and spectacular views over the Atlantic; all have broadband Internet access. Cuisine is well presented and award winning. It is plain to see why Bedruthan Steps won the coveted *Hotel of the Year 2005* at the Cornwall Tourism Awards.

Family friendly hotel with fantastic views and facilities.

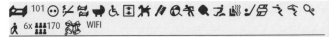

101 6x 170 WIFI

Directions: A30 to Bodmin, then A389 Wadebridge & Padstow. 7m on B 3276 Newquay Road.

Nearby attractions
Lanhydrock Garden, Newquay Zoo, Tate St Ives, Eden Project.

Distances
Padstow 7, Newquay 5, London 295.

Rates Single inc dinner & breakfast from £80; double from £160.
Meals Indigo Bay AA ☺ restaurant; alc, lunch & diets available; last orders 2100; bfst fm 0730.
Other activities Crèche. Golf nearby.
Visa, Maestro, Mastercard accepted.

6

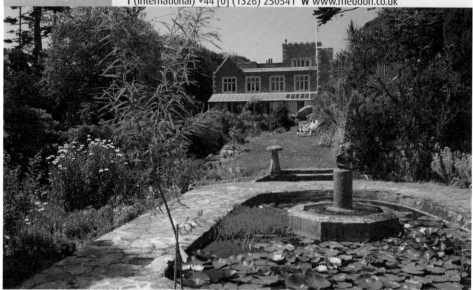

Meudon Hotel
Mawnan Smith, Falmouth, Cornwall TR11 5HT
T (0870) 418 8000 F (01326) 250543 E wecare@meudon.co.uk
T (International) +44 [0] (1326) 250541 W www.meudon.co.uk

Nestling on the south Cornish coast in thickly wooded country-side between the famous 'Packet' harbour of Falmouth and the romantic Helford estuary, Meudon is a unique family run luxury hotel set in a timeless sub-tropical valley leading to its own private beach at Bream Cove. Originally a country mansion built at the turn of the 19th century, two 17th-century former coast-guards' cottages were incorporated into the hotel and a large modern bedroom wing was added. Public rooms are furnished with antiques, fine paintings and fresh flowers and all bedrooms overlook the spectacular gardens. The award winning restaurant, under the supervision of chef Alan Webb, specialises in local seafood, lobster, crab and oysters, delivered daily by local fishermen. Cornwall's many resorts, castles and gardens, including the Eden Project, are accessible by car. Golf on six local courses is free to residents and riding, sailing and Cornwall's coastal path and many attractions are on the doorstep. Mr & Mrs Harry Pilgrim developed the hotel and their son Mark now manages it, representing the fifth generation - truly a Pilgrims' Progress of fine Cornish hotel keeping.

Family owned hotel with fantastic gardens and private beach.

Directions
A39 to Falmouth, rt at Hillhead rndbt, 4 miles sign Maenporth.
Nearby attractions
Trebah & Glendurgan Gdns, Cornwall Maritime Mus, Eden Project.
Distances
Falmouth 5, Helston 8, London 259.

29 (£7 p.n.) 50

Rates Room, breakfast & dinner from £70 per person. Separate cottage (sleeps 4/5) available from £525 per week.
Meals 5-cse tdh dinner £33; alc, lunch & diets available; last orders 2100.
Leisure Breaks
Winter Warmers Nov-end Feb, 3 nights, dinner, b & b £70 pppn.
Christmas 3 nights from £180 pppn.
Other activities Hotel yacht, free golf, sub-tropical gardens and private beach.

 Visa, Diners, Mastercard accepted.

Cornwall, Falmouth

Mullion Cove Hotel

Mullion, Lizard Peninsula, Cornwall TR12 7EP

T (0870) 418 8014 **F** (01326) 240998 **E** mullion.cove@btinternet.com
T (International) [0] (1326) 240328 **W** www.mullioncove.com

7

It is worth the journey down to farthest south-west Cornwall to experience the privacy and wild setting of Mullion Cove Hotel, set high above the beach in its own corner of tranquillity. The lounge looks down to the harbour and across to Mullion Island, a haven for rare bird species and out along 30 miles of spectacular coastline. A number of bedrooms have been converted into *Superior Plus* accommodation, with sea views, flowers, fruit and other extras. In the dining room the menu changes daily and features fresh fish and shellfish, often caught the same day in the cove below, locally reared meats and fresh vegetables, salads and herbs from the hotel's own garden. For recreation there is a heated outdoor pool or you can stroll to the picturesque Mullion Village, walk the Cornwall Coastal Path running in front of the hotel, play a round of golf on a nearby links course or visit one of Cornwall's exotic gardens. Set in an area of outstanding natural beauty, the Lizard Peninsula has many little sandy beaches and harbours. The Gulf Stream ensures an early Spring and, in this corner of Britain, even Autumn wants to linger longer.

🛏 30 🎵🕹 🔱 🗒 ⚡ 🐕(£5 pn fee) 🅿 30

Spectacularly set hotel combining traditional values & modern comfort

Rates Dinner, room & breakfast from £70 per person; suites from £175.
Meals Tdh dinner £25.95; lunch & spec. diets available; last orders 2045.

Directions
A39 Truro, then twds Falmouth, A394 to Helston, then A3083 twds Lizard.

Leisure Breaks
Discounts available for stays of three nights or more throughout the year.
Other activities Riding (2m), golf (2m).

Nearby attractions
Trebah Gdns, Maritime Mus, Tate St Ives, Godolphin Hse, St Michaels Mt

Distances
Helston 7, Truro 26, London 323.

 & major credit cards accepted (exc. Diners).

Cornwall, Lizard Peninsula

Trevalsa Court Country House Hotel & Restaurant

8

Mevagissey, Cornwall PL26 6TH

T (0870) 860 8465 **F** (01726) 844482 **E** stay@trevalsa-hotel.co.uk
T (International) [0] (1726) 842468 **W** www.trevalsa-hotel.co.uk

Trevalsa Court Hotel is set above the wonderful sandy Polstreath Beach. When you enter the portals of this immaculately maintained 1930s country house, you are in a world of calm and unobtrusive hospitality. Trevalsa's well travelled and cultured owner Klaus Wagner together with manager Matthew Mainka run the hotel with enthusiasm, an aesthetic eye and a dedicated team of young professional staff. Breakfast and dinner are taken in the atmospheric panelled dining room decorated with understated grace and carefully lit. Fresh fish seems to arrive from the local fishmonger almost as you sit and order. The daily changing menu concentrates, wherever possible, on locally sourced and freshly cooked produce. Bedrooms, tastefully decorated in muted colours, have wonderful sea views. The drawing room has wooden floors, gentle classical background music and sumptuous leather sofas. Outside guests can wander in the large and immaculately kept gardens, walk the Cornwall coastal path, or explore Mevagissey's attractive harbour and interesting shops. The Eden project and Lost Gardens of Heligan are within a 15-minute drive.

Boutique seaside hotel with a high attention to food.

🛏 12 ♩ ⚘ ⚠ ⚲ ☂ 🐕 🅿 14

Directions
A30/A391 St Austell, then B3273 to Mevagissey; hotel on left.

Nearby attractions
Eden Project, Lost Gardens of Heligan, Lanhydrock.

Distances
St Austell 5, Truro 20, London 287.

Rates Single inc. breakfast from £65; double from £98.
Meals Tdh dinner £29; lunch on request; spec. diets avail; dinner 1900 - 2100.
Leisure Breaks
3-night Eden Break, dinner, bed & breakfast; 2-night Romantic Break - champagne in room, candle-lit dinner. Prices on application.
Other activities Golf, squash, gym/fitness centre nearby.

 & major credit cards accepted.

Cornwall, Mevagissey

This Grade II Listed Georgian building was once owned by John Tredwen, the last of the local sailing shipbuilders. It has recently been bought and refurbished by Nick and Cazz Orchard, who also own the stylish Tregea Hotel and Ruskin bed & breakfast nearby. Cross House sits in the heart of this thriving village, in an area of tranquility looking down towards the harbour. It is the perfect embodiment of Padstow's unique atmosphere. Guests can relax on the terrace under a colonial umbrella before setting off to explore the myriad shops and restaurants in the town: Rick Stein's Seafood Restaurant or The Estuary Restaurant in the Tregea Hotel. Further afield the energetic can walk the Cornwall Coastal Path or hire a bicycle to ride the Camel Trail, from Padstow to Bodmin. The estuary is also an ideal spot for many watersports and two excellent 18-hole golf courses are nearby - Trevose and St Enodoc. Prideaux Place Deer Park is next door and there are many beautiful gardens and an endless array of wildlife to study, from puffins to seals and basking sharks.

🛏 11 🍽 ⓐ △ 🏃 🐾 🅿 5

Cosy small hotel a short walk from picturesque Padstow harbour.

Rates Room inc. breakfast £70-150.
Meals Lunch available during summer months; bfst from 0800.

Leisure Breaks
October-March, three nights for the price of two.
Other activities Golf, watersports, bicycling nearby.

Mastercard, Visa, Maestro, Delta cards accepted. Open all year.

Directions
A30 to Bodmin, then A389 to Wade-bridge and Padstow. Hotel in centre.
Nearby attractions
Lanhydrock Garden, Newquay Zoo, Tate St Ives, Eden Project. Camel Trail
Distances
Newquay 12, Bodmin 16, London 290

Cornwall, Padstow

Treglos Hotel
Constantine Bay, Nr. Padstow, Cornwall PL28 8JH
T (0870) 860 8402 **F** (01841) 521163 **E** stay@tregloshotel.com
T (International) +44 [0] (1841) 520727 **W** www.tregloshotel.com

Overlooking the broad sandy sweep of Constantine Bay and Trevose Head, four-star rated Treglos offers an ideal base from which to explore the North Cornish coast with its rugged and dramatic coastal paths and golden beaches. Owned by the Barlow family for 40 years, the hotel is friendly and welcoming. The tastefully decorated bedrooms are inviting with views over the elegantly landscaped gardens to the bay beyond. Guests can choose between the *Glo* treatments in the hotel's spa or a dip in the glorious indoor pool and jacuzzi. Alternatively they can head for one of the eight nearby golf courses including Treglos's own at Mawgan Porth. Guests can unwind in the conservatory, take tea on the terrace and dine in the highly rated restaurant. Mouth-watering dishes are created, making full use of herbs from the hotel garden. Freshly landed local fish is a speciality. Treglos is relaxing, invigorating and hospitable, making for an unforgettable stay. For those who prefer to self-cater but still enjoy all the facilities the hotel has to offer, there are two and four person apartments and 'Little Treglos', a 4-person bungalow in the grounds of the hotel.

Family owned resort hotel on Cornwall's picturesque North Coast

🛏 42 (inc 5 ♨) ⚥ ♩ ⚘ ♿ ❄ ⏰ ⛳18 🎳 ⚗ ♨ ⚓ // ☀ ♨♨♨ 20 🐕
(fee payable) 🅿 42

Directions
A30 Bodmin; after 4m rt on B3274 to Padstow, B3276 2m to St Merryn, rt to Constantine Bay. **Nearby attractions:** Lanhydrock Garden (NT) , Eden Project, Lost Gardens of Heligan, Padstow port.

Distances
Padstow 4, Bodmin 17, London 290.

Rates Single with breakfast from £67; double from £134.
Meals Quie's AA ❁ Restaurant £27 3-cse tdh; lunch & diets avail; last ord 2100
Leisure Breaks Thursday to Thursday or Sunday to Sunday reductions of £4.50 per person per day; certain non-sea view rooms have 5-10% discounts.
Other activities Fishing, golf, watersports, riding & tennis nearby.

CCs Visa & Mastercard accepted. Closed December to February.

Cornwall, Nr. Padstow

The Old Coastguard Hotel

The Parade, Mousehole, Penzance, Cornwall TR19 6PR

T (0870) 418 8068 **F** (01736) 731720 **E** bookings@oldcoastguardhotelco.uk
T (International) [0] (1736) 731222 **W** www.oldcoastguardhotel.co.uk

11

Thoroughly up to date yet steeped in tradition, the Old Coastguard Hotel looks out across gardens to the timeless harbour of Mousehole. Guests can watch the world sail by from the shade of colonial-style brollies on the terrace, as they select from the mouth-watering menu. This might start with a trio of salmon, move onto char-grilled lamb cutlets with herb couscous and finish with one of their home made desserts like Garden Rhubarb & Apple Crumble. The sea is reflected in the indigo and cream colour schemes of the bedrooms and bathrooms and the beautiful wooden flooring brings to mind the deck of a yacht. Half of the hotel's bedrooms are located in The Lodge, set in the grounds at the water's edge with a panoramic view of Mounts Bay. Outside the sub-tropical garden leads to a rocky beach with pools to explore. The nearby harbour has a small safe sandy beach. The artistic traditions of Mousehole are felt throughout the hotel with its sense of space and light. Guests can visit a plethora of local galleries, sandy coves, rugged cliffs and secret wooded valleys. A place to relax, recharge and renew.

Former coastguard's cottage by one of Cornwall's oldest fishing ports

🛏 20 ⚮ ♪ ⟳ ♀ △ ☆ ✗ P 18

Rates Single inc. breakfast from £40-100; double £80-160. [Ad]
Meals Alc dinner ca £35; lunch & spec. diets avail; last orders for dinner 2200; bfst fm 0745.
Leisure Breaks Nov-Mar three nights dinner, b & b £100 per pers. 3rd eve meal free if two dinners are taken.
Other activities Golf, spa, swimming pools, gym/fitness centre nearby.

Directions
A30 Penzance, then follow signs to Mousehole, hotel on left.
Nearby attractions
St Michaels Mount, Land's End, Tate Gallery, St Ives.
Distances
Penzance 2, Lands End 10, London 321

 & major credit cards accepted

Cornwall, Penzance

The Talland Bay Hotel
Porthallow, Cornwall PL13 2JB
T (0870) 418 8034 **F** (01503) 272940 **E** info@tallandbayhotel.co.uk
T (International) +44 [0]1503 272667 **W** www.tallandbayhotel.co.uk

This old Cornish manor house - mentioned in the Domesday Book - is perched high above the sea and commands idyllic views over the bay from its two-acre sub-tropical garden. The library, bar and sitting room are like private rooms in an elegant, cosy home. Each of the 23 bedrooms and three cottages has its own individual style. The blend of traditional furniture and more modern bold colouring works well to acheive a fresh, contemporary atmosphere. Bathrooms are fresh, with elegant fittings, fluffy white towels and bathrobes and Moulton Brown goodies. Some rooms directly access the garden. Cuisine is modern British and includes wonderful day caught fish, scallops and crab, most of which are landed just two miles away at Looe. Oysters and mussels come from the Fowey estuary; smoked salmon comes from Charlestown. There is a Tasting Menu and a frequently changing 4-choice per course gourmet dinner menu. Talland Bay is comfortable with understated elegance. Service is efficient yet discreet and it is the kind of place where strangers chat without compromising each other's privacy. Altogether delightfully *English* in the best sense of the word.

One of Cornwall's premier country manor house hotels, in a striking setting

🛏 26 (inc 3 🛏) ⊰ ⌕ 🔟 🖋 ✒/🛏 🔍 ⬛⬛ 20 🐾(£7.50 pn fee) 🅿 20

Directions
A38 Plymouth to Looe, A387 Looe-Polperro, turn left at small Xrds, to TBHotel

Nearby attractions
Lanhydrock Garden, Eden Project, Lost Gardens of Heligan, St Keyne Music Machines

Distances
Looe 4, Plymouth 21, London 229.

Rates Small double with breakfast from £80; country view double/twin from £95; superior sea view double/twin from £150; suite from £170.

Meals Tdh dinner £25 2-cse/£32.50 3-cse; diets available; last orders 2100.

Leisure Breaks Winter breaks from £65; 3-night Christmas Breaks from £485; 2-nt New Years Eve breaks from £220.

Other activities Fishing, golf, watersports, riding, squash & tennis nearby.

Accreditations & awards AA★★★ ☺☺☺ Good Food Guide 5/10 Newcomer of the Year Award.

CCs Visa & Mastercard accepted. Open all year.

Cornwall, Porthallow

The Rosevine Hotel

Portscatho, Roseland, Truro, Cornwall TR2 5EW

T (0870) 860 8492 **F** (01872) 580230 **E** info@rosevine.co.uk
T (International) +44 [0](01872) 580206 **W** www.rosevine.co.uk

13

Rosevine is a family run hotel framed by immaculate sub-tropical gardens which lead down to the safe, sandy Porthcurnick Beach (*pictured left*) or to the fishing village of Portscatho with its Smugglers Inn. Guests can enjoy tea in the conservatory or lunch on a grassy terrace and watch the boats sail by or simply breathe in the garden aromas. The hotel is very family friendly, with a games room and even a tiny tots paddling pool and jacuzzi. A nice touch is the *Welcome Package*, consisting of disposable camera, stamped postcards, 'emergency chocolate rations' and maps for longer walks. A dip in the indoor pool is an ideal preparation for the culinary experience of the dining room, winner of three RAC blue ribbons and three AA rosettes for four years in succession. Here the freshest ingredients are used to create a memorable dining experience. After a comfortable night, you will wake up to the glorious views, feeling refreshed and ready to explore all the wonderful sights of this special uncrowded and secretive part of the Roseland peninsula.

 17 ⚷ ♿ 🛏 ♣ ✝ ❄ 🛁 🏰 ♨ 🎵 🐕 🐎 🐾 🅿 40

Family friendly small hotel on the picturesque Roseland peninsula

Rates Single with breakfast £90-£196; double inc brfst £175-200.
Meals Didiers Restaurant tdh dinner £38; alc & diets avail; last orders 2130.
Leisure Breaks Garden Breaks, Chocaholic Weekends, Seafood Spectaculars. Contact hotel for details.
Other activities Golf, riding, sailing, canoeing, coastal path nearby.

Directions
A30/A39 to Truro, then A390/B3287 to Tregony, A3078 Portscatho, hotel on left

Nearby attractions
Minack Theatre, Flambards, Eden Project, Lost Gardens of Heligan

Distances
St Mawes 6, Truro 15, London 310

 & all major credit cards accepted. Open all year exc. 28 Dec- 2 Feb.

Cornwall, Porthscatho

Rose-in-Vale Country House Hotel
Mithian, St Agnes, Cornwall TR5 0QD
T (0870) 418 8006 **F** (01872) 552700 **E** reception@rose-in-vale-hotel.co.uk
T (International) +44 [0]1872 552202 **W** www.rose-in-vale-hotel.co.uk

There could be no more appropriate name for a Georgian country manor so entirely shrouded in fragrant roses snuggled in its own 11-acre valley. Situated just outside the charming old village of Mithian and built in the 1760s as a winter residence for a tin mine captain, this is a truly tranquil spot. James and Sara Evans bought the hotel in 2006 and have injected it with new vitality. The Valley Restaurant, under the supervision of head chef Colin Hankins, offers a wide range of locally sourced food with seafood lovers well catered for. There is also an imaginative wine list. Bedrooms include the Rose Suite and many have four-poster or draped king size beds. Some rooms can accommodate families and ground floor rooms cater for guests needing level access. All are attractively decorated in pretty English country house style fabrics. The Southwest Coastal Path is near the hotel as are the delightful beaches of Perranporth, Chapel Porth and Trevaunance Cove. In addition, there are six golf courses nearby and many of Cornwall's historic houses and gardens are within easy reach.

Special hotel in a glorious setting with a timeless atmosphere.

18   12 (£5 pn fee)   30

Directions
A30 to 4m short of Redruth, then B3277 rt to St Agnes. Signs Rose-in-Vale 500m.

Nearby attractions
Chyverton & Trelissick Gdns, Truro, Eden Project, Lost Gardens of Heligan

Distances
Truro 8, Redruth 8, London 269.

Rates Single with breakfast from £68; double from £120.
Meals Tdh dinner £32; diets available; last orders 2045.
Leisure Breaks Spring Gardens Breaks inc. entry into var. gardens - Eden, Heligan etc. Golf Breaks inc. green fees at four local courses. Also 4 nights dinner, b & b for price of three. Winter pacakages also avail. inc. upgrades.
Other activities Riding, golf, coastal path nearby.

Visa & Mastercard accepted. Open all year.

Cornwall, St Agnes

The Garrack Hotel & Restaurant

Burthallan Lane, St Ives, Cornwall TR26 3AA

T (0870) 418 8003 **F** (01736) 798955 **E** spost@garrack.com
T (International) +44 [0]1736 796199 **W** www.garrack.com

15

The discerning traveller seeking a classic small country house hotel could hardly do better than to stay in the family-run Garrack with its spectacular views over the old town of St Ives and the sea. It has two acres of gardens, is near the coastal footpath and its excellent leisure centre caters for most eventualities. The personal touch and friendliness of the Garrack is reflected in the main lounge with its log fire in winter, books, magazines and board games. In addition there is a small TV lounge and a bar lounge. Whilst the bedrooms in the main house are traditional in keeping with the building, an extension has additional rooms of more modern design but equal comfort. Some rooms have four posters, others whirlpool baths. There are family rooms and a room for the disabled. The hotel restaurant is justifiably renowned for its sea-food with lobsters fresh from the hotel's storage tank, and much of the other food is locally sourced. It would take several weeks to work through the wine list. The Garrack is a rarity - one of those places which it was a delight in itself to visit - and so hard to leave.

🛏 18 ♿ 🍴 🐾 🏊 ⚓ 🚗 🎿 🎣 ⚏ 12 🐕(£10 fee) 🅿 30

Family owned hotel overlooking St Ives town and beach.

Rates Single with breakfast from £75; double from £134.
Meals Garrack Rest. 3-cse tdh dinner £24.50; alc & diets avail; last orders 2100
Leisure Breaks Out of season breaks, Nov-March (excl. Xmas/New Year & Easter). Ring for details or visit our website.
Other activities Riding, golf 4 miles.

 & major credit cards accepted. Open all year exc. five days at Xmas.

Directions
A30 to Hayle/Lelant, then B3311 via Halsetown. Flw brown signs Tate Gall'y
Nearby attractions Eden Project, Geevor Mine, Land's End, Tate St Ives, St Michael's Mount
Distances
Penzance 10, Redruth 14, London 319.

16 The Gurnard's Head

Treen, Zennor, St Ives, Cornwall TR26 3DE

T (0870) 860 8494 E enquiries@gurnardshead.co.uk
T (International) +44 [0] (1736) 796928 W www.gurnardshead.co.uk

The Gurnards Head sits cheerfully in a splendid cliff top position, its yellow ochre walls beckoning from afar. Here the welcome is as warm and attractive as its Moroccan inspired colour scheme. Marine blues and deep sultry yellows brighten the spirits of any guest. Walls are hung with local art from this incredibly creative region, with the Tate Gallery next door and endless land and sea scapes all around. Bedrooms are fresh and uncluttered (no TVs) with views of either the sea or inland over heather clad moors. The dining room is informal, with scrubbed pine tables and native art creating a relaxed atmosphere. Fresh local produce forms the backbone of a straightforward, yet enticing, menu reflecting the area's specialities: fresh turbot, home grown artichokes, pancetta and lentils or Cornish pilchards on toast with a cucumber relish. The Gurnards Head has recently been bought and refurbished by the Inkin family (*see the* Felin Fach Griffin *in the Wales section of this book*). Here you will find the same warm welcome, upbeat energy and young enthusiasm. Gurnards is an ideal base from which to explore the wild scenery of this Cape Cornwall peninsula.

Small clifftop inn - Cornish hospitaity with a contemporary twist

🛏 7 🍴 🐕 🔍 🅿 40

Directions
A30 to Penzance (ring road) then rt after heliport to New Mill & Porthmeor

Nearby attractions
Eden Project, Land's End, Tate St Ives, Minack Theatre, St Michael's Mount

Distances
Penzance 7, St Ives 7, London 326

Rates Single with breakfast from £42.50; double from £72.50.

Meals 3-cse tdh dinner £23.50; alc & diets avail; last orders 2130; bfst fm 0730

Leisure Breaks Weekend group parties; multi night offers November-March. Ring for details or visit our website.

Other activities Fishing, birdwatching, sailing, volleyball, golf nearby

CCs Mastercard, Visa & Maestro credit cards accepted. Open all year .

Blagdon Manor Hotel
Ashwater, Devon EX21 5DF
T (0870) 860 8401 **F** (01409) 211634 **E** stay@blagdon.com
T (International) +44 [0] (1409) 211224 **W** www.blagdon.com

17

Warmth of welcome is second to none from proprietors Elizabeth and Stephen Morey and their two chocolate labradors Nutmeg and Cassia. Nothing is ever too much trouble to ensure that your stay is memorable and relaxing at this one time Devon farmhouse, now a successful, lovingly restored small hotel. Heavy oak beams and worn slate flagstones blend with hand stitched soft furnishings. The scent of flowers in summer or the hint of woodsmoke in winter combine to create a beguiling and tranquil charm. The Moreys exude professionalism, and give personal attention within a relaxed atmosphere. Stephen, with 26 years' experience, cooks with sincere enthusiasm, utmost passion and skill, whilst sourcing everything from Devon's incredible larder. Guests return again and again to this little gem and once sampled, the hosts are confident you will be counting the days until your next visit. The high degree of repeat business bears this out. There is much to see and do in this corner of Devon - golf, fishing or shooting, the Eden Project, Falmouth's Maritime Museum or a visit to one of the many local stately homes and gardens.

 7 ⚞ 🐕 🅿 20

Award winning small hotel on the edge of Dartmoor

Rates Single with breakfast fm £85; double from £120.
Meals 3-cse tdh £35; lunch & spec. diets avail; last orders 2100; bfst fm 0800.
Accreditations & awards AA Top 200 ★★ ☺☺
Other activities Giant chess; sailing, boating, shooting, fishing, tennis, golf, indoor swimming pool nearby.

Directions A30 Launceston then A388 Holsworthy rd; past Chapman's Well take 2nd sign to Ashwater, then 1st rt; hotel on rt
Nearby attractions
Rosemoor RHS Gardens, Roadford Reservoir, Dartmoor Nat'l Park, Tintagel.
Distances

CCs Visa, Mastercard & Switch accepted. Closed 2 wks January/2 wks October.

Launceston 8, Exeter 43, London 218.

Devon, Ashwater

The Berry Head Hotel

Berry Head Road, Brixham, Devon TQ5 9AJ
T (0870) 418 8004 **F** (01803) 882084 **E** stay@berryheadhotel.com
T (International) +44 [0] (1803) 853225 **W** www.berryheadhotel.com

The Berry Head Hotel is set in a superb water's edge position in six acres of it own gardens and woodland, in the seclusion of the Berry Head Country Park, which is noted for its bird life and rare wild flowers. The hotel is steeped in history. It was built as a military hospital in the Napoleonic Wars and was later the home of the Reverend Francis Lyte, who wrote the famous hymn *Abide with Me* at the hotel, no doubt inspired by the glorious sunsets. The historic fishing port of Brixham, where William of Orange first landed to claim the English crown, is only a short walk away. The hotel offers relaxing accommodation and all rooms have up to date facilities as well as a baby listening service. The comfortable lounge and the restaurant, which overlooks the terrace, enjoy spectacular views of Torbay and the Devon coast. The emphasis here is upon good food, wine and company in a rather special setting. Set in national parkland with miles of coastal walks, fishing, birdwatching and sailing at hand, yet close to the major resort of Torquay, this is an ideal hideaway for a short break and the perfect location for any occasion, wedding or conference.

Water's edge hotel set in 6 acres of gardens & woodland in country park

🛏 32 ⊕ 🛒 ⚲ ⚬ ⛵ ♨ 200 🐕 🅿 30 🐾

Directions A3022 via Torbay to Brixham, follow signs to marina, continue past onto Berry Head Road.

Nearby attractions
Oldway Mansion, Torre Abbey, Golden Hind replica, The Deep theme park.

Distances
Torquay 8, Exeter 30, London 230.

Rates Room & breakfast fm £48 per pers; dinner, room & bfst fm £58 pppn
Meals Last orders 2130; bar meals til 2130; spec. diets avail; children welcome
Leisure Breaks Two nights, dinner, b & b from £88 per pers/3 nts fm £132.
Other activities Boules. Outdoor (seawater) pool 200 yds, squash, sailing, boating, shooting, fishing, tennis and golf nearby.

 Visa, Mastercard, Switch & Solo accepted. Open all year.

Combe House - Hotel & Restaurant
Gittisham, Honiton, Nr. Exeter, Devon EX14 3AD

T (0870) 418 8010 **F** (01404) 46004 **E** stay@thishotel.com
T (International) [0]1404 540400 **W** www.thishotel.com

This romantic privately owned Grade I Elizabethan manor of 16th century origin lies in 3500 acres of lush mature parkland, approached via a mile of winding drive. The magnificent Entrance Hall, with its huge log fire and squashy sofas, gives a flavour of things to come. Antiques, family portraits and fresh flowers abound throughout the house. Ken and Ruth Hunt are justifiably proud of the menus produced by master chef Philip Leach. April dishes included roasted wood pigeon, seared foie gras and grilled red mullet with clam linguini. Seasonal herbs and vegetables come from the hotel's own kitchen garden. The wine list is well chosen, with a renowned Chablis collection. Private dining is available in the Panel Room or in the Georgian Kitchen. Bedrooms are decorated in informally elegant country house style, have spacious bathrooms and sweeping views over the estate to the Devon countryside beyond. The Jurassic Heritage Coastline is over the hill and Dartmoor 25 minutes away. Gittisham has a Norman church and pretty thatched cottages. Combe House is also available for exclusive use.

🛏 15 🛋 ♣ ♪ (3/4 m) 🐎 🐴 ‼ 50 🦌 (100-150)

Romantic Elizabethan mansion set in 3500 acres of mature parkland.

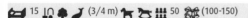

Rates Single with breakfast from £129; double from £148.   Open all year.
Meals Tdh dinner; diets available; last orders 2100.
Leisure Breaks Up to March 2006 stay two nights fm £198 per pers, dinner, b & b (two sharing). Children under 12 in parents' room £15 per nt, b & b.
Conference tariff 24-hr res rate single fm £162/dble fm £284; day del rate £45
Other activities 4 x 4 Landrover Experience West Country Centre - 5 mins' away
Awards AA Top 200 ★★★ 83%, ◎◎ RAC Gold Ribbon, Restaurant of the Year 2005 - Devon Life Awards, Best Country House Hotel 2004 - Sun Times Tr. Mag. *Country Hotel of the Year* - Good Hotel Guide 2007. Visa, Mastercard, Switch, Delta, accepted

Directions
M5 Exit 28/29 to Honiton. Half mile after A30 town bypass, left to Gittisham
Nearby attractions
Killerton & Knightshayes (NT). Honiton (antiques), Exeter Cath, Lyme Regis
Distances
Honiton 2, Exeter ⊕ 10, London 155.

Devon, Honiton

Home Farm Hotel

Wilmington. Nr. Honiton, Devon EX14 9JR

T (0870) 860 8496 **F** (01404) 831411 **E** info@thatchedhotel.co.uk
T (International) [0]1404 831278 **W** www.thatchedhotel.co.uk

Home Farm is a delightful romantic Devon hotel and restaurant located only minutes from both Axminster and Honiton. Home Farm offers character bedrooms, fine food and wine and friendly service. Originally a 16th century thatched farmhouse, Home Farm now presents an intimate fine dining restaurant with rooms and caters for leisure and business traveller alike. All bedrooms have widescreen LCD TVs, Digital Freeview Channel and complimentary wireless internet connections, as well as the usual amenities. In the newly refurbished restaurant chef Lee Villiers makes use of the finest local produce. Make sure to leave room for his tempting desserts, such as *chocolate & bailey's tower* or *walnut meringue torte.* Honiton is the gateway to the West Country and there is much to see in the area: National Trust properties at Killerton and Knightshayes Court, amusement and wildlife parks, model villages, working museums and farms, abbeys, castles and bird sanctuaries. Home Farm is set in four acres of grounds and golf, sea bathing, riding, tennis and invigorating cliff walks are available nearby.

Former thatched farmhouse at the West Country's gateway

 12

Directions
M5 or A30 to Honiton, then A35 signed Axminster. Wilmington 4m.

Rates Single with breakfast from £50; double from £84
Meals Tdh dinner £24; alc, lunch & diets avail; last orders 2100; bfst fm 0800.

Nearby attractions
Wilmington Hayes Gdns, Seaton Tramway, Killerton, Knightshayes NT

Other activities Golf, riding, walks, tennis, sea bathing nearby.

Distances
Honiton 4, Axminster 6, London 156

 & major credit cards accepted

Devon, Honiton

The Cottage Hotel

21

Hope Cove, Kingsbridge, Devon TQ7 3HJ

T (0870) 418 8005 **F** (01548) 561455 **E** info@hopecove.com
T (International) +44 [0] (1548) 561555 **W** www.hopecove.com

Hope Cove is what the name implies: a beautiful village situated along the rugged South Devon coastline. The Cottage Hotel enjoys a superb position, overlooking the picturesque harbour and cove, set in $2^1/2$ acres of shrubs and lawns which lead, via sloping footpaths, to the largest of two beaches, where you can bathe in safety. The hotel has 26 differently furnished en suite bedrooms. The Ireland family have run The Cottage since 1973 and provide a warm, personal service, whilst constantly updating the facilities. The Restaurant is renowned amongst visitors and locals alike. Locally caught crab, lobster and fish are on the menu and the house wines are truly special. The Cottage is popular with families - there is a games room and special high teas are available, as well as child alarms. Along this Heritage Coastline there are challenging walks affording superb views. The area is famous for its unique flora and fauna, including the Nature Reserve at Slapton Ley. Many sporting activities are available nearby with ten golf courses within easy reach - the hotel having concessions at Bigbury.

🛏 26 🔍 🛥 ⚓ 🎠 🚶 🔍 ♨ 50

Popular family hotel overlooking harbour and protected cove.

Rates Dinner, room & breakfast from £57.50 per person.
Meals Bar meals 12-1.30 pm; last orders 2030.
Leisure Breaks 1st Nov-30 April inc. 2-night stay £35-£56; 7-night stay fm £33.50-£53 acc. to room. Prices per person pr night and include accomm, breakfast & 6-course dinner + coffee, service + VAT
Other activities Riding (3m), golf (4m), tennis & squash (6m).

Open all year exc. Jan 2-30th. Debit cards accepted.

Directions
A381 Salcombe rd out of Kingsbridge, 3m rt via Galmpton to Hope Cove.
Nearby attractions
Dartington Hall, Shorpitor, Overbecks, Dartmoor National Park.
Distances
Kingsbridge 7, Plymouth 25, London 236

Devon, Hope Cove

Bovey Castle
Moretonhampstead, Dartmoor National Park, TQ13 8RE

T (0870) 418 8018 F (01647) 445120 E enquiries@boveycastle.com
T (International) +44 [0] (1647) 445000 W www.boveycastle.com

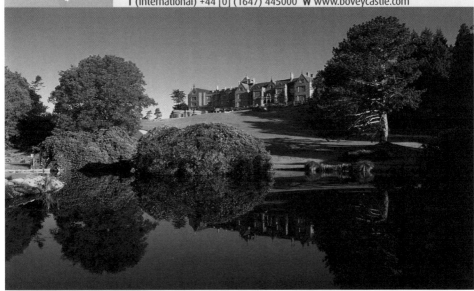

You don't need a book in the Cathedral Room *(pictured top left)* - at least not until you have ingested your gorgeous surroundings and the view across unspoiled acres of Dartmoor. Bovey Castle, a magnificent Edwardian mansion, was built as a private home for Viscount (WH Smith) Hambledon, who was also First Lord of the Admiralty. Three years ago Peter de Savary acquired the hotel and nothing was spared in the elegant and sumptuous restoration. A medieval twist here, a bit of art deco there, peppermint green hand-painted wall coverings, fascinating art, rich yet relaxing colours, a private cinema and a smoking room in the cellar give an idea of the style. Guests could be forgiven for thinking they were part of a grand house party. Luxury and fun are the watchwords. The 65 rooms and suites offer exceptional levels of comfort. The menu is superb. The golf course, built in 1926 as a sister to Gleneagles and Turnberry, has been restored to championship standard; the spa is brand new. Facilities include tennis, shooting, croquet, riding, 4x4 driving and there are plenty of wholesome activities for children too. This is truly the place for that special break.

Sumptuously restored Edwardian manor set in 270 acres of parkland

Directions
M5 to Exeter. A30 W 15m to Whiddon Down, left A382 to Moretonhampstead. Hotel on left 2m on B3212 Tavistock rd

Nearby attractions
Dartmoor, Powderham Castle, Exeter Cath, Dartmouth & Regatta Naval Mus.
Distances Exeter 25, London 182.

Rates Single with breakfast from £155; double from £225.
Meals Palm Court tdh dinner £38.50 +VAT; lunch & diets avail; last orders 2130
Leisure Breaks Subject to availability. Call Reservations or view website.
Other activities Watersports 18m. Balloon & helicopter flights can be arranged.

 & all major credit cards accepted. Open all year.

The White Hart Hotel

The Square, Moretonhampstead, Dartmoor, Devon TQ13 8NF
T (0870) 418 8217 **F** (01647) 441341 **E** enquiries@whitehartdartmoor.co.uk
T (International) +44 [0] (1647) 441340 **W** www.whitehartdartmoor.co.uk

The White Hart has stood in the market square of Moreton-hampstead for 350 years and has played a pivotal role in history. The Pymouth to London coach used to change horses here. During the Napoleonic Wars it was a meeting place for French officers on parole from Dartmoor prison. It was bought in 2003 by Peter de Savary who has refurbished it with impeccable taste and with no expense spared. The en suite bedrooms are decorated in great style with luxury facilities such as flat screen TVs and CD players. The ground floor includes a lovely bar with stripped flooring, a tasteful and relaxing lounge, a luxurious brasserie restaurant which serves a seasonal menu of fresh, local produce, a courtyard and a Stag suite for functions, meetings and parties. A typical menu might start with Speldiono of Tiger prawns, continue with a rib eye of beef and finish with a trio of home made ice creams. On the first Sunday of each month a jazz band plays at lunchtime. There are great walks and cycle rides in the area. Golf and spa packages can also be arranged upon booking (subject to availability), using the leisure facilities of nearby Bovey Castle.

Refurbished Dartmoor hotel with 350 years of history

🛏 28 ✗ 🐾(£6 pn fee) 2x ⛊ 60/14 🅿 🎿

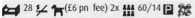

Rates Single with breakfast from £60; double from £98.
Meals Brasserie, bar, lounge, Stag suite. 3 courses from £25; lunch & spec. diets avail; last orders 2130; bfst fm 0730 (earlier by request).
Other facilities Golf, walks, cycling nearby. 12 miles fishing on Upper Teign.
Accreditations AA ★★★ RAC

& all major credit cards accepted. Open all year.

Directions M5 to Exeter, then A38 to Bovey Tracey, then A382 to Moretonhampstead. Hotel in town centre.
Nearby attractions
Dartmoor National Park,Castle Drogo, Becky Falls, Fingle Bridge.
Distances
Torquay 19, Exeter 18, London 182.

Devon, Moretonhampstead

Ilsington Country House Hotel

Ilsington Village, Nr. Newton Abbot, Devon TQ13 9RR
T (0870) 418 8015 **F** (01364) 661307 **E** hotel@ilsington.co.uk
T (International) +44 [0] (1364) 661452 **W** www.ilsington.co.uk

This peaceful country house hotel is situated in ten acres of the dartmoor National Park and offers spectacular views over some of the most beautiful scenery in England. Bedrooms are well appointed and comfortable and the reception rooms offer a choice from the library or attractive lounge bar with roaring log fire in winter to the new conservatory. In May 2006 a brand new restaurant was opened. Carefully designed and planned, the restaurant has dramatic views over Dartmoor to Haytor Rocks. Large picture windows ensure that all diners have an excellent view over the rolling countryside. Head Chef Mike O'Donnell presides in this stunning setting. He has been at the hotel for nine years and is the proud holder of AA ⊚⊚. His contemporary cooking uses predominantly locally sourced ingredients. The hotel also offers its own leisure facilities including indoor pool, spa, steam room, sauna and state-of-the-art gymnasium. The ideal combination either to work out or to wind down. Ilsington Village is dominated by the 12th century St Michael's Church. Further afield are the riches of Dartmoor's tors, open moorland and dramatic wooded valleys, fishing, golf and gardens to visit .

Peaceful country house hotel on the edge of Dartmoor National Park

🛏 25 △ ⧉ ⅄ ⊞ 🕮 🝙 ⚒(£8 pn fee) 🅿 70 ⁙ 110

Directions
A38 to A382 Bovey Tracey junct, then small rd through Liverton to Ilsington.

Nearby attractions
Moorland Crafts Ctre, Dartmoor Nat. Park, Becka Falls, Hound Tor, Haytor

Distances
Bovey Tracey 2, Exeter 20, London 236

Rates Single with breakfast from £92; double from £136.

Meals Tdh ⊚ ⊚ dinner £32,50; lunch & spec. diets avail; last orders 2100.

Leisure Breaks Discounted dinner, b & b rates available to guests staying two days or more. Call or see website for special Winter offers.

 Mastercard & Visa accepted. Open all year.

Devon, Newton Abbot

Collaven Manor Hotel

Sourton, Okehampton, Devon EX20 4HH

T (0870) 418 8007 **F** (01837) 861614 **E** collavenmanor@supanet.com
T (International) +44 [0] (1837) 861522 **W** www.collavenmanor.co.uk

25

Those readers looking to stay in a small country manor house need look no further. Collaven is a picture book Devon manor both externally and internally. Dating form the 15th century, it stands in four acres of picturesque garden and paddock. It has been sympathetically restored to cater for discerning guests as it would have done in the days of its earlier owners. Notable among these are the Hamilton family (of Nelson fame) and the house positively exudes Devon history. On entering the manor via the baronial Reception Hall, the visitor is greeted by a feeling of warmth and comfort, enhanced by log fires in winter and cooled by medieval thick walls in summer. The candle lit Hamilton Restaurant offers a 4-course dinner, changing daily, with the emphasis on the Best of British cuisine, with Continental and Oriental influences. There is always a vegetarian option on the menu. Here the atmosphere is serene, the setting tranquil but, for the adventurous, the moors are on the doorstep, to delight the walker, naturalist or outdoor sportsman.

🛏 9 🍴 🔊 🐕(£5 fee) 🅿 50 ⚏ 30

Small family hotel with 15th-century origins on the edge of Dartmoor.

Rates Single with breakfast from £61; double from £99.
Meals Tdh dinner £25.50; lunch by arr't; vegetarian dishes a speciality; last orders 2030. Bfst from 0830.
Leisure Breaks 2/3 night breaks avail. from £59 per person per night. 4 nts + fm £55 pr pers pn. Includes tdh dinner, full Eng. bfst & VAT.
Other activities Fishing, golf, riding, indoor pool nearby.

Mastercard, Visa, Delta & Switch accepted. Open all year.

Directions
A30 to 2m W of Okehampton, then A386 twds Tavistock. Hotel 1 mile on rt
Nearby attractions
Heligan, Eden Project, Lydford Gorge, Castle Drogo, Rosemoor Gardens.
Distances
Okehampton 7, Exeter 22, London 192.

Tides Reach Hotel

South Sands, Salcombe, South Devon TQ8 8LJ

T (0870) 418 8009 **F** (01548) 843954 **E** enquire@tidesreach.com
T (International) +44 [0] (1548) 843466 **W** www.tidesreach.com

Tides Reach is a complete gem of a hotel, set just back from the famous South Sands beach. Here you will find everything you could possibly desire for a relaxing, invigorating break in Salcombe. The hotel has been run by the Edwards family for over forty years and their attention to each individual guest is second to none. Staff are courteous and good humoured. Whether you are in the hot tub, sauna, indoor pool, snooker room or conservatory overlooking the beach, someone is always at hand to provide a drink or a snack, or just to chat. The food is of a very high standard with wonderfully varied choices, like fillet of Salcombe sea bass served with aubergine caviar or char-grilled wild boar cutlet with crispy air dried ham and a balsamic jus, or roast pheasant on a pink peppercorn sauce with game chips. Starters and puddings are just as spoiling. If you can bear to venture outside the hotel, Overbecks Garden is within walking distance and the NT properties of Coleton Fishacre, Saltram, Buckland Abbey and Cotehele are just a short drive away.

Beach-side hotel with most outdoor activities available on site.

🛏 35 🏃 ♣ 🎿 🎣 ♨ ⚓ ♿ 🎱 ♫ 🍴 🎳 🐕(£5 fee) **P** 100

Directions
Sandhills Rd out of Salcombe twds Combe. Hotel in South Sands Bay.
Nearby attractions
Overbecks Gardens & Museum (NT), Sth Devon coastline, Dartmoor Nat Pk
Distances
Kingsbridge 7, Plym'th 26, London 214

Rates Single with breakfast from £82; double from £136.
Meals Garden Room Rest't tdh dinner £35; spec. diets avail; last orders 2100.
Leisure Breaks Out of season bargain breaks are available. Prices vary acc. to season. Min. two nights - no maximum. Any days.
Other activities Fishing 1 mile; golf & riding 6m; tennis ¹/₂ mile.

 & major credit cards accepted. Open all year.

Devon, Salcombe

Palace Hotel

Babbacombe Road, Torquay, Devon TQ1 3TG
T (0870) 418 8016 F (01803) 299899 E info@palacetorquay.co.uk
T (International) +44 [0]1803 200200 W www.palacetorquay.co.uk

Once home to the Bishop of Exeter and built in 1841 in the Italianate style much favoured by the Victorians, this imposing, elegant peppermint green building has been a privately owned hotel since 1921. Magnificently situated in 25 acres of its own grounds, yet close to the bustling centre of Torquay, it creates a wonderfully secluded space in the Babbacombe village area of this largely Regency resort which was home to Agatha Christie and the backdrop for many of her mysteries. The hotel is blessed with a wealth of sporting facilities. Bedrooms are comfortably decorated and some of the suites have fine balconies. The sitting areas are spacious and smart, recently decorated in soft sand and burgundy colours. The impressive restaurant has grand marbled panels and dining is international in flavour and accompanied by gentle piano music. Lighter meals are available in the lounges or in the summer on the terrace. In short, once arrived at such an hotel, which is a resort in itself, you may be tempted never to leave its grounds, ending each day perhaps with an after-dinner stroll around the floodlit sub-tropical gardens.

 140 (inc 17) ⊙ ♿ ↖ ↘ ♿ ⚒ ♥ ♦ ⚙ ⚗ 11 ♨1000 ⚓ 🅿 150

Resort hotel set in 25 acres of parkland, with many facilities.

Rates Single with breakfast from £65; double from £130.
Meals Tdh dinner £26; alc, lunch & diets avail; last orders 2130; bfst fm 0730
Leisure Breaks
Special breaks available throughout the year, from £54 pppn, dinner, b & b for two nights or more.

Other facilities Sailing, watersports, fishing, riding nearby.

 & all major credit cards accepted.

Directions
M5 Exeter, A380/A3022 to town centre, then B3199 Babbacombe.
Nearby attractions
Oldway Mansion, Paignton Zoo, Torre Abbey, Babb'e Model Village.
Distances
Plymouth 32, Exeter 23, London 223

Devon, Torquay

28 Kitley House Hotel
Kitley Estate, Yealmpton, Plymouth PL8 2NW
T (0870) 860 8404 **F** (01752) 881667 **E** sales@kitleyhousehotel.com
T (International) +44 [0](1752) 881555 **W** www.kitleyhousehotel.com

Approached by a mile-long drive through a 300-acre estate of wooded parkland along the Yealm estuary, Kitley House is an oasis of quiet luxury providing a relaxing alternative to urban Plymouth. The Grade 1 Listed country house is one of the earliest Tudor Revival houses in England, and has now been restored to its former glory. The principal rooms have high moulded ceilings and elegant sash windows. From the book-lined Terrace Restaurant, diners can watch the soft progress of the lake. The sweeping divided staircase, lit by an impressive stained glass window, leads up to seven state rooms, some inter-connecting. The top floor bedrooms are more intimate with a lovely feel and delightful views. Andrew Huckerby is the charming proprietor who ensures that all guests are made welcome and comfortable. There is fishing in the hotel's private lake and other watersports nearby. Kitley is an excellent base from which to explore Dartmoor. The Southwest Coastal Path, Wembury Church and Bay and Burgh Island.

Tudor Revival era country house on the banks of the Yealm

19 (inc 7 state rooms) 🛏 ♨ ♪ ✓ 🕯 ☎ ♨ 🅿 60 🎿

Directions Fm East, A38 to South Brent, then A3121 signed Modbury, then A379 thru Yealmpton; hotel 1.5m on left.

Nearby attractions
Eden Project, National Aquarium, Dartmoor, Wembury, Plymouth.

Distances
Plymouth 6, Kingsbridge 14, London 223

Rates Single with breakfast from £75; double from £95.

Meals Terrace Restaurant alc dinner av £29.50; lunch & diets avail; last orders 2100; bfst fm 0700.

Leisure Breaks 2-night breaks, dinner, b & b from £84.50 per person per nt.

Other facilities Massage. Golf, sailing, tennis, squash, riding within 5 miles.

 & all major credit cards accepted. Open all year.

Devon, Yealmpton

T (0870) 860 8405 F (0117) 937 2251 E info@epresort.com
T (International) +44 [0] (117) 937 4288 W www.epresort.com

Surrounded by two golf courses, The Park is a leisurely, unfussy and friendly place to stay near the Georgian World Heritage City of Bath. The main house is comfortably classical, well restored and impressive with a vaulted Masonic dining room and graceful domed reception rooms. 17 freshly refurbished bedrooms are spread around an attractive quad - once the inspirational setting for Anna Sewell, author of Black Beauty. Rooms are contemporary yet timeless with limestone clad bathrooms and flat screen plasma TVs. Pretty knot gardens are cleverly positioned for peaceful wandering and contemplation. A light menu is available in the Golf Club Restaurant, where the atmosphere is more casual, while the refurbished Oakwood Restaurant specialises in fine dining. More bedrooms and a leisure centre are planned. The separate Manor in the Park is an ideal venue for business meetings or weddings. Only four miles from the city centre, yet in peaceful countryside, The Park is an important addition to the Bath hotel scene.

Stately hotel with golf courses on the outskirts of Bath.

🛏 17 ☺ ⌗ ♠ ↑₁₈ ⍨ 🖥 ⚑²⁰⁰ 🅿 ¹⁵⁰ ⚘

Rates Single with breakfast from £135; double from £185.
Meals Oakwood Restaurant tdh £35; alc, lunch & diets avail; last orders 2130 breakfast fm 0700.
Leisure Breaks
2 night Golf Break, 3 rounds of golf, luxury accomm, b & b + dinner from £210 per person.

Directions From M4 junc 18 A46 twds Bath, then rt on A420 signed Bristol. Hotel 2m on left in Wick.
Nearby attractions
Roman Baths & Museum, Abbey, Assembly Rooms, Pump Room.
Distances
Bristol 10, Chippenham 12, London 104.

& all major credit cards accepted. Open all year.

Somerset, Bath

30

The Windsor Town House Hotel
69 Great Pulteney Street, Bath, Somerset BA2 4DL
T (0870) 418 8012 F (01225) 422550 E sales@bathwindsorhotel.com
T (International) [0]1225 422100 W www.bathwinddsorhotel.com

A Grade I listed building, sympathetically restored into a fine townhouse hotel in keeping with its location, Gt Pulteney Street, which was built between 1769 and 1794 and is one of the most elegant boulevards in Europe. On arrival at the Windsor, one immediately feels a sense of welcome, the public areas being spacious and bright but retaining a warm, homely feeling. A unique feature of the hotel and unique to Bath is the *Sakura* Japanese restaurant which overlooks the hotel's garden with its giant pebbles and bamboo trees. The restaurant, open Tuesday-Saturday, is personally supervised by Mrs Sachiko Bush and offers three styles of Japanese cooking: *Shabu Shabu, Sukiyaki* and *Seafood nabe*. For those unfamiliar with Japanese cuisine, there are English descriptions and sampling tips. An opportunity not to be missed. Each bedroom is different and decorated with Georgian and traditional English patterns. The Windsor is in the heart of Bath, a World Heritage site, with rooms facing either the Georgian façades of the city inspired by Palladio or the hills to the South. The Windsor is ideally situated for those wishing to explore this historic city on foot or to visit attractions in the area by car.

Centrally located townhouse hotel with Japanese restaurant.

 14 (inc 1 ⚅) ⊙ ⚡ (throughout) 🛏14 🅿 16

Directions
M4/A4 to Bath, then ring road A36. Rt into Gt Pult'y St opp. Holbourne Mus

Nearby attractions
Roman Baths & Museum, Abbey, Assembly Rooms, Pump Room.

Distances
Bristol 12, Chippenham 13, London 104

Rates Single with breakfast from £85; double inc. breakfast from £145. [Ad]

Meals AA ◎ Japanese Restaurant tdh dinner £25; alc, lunch avail; last orders 2130; breakfast fm 0730.

Midweek Breaks Prices on application.

 & all major credit cards accepted. Open all year.

The Luttrell Arms

High Street, Dunster, Somerset TA24 6SG

T (0870) 418 8019 **F** (01643) 821567 **E** mail@luttrellarms.fsnet.co.uk
T (International) +44 [0]1643 821555 **W** www.Behere.co.uk

31

Set in a commanding position at the top of historic Dunster's High Street and overlooking the castle, this 15th century hotel was used in medieval times as a guest house by the Abbots of Cleeve. They would approve of its status today, under the management of Paul Toogood, who has returned to his home town and to the hotel where he first worked as a barman at the age of 18! All 28 bedrooms have stylish antique furniture and immaculate tiled bathrooms. The five 4-poster rooms have particular character, the Dunkery Beacon room is pictured left. The Grabbist Room intriguingly includes its own small writing room which looks up to Grabbist Hill where Mrs Jean Alexander wrote *All Things Bright and Beautiful*. Superior rooms include discreetly disguised stereos, TVs, fridges, ironing boards and bathrobes. The diverse and interesting cuisine includes such options as a dish of chicken and lobster or a terrine of local rabbit with horseradish brioche. Alternatively excellent bar snacks are available *al fresco* in the garden in summer. Altogether this is a perfect spot from which to explore Exmoor's many sights including several notable nearby gardens.

 28 (✂) inc 5 ♨ 🐕 (£5 per nt) **P**

Historic inn overlooking old town and castle on Somerset's coast

Rates Single with breakfast from £65; double from £95.
Meals Alc dinner; lunch & spec. diets avail; last orders 2200; bfst fm 0800.

Directions
M4 Bridgwater, then A39 to Dunster. Hotel at top of High Street.

Leisure Breaks
Min. two nights, dinner b & b from £63 per person per night.

Nearby attractions
Rosemoor, Hestercombe & Cothay Manor Gardens, Dunster Castle.

Distances
Minehead 2, Bridgwater 22, London 165

 & all major credit cards accepted. Open all year exc. Xmas (for accom.)

Somerset, Dunster

Fact File
Illustrated Guide to
Historic Houses and Gardens,
Attractions and Walks

Central Southern England

A remarkable mosaic of things to do and places to visit. The scenery is diverse, with a beautiful coastline ranging from limestone cliffs to woodland shores and wonderful sandy beaches. Inland there are peaceful wooded valleys, forests, rolling downland, picturesque thatched cottages and wide open spaces. Always something different just around the corner.

Thames at Marlow

Oxford

Shaftesbury

Further information:
Tourism South East
40 Chamberlayne Road,
Eastleigh, Hampshire SO5 5JH
Tel: 02380 625525

www.tourismse.com

Berkshire, Buckinghamshire & Oxfordshire

Changing Guard at Windsor Castle

Oxford

Much of **Berkshire, Buckinghamshire** and **Oxfordshire** serve as commuter territory, but the area is still one of great beauty, with many historic houses, gardens and parks. The Thames sweeps eastwards in broad graceful curves, cutting through the beeches of the Chiltern Hills.

Berkshire's most famous building, seen by every leaving and arriving passenger at Heathrow is **Windsor Castle**. Built by Edward III in the 14th century and restored by later monarchs, most apartments are now open to the public after the 1992 fire. It is the largest and oldest occupied castle in the world and encapsulates more than 900 years of English history. **Cliveden**, former seat of the Astor family and now a famous hotel, is nearby.

Buckinghamshire, to the northeast, contains the Capability Brown landscape designed **Stowe**, now a famous public school and also the city of **Milton Keynes**, with its famous plastic cows and longest (wet) ski slope in Britain.

Oxford's dreaming spires, echoing quads and cloistered college lawns have a timeless beauty. The **Ashmolean Museum**, Britain's oldest public museum. opened in 1683 and contains gold and jewellery believed to have belonged to King Alfred, the lantern carried by Guy Fawkes and riches form ancient Egypt and Greece. The **Bodleian Library**, founded in 1596, contains over one million volumes, including a copy of every book published in the UK since 1900.

Milton Keynes

Just north of Oxford at **Woodstock** sits **Blenheim Palace**, given to the first Duke of Marlborough by a grateful nation in 1705 after the eponymous victory and built between 1705 and 1722 by Sir John Vanburgh. It was the birthplace of Sir Winston Churchill and is one of Britain's most visited Great Houses.

TOP 10 Historic Houses Gardens and Parks

Ardington House, near Wantage
Broughton Castle,
  near Banbury, Oxon
Blenheim Palace, near Woodstock
Claydon House, Buckinghamshire
Cliveden, Berkshire.
Dorney Court, Windsor, Berks
Ashmolean, Bodleian & Oxford
  University's Botanic Garden,
Stonor Park, near Henley, Oxon.
Stowe Gardens and Park, Bucks.
Windsor Castle, Park and Savill
  Woodland Garden

TOP 10 Attractions

Bekonscot Model Village,
  Beaconsfield, Bucks
Bletchley Park, Milton Keynes
Chiltern Open Air Museum,
  Chalfont St Giles, Bucks
Cotswold Wildlife Park, Burford
Didcot Railway Museum, Oxon
Eton College and Chapel, Berks
Hellfire Caves, West Wycombe
Highclere Castle, Nr Newbury,
Legoland, Windsor
Waddesdon Manor &
  Rothschild Collection, Bucks

TOP 10 Walks and Nature Trails

Chess Valley Walk > Chenies >
  Chalfont & Latimer Sta, Bucks
Heritage Walk, Reading, Berks
Kennet & Avon Canal >
  Aldermarston, Berks
Look Out Countryside & Heritage
  Centre, Nr Reading, Berks
Ludgershall > Wotton House walk,
  Bucks
Mill End > Remenham > Aston
  Thamesside walk, Oxon
North Oakley > Hannington >
  White Hill, nr. Kingsclere, Berks
Guided Walking Tours, Oxford
The Ridgeway:
  Uffington White Horse (Oxon) to
  Caversham (Berks)
Riverside & Country Walk to
  Speen Moors, Berks

TOP 10 Historic Houses Gardens and Parks

Hampshire, Wiltshire & Dorset

Athelhampton House & Gardens, Dorchester, Dorset.
Abbotsbury Gardens, near Weymouth, Dorset
Beaulieu, New Forest, Hampshire
Bowood House & Gardens near Calne, Wiltshire
Broadlands ,Romsey, Hants
Longleat, near Bath, Wiltshire
Sir Harold Hillier Gardens & Arboretum near Romsey
Stratfield Saye, and Wellington Country Park, near Basingstoke
Stourhead, Stourton, near Warminster, Wilts
Wilton, near Salisbury, Wilts

TOP 10 Attractions

Avebury Stone Circles, Wiltshire
Corfe Castle, Weymouth, Dorset
Fords Abbey & Gardens, Chard
Lulworth Castle & Cove, Dorset
Marwell Zoological Park, Winchester, Hants
New Forest Museum & Visitor Centre, Ashurst, Hants
Osborne House, Cowes, I-O-W
Portsmouth Sea Life Centre & D-Day Museum, Hants
Royal Naval Museum, Portsmouth, Hants
Stonehenge, Avebury, Wiltshire

TOP 10 Walks and Nature Trails

Avebury > West Kennet Long Barrow > The Sanctuary, Wilts
Avon Valley Path, Salisbury to Christchurch
Hardy's Dorset Walk
Itchen Way: Southampton to Hinton Ampner
The Ridgeway: Avebury > Wantage
Solent Way: Milford-on-Sea to Emsworth
South West Coast Path from Bridport to Bournemouth
Test Way: Inkpen Hill to Romsey
Three Castles Path: Windsor to Winchester
Wayfarers Walk: Highclere to Hambledon, Hants

The **Solent** waterway between **Southampton** and the **Isle of Wight** is the sailing playground of southern England. The island itself has Queen Victoria's **Osborne House** to explore and the marinas of **Bembridge** and **Cowes**, with its famous regatta every August.

Portsmouth Harbour in **Hampshire** is home to Nelson's Victory, the Mary Rose, the restored Elizabethan galleon recently brought to the surface and HMS Warrior, Britain's first iron-clad warship. **Southampton** is a great port and maritime centre. The **New Forest** is home to wild deer and ponies and is the oldest forest in the UK. On the way north the visitor passes through **Winchester** with its 11-13th century cathedral and castle remains, where King Arthur's reputed Round Table can be viewed. **Beaulieu** and its **National Motor Museum** in the New Forest is a great family attraction.

Wiltshire to the West, was the cradle of Druidic and Saxon life and **Stonehenge** must be one of the seven wonders of Britain, a 'must see' for visitors. Nearby the **Avebury Stone Circle** is equally puzzling. **Salisbury** Cathedral's 404ft spire is the tallest in England. Southwest lies **Dorset**, Thomas Hardy's county, with the ancient cities of **Dorchester** (Roman remains) and **Casterbridg**e (modern day Shaftesbury). In **Cerne Abbas** the infamous 180ft high Chalk Giant looks down on the village. There are several other prehistoric earthworks and chalk horses carved into hillsides in this area. Dorset

Corfe Castle

also has the extraordinary **Jurassic Coast**, stretching from **Lyme Regis** to **Portland Bill** and including Chesil Beach, a 40ft bank of shingle stretching ten miles.

Lulworth Cove

Avebury

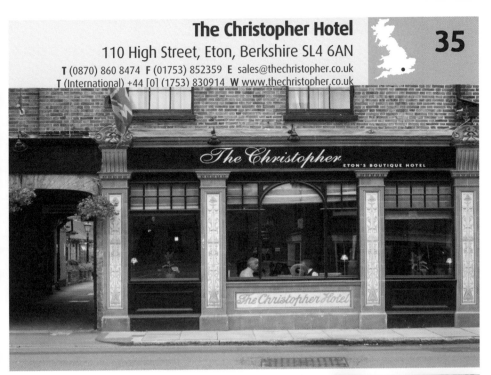

The Christopher Hotel

110 High Street, Eton, Berkshire SL4 6AN

35

T (0870) 860 8474 **F** (01753) 852359 **E** sales@thechristopher.co.uk
T (International) +44 [0] (1753) 830914 **W** www.thechristopher.co.uk

The Christopher Hotel in Eton is a former 17th century coaching inn with a colourful and elaborate past. Situated in a prominent position on Eton High Street, today it is a modern boutique hotel full of comfort and style and ideal for the discerning guest whether on business or pleasure. Guests will find 33 well equipped rooms of contemporary interior design using natural materials and organic colour schemes. Each room has a modem point and wireless Internet access. Bathrooms are bright and contemporary, with many little luxuries. Guests can unwind and enjoy snacks and beverages in the light and tastefully furnished wine bar, *Strok's* . Alternatively there is a discount on dinner in the nearby sister hotel Sir Christopher Wren's, which aslo has a fully equipped spa. The Christopher is ideally situated close to Windsor town centre, Slough and the M4 and near to the many attractions of the Thames Valley. Whatever the reason for your trip: overnight business stays, weekends away or visiting friends and family, the Christopher is the ideal choice.

🛏 33 🚻 ♿

Former 17th century coaching inn in Eton's High Street

Rates Single inc. breakfast from £100; double from £130   Ad

Other facilities Video + satellite TV. Health club, jacuzzi, sauna, massage, spa at sister hotel nearby.

 & major credit cards accepted. Open all year.

Directions
Leave M4 @ junc 6, A355 twds Windsor, rt to Eton, hotel on right

Nearby attractions
Windsor & Windsor Castle, Eton College, Dorney Lake, Savill G'dns

Distances
Maidenhead 2, Heathrow 8, London 19

Berkshire, Eton

Ye Olde Bell

High Street, Hurley, Nr. Maidenhead, Berkshire SL6 5LX

T (0870) 860 8497 **F** (01628) 825939 **E** oldebellres@dhillonhotels.co.uk
T (International) +44 [0] (1628) 825881 **W** www.dhillonhotels.co.uk

Ye Olde Bell at Hurley is where your publisher spent the first night of his honeymoon many years ago. Now back in the hands of a small group Dhillons Hotels (see Stoke Place and The Crown at Amersham in the following pages), it has now been refurbished and has a committed staff to the extent that we feel confident in recommending it once again to Signpost readers. Set in beautiful gardens and only 30 minutes from Heathrow, this charming inn dates back to 1135 and incorporates a 16th century Tudor barn, perfect for weddings, celebrations and conferences. The hotel offers a range of en suite bedrooms including some luxurious four posters. Wholesome British cuisine is available in the welcoming restaurant, which enjoys views of the gardens. The Bell is well situated for the airport, the motorway network, Maidenhead, Marlow and Henley, yet is very quiet, being at the end of a cul de sac. The river Thames is but a short walk away and there are several gardens and stately homes to visit in the area.

Inn of Norman origins situated just 30 minutes from Heathrow airport

47 (£10 per night) WIFI

Directions
Leave M4 junc 8/9, then A423 twds Henley. Hurley 1m off rd to right.

Nearby attractions
Windsor & Windsor Castle, Legoland Cliveden, Hambleview Lock.

Distances
Maidenhead 4, Henley 4, London 28

Rates Single inc. breakfast from £109; double from £119
Meals 3-cse tdh dinner £30; alc, lunch & diets avail; last orders 2200; bfst fm 0700.
Leisure breaks Weekend rate, b & b £99 per room.
Other facilities Satellite TV.

& major credit cards accepted. Open all year.

The Great House at Sonning

Thames Street, Sonning-on-Thames, Berkshire RG4 6UT

T (0870) 860 8482 **F** (0118) 944 1296 **E** greathouse@btconnect.com
T (International) +44 [0] (118) 969 2277 **W** www.greathouseatsonning.co.uk

37

The six separate buildings which form the Great House at Sonning are situated on a four-acre site with superb frontage to the river Thames. The oldest part of the Great House Estate was formerly the White Hart, which dates back to Elizabethan days. The recently reconstructed Sonning Clocktower has 18 new bedrooms, opened in August 2006, bringing the total to 59. All have the facilities expected of a hotel of this quality. Wireless broadband is now available in all bedrooms, meeting rooms and public areas. Sonning is a picturesque conservation village between Reading and Henley, with easy access to the A4 and M4. The Great House's rural, riverside location provides luxury accommodation and fine dining in the Regatta Restaurant. Conference facilities and weddings for up to 120 guests are fully catered for. During the summer months, you can dine *alfresco* on the terrace. If you see three men in a camping skiff glide by, don't be surprised! The Great House recalls an age of 1920s riverside elegance and style, blended with 21st century comforts.

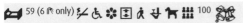

Well known riverside hotel with private moorings.

Rates Single inc. breakfast from £149; double from £179.
Meals Regatta and Ferrymans Restaurant. Alc, Sunday lunch, spec. diets available; last orders 2200 (2230 w/ends); bfst fm 0700 (0800 w'ends).
Leisure Breaks Fri/Sat/Sun £119 per double room b&b; £149 dinner, b & b.
Other activities Golf, spa, indoor swimming pool nearby.

Directions
 M4/end of A329M twds Reading. Trn right onto A4 then left twds Sonning.
Nearby attractions
Windsor & Windsor Castle, Mapledurham House, Eton College, Ascot
Distances
Reading 3, Maidenhead 13, London 33.

 & major credit cards accepted. Open all year.

Berkshire, Sonning

38

Sir Christopher Wren's House Hotel

Thames Street, Windsor, Berkshire SL4 1PX

T (0870) 860 8473 **F** (01753) 860172 **E** reservations@wrensgroup.com
T (International) +44 [0] (1753) 861354 **W** www.sirchristopherwren.co.uk

The building was designed and built by the celebrated architect Sir Christopher Wren, best known for the design of St Paul's Cathedral, whose father was the Dean of Windsor. The hotel nestles on the banks of the Thames by the pedestrian bridge to Eton. It opened in the 1920s as the Riverholme Restaurant and Guest House and was purchased by the privately owned Wren's Group in 1995. Substantial investment over the years has ensured that the hotel, whilst catering for the demands of today's traveller, preserves the charm of yesteryear. The 96 bedrooms feature a host of period features in line with the building's Grade II listing, while the modern health, fitness and beauty spa help to relieve the stress of today's hectic world. Sir Christopher Wren's House is within walking distance of Windsor Castle, the Theatre Royal and Windsor's other attractions. Strok's Restaurant overlooks the river and specialises in modern European cuisine. Bars include the Martini Bar, Champagne Terrace and the Pavilion. The hotel is conveniently located for Heathrow, Central London and the many attractions of the Thames Valley.

Comfortable hotel in the shadow of the castle overlooking the Thames

96 (15 only) 100 WIFI

Directions
M4 junc 6, A355 for Windsor, left at rdbt, then left at lights.

Nearby attractions
Windsor & Windsor Castle, Legoland Eton College, Ascot Racecourse.

Distances
M4 -3, Slough 2, Bagshot 10, London 21

Rates Single inc. breakfast from £175; double from £240. [Ad]
Meals Strok's AA ☺☺ Restaurant. Alc, lunch, spec. diets available; last orders 2145; bfst fm 0730.

 & major credit cards accepted. Open all year.

Berkshire, Windsor

The Crown Hotel

16 High Street, Old Amersham, Buckinghamshire HP7 0DH

T (0870) 860 8498 **F** (01494) 431283 **E** crownres@dhillonhotels.co.uk
T (International) +44 [0] (1494) 721541 **W** www.dhillonhotels.co.uk

The Crown is the latest addition to the Dhillon hotel group (see *The Bell at Hurley* and *Stoke Place* in this section). Once an Elizabethan coaching inn, The Crown found fame when it was featured in the hit comedy *Four Weddings and a Funeral* (see bedroom, bottom right). The addition of 14 contemporary styled rooms has created a delightful mixture of old world charm combined with contemporary facilities. With its full timber beams and open log fires, the Crown is the perfect setting for a romantic weekend break. This charming hotel also has a cobbled courtyard where you can enjoy *alfresco* dining during the summer months. Amersham High Street has Georgian houses and cobbled courtyards leading to thatched cottages. Its Market Hall and almshouses both date from the 17th century. The church, which was restored in the 19th century, dates from 1140 and has fine brasses and monuments. Although only 30 minutes from Central London and five miles from the M25, Amersham is on the edge of the gentle Chiltern Hills with the Ridgeway Path and several houses and gardens nearby to visit.

 37 (4 x 🛏) 🍴 ♿ ❀ ☺ ♻ 🖥 ♨ 🕸 ✝ WIFI

Old coaching inn in the centre of Amersham Old Town

Rates Single inc. breakfast from £110; double from £145
Meals 3-cse tdh dinner £40; alc, lunch, spec. diets available; last orders 2230 bfst fm 0700.
Leisure Breaks Weekend breaks, b & b, £99 per room.

Directions
From junc 1 M40 take A40, the n A413 to town centre.

Nearby attractions
Bekonscot Model Village, Chenies Manor House, Hughenden Manor.

Distances
Chesham 2, Beaconsfield 5, London 26

 & major credit cards accepted. Open all year.

Buckinghamshire, Amersham

40

Taplow House Hotel
Berry Hill, Taplow, Nr. Maidenhead, Bucks SL6 0DA

T (0870) 418 8128 F (01628) 783985 E reception@taplow.wrengroup.com
T (International) +44 [0] (1628) 670056 W www.taplowhouse.com

Taplow House, situated in six acres of beautiful gardens on the outskirts of a lovely old village in the Thames Valley, offers peaceful quiet for weary travellers. It dates from the 17th century and was originally a gift from King James I to Hampson, Governor of Virginia. Located near the magnificent forest of Burnham Beeches, Taplow has its own trees - an ancient cedar and Europe's largest and oldest tulip tree, planted by Queen Elizabeth I. Inside the 32 bedrooms are tastefully and elegantly designed to enhance your visit here. *Strok's* Restaurant over-looks the grounds and has been awarded two AA rosettes for use of best British produce. In Winter there is a roaring log fire and the attentiveness of the friendly staff will enhance your visit. There is also a relaxing and welcoming Whisky Bar with a wide selection of classic malts, other fine spirits and draft beer. Taplow offers a rare combination of period charm, great comfort, state-of-the-art business facilities and an outstanding restaurant just 15 minutes from Heathrow Airport and 10 from historic Windsor.

Comfortable hotel in extensive grounds near to all transport hubs

Directions Leave M4 Junc 7 (Slough West); left on A4 twds Maidenhead. Rt up Berry Hill 2m signed Taplow/Cliveden
Nearby attractions
Windsor & Windsor Castle, Thorpe Park, Legoland, Cliveden NT, Thames
Distances
Maidenhead 2, Heathrow 10, London 24

32 🛏 ... 100

Rates Single inc. breakfast from £80; double from £95.
Meals *Strok's* ◎◎ Restaurant. Alc, lunch, spec. diets & bar meals avail; last orders 2130; bfst fm 0700.
Leisure Breaks 1. Classic 1-nt dinner, b&b £160 based on two sharing. 2. Weekend Winddown 1 nt (fridays only acc to avail.) b&b £100 per rm inc. glass champagne on arrival. Others available - see website.

 & major credit cards accepted. Open all year.

Buckinghamshire, Taplow

Stoke Place

Stoke Green, Stoke Poges, Bucks SL2 4HT

T (0870) 860 8499 **F** (01753) 512743 **E** enquiries@stokeplace.co.uk
T (International) +44 [0] (1753) 534790 **W** www.stokeplace.co.uk

41

Stoke Place is an exquisite 17th century Queen Anne mansion set in 25 acres of secluded parkland, landscaped by Capability Brown. From 1764 until 1963 it had been in the Howard family. In 1967 a fire destroyed the middle section of the house. It has been beautifully and sympathetically restored to a luxurious boutique-style retreat, offering elegance combined with convenience, efficiency and sensational service. Perfectly situated for business or leisure, Stoke Place is within the conservation area of Stoke Green, yet located just 25 minutes from Central London. It's not difficult to immerse yourself in rural pastimes at Stoke Place. Outdoors there is clay pigeon shooting, fishing and picturesque walks. Inside you can relax in the newly restored drawing room, dine in the Garden Room, with its chandeliers, sumptuous furnishings and views over the grounds, savouring the modern British menu, before retiring to your individually appointed bedroom with its Frette bed linen, pocket sprung mattress, DVD player, wide plasma screen TV and 24-hour wireless internet connection.

29 5x WIFI

Gracious mansion with contemporarily styled bedrooms & public rooms

Rates Double/single room with breakfast from £200.
Meals Tdh dinner in Garden Room Restaurant £40; bar meals available; alc, lunch & diets available; last orders 2200; bfst fm 0700.
Leisure Breaks Weekend rate £210 per room b & b.
Other facilities Massage, CD players, satellite/SKY TV

Directions M4 Junc 6 to Slough then B416 twds Gerrards X. At Stoke Green Cnr, fork rt to Wexham Park Hosp. Hotel 50 yds on rt.
Nearby attractions
Windsor Castle, Cliveden, Legoland, Thorpe Park, Burnham Beeches.
Distances
Slough 2, Heathrow 10, Ctrl London 23

& major credit cards accepted. Open all year.

Buckinghamshire, Stoke Poges

42

Plumber Manor
Sturminster Newton, Dorset DT10 2AF
T (0870) 418 8024 **F** (01258) 473370 **E** book@plumbermanor.com
T (International) +44 [0] (1258) 472507 **W** www.plumbermanor.com

This imposing Jacobean manor house is set in idyllic countryside "far from the madding crowd". The Divelish stream weaves its way through delightful grounds, extensive lawns and fine old trees. Dating from the 17th century, the manor has been the home of the Prideaux-Brune family. Since 1973 the careful management of Richard, Alison, Brian (in the kitchen) and now Tim has led to the creation of a first class hotel and restaurant. Richard knows many of his regular diners personally and is always on hand for advice, both about current dishes on the ever changing menu and about what to see in this charming part of Dorset. When we dined there last year we tried the excellent 'medley of seafood' starter, followed by succulent *medallions de boeuf*. Do remember to leave room for one of the excellent Plumber puddings! The wine list is of the same standard, well-chosen and with ever changing freshness. There are six elegant bedrooms within the main house and a further ten in the courtyard and converted barn. Plumber is welcoming, comfortable and has a charming atmosphere in which to relax and savour first class hospitality, cuisine and service.

Family-owned Jacobean manor house 'far from the madding crowd'

🛏 16 ⌂ 🛗 ♨ (16) ⚲ 🐕 (by arr't)

Directions
Turn lft opp Sturminster Mill on A357 in Stur Newt on Hazlebury Bryan rd. Hotel on lft

Nearby attractions
Abbotsbury Tourisn, Weymouth, Sherborne Castle, Fleet Air Arm, Ilchester.

Distances
Blandford 8, Sherborne 12, London 125.

Rates Single room with breakfast from £95; double inc. bfst from £110.

Meals 2-cse tdh dinner £24/3-cse £27.50. Alc, lunch & spec. diets available; last orders 2130.

Sensibly priced short breaks Min 2-night stay bed & breakfast £100-150 per couple per night/3 nights £90-140 per couple per night. Nov 1st-March 31st.

Other facilities Fishing, golf, riding, shooting nearby by arrangement.

 & major credit cards accepted. Hotel open early March- late January.

Dorset, Sturminster Newton

Manor House Hotel

Studland Bay, Nr. Swanage, Dorset BH19 3AU

T (0870) 418 8023 **F** (01929) 452255 **E** themanorhousehotel@lineone.net
T (International) +44 [0] (1929) 450288 **W** www.themanorhousehotel.com

43

The site of the Manor House is mentioned in the Domesday Book and parts of the present rambling Gothic house date back to 1750. Set within 20 acres of elevated grounds, the hotel commands beautiful views overlooking the beaches and waters of Studland Bay. History and character are in abundance; the hotel's medieval carvings are said to have come from the residential quarters of Corfe Castle, home of the famous Mary Banks, who defended it so bravely against Cromwell's troops. Most of the en suite bedrooms (four with four-poster beds) have spectacular views over the bay and out to Old Harry Rocks. Wall carvings in the Westminster Bedroom are of particular interest, reputed to have come from the Old Palace of Westminster, circa 1636.
A delightful conservatory has extended the dining area, where décor is sophisticated, and the atmosphere and service is most warming. The menu has an excellent choice of fresh local produce and the delicious Studland Lobster is a must! The Manor House is an ideal base from which to explore the beauty, beaches and nature trails of Studland and surrounding Dorset.

🛏 21 ⌂ ⛰ ⌕ 🐴 ⚲

Gothic manor house set in 20 acre grounds overlooking Studland Bay.

Rates Dinner, room & breakfast from £82 per person.
Meals Spec. diets and bar lunches available; last orders 2100.
Leisure Breaks Three night special = 15% off daily rate; 5 night special = 20% off daily rate. Weekly rates also available.
Other activities Riding (¼m). golf (1m). Children over 5 welcome.

 & major credit cards accepted. Hotel closed 3 weeks in January.

Directions A351 or A352 to Wareham, then left at Corfe Castle B3351 to Studland. Take Rectory La in cntr of village.
Nearby attractions Brownsea Island, Corfe Castle, Kingston Lacy.
Distances Swanage 3, B'nemth 8 (fry), London 135

Dorset, Studland Bay

Knoll House Hotel
Studland Bay, Dorset BH19 3AH
T (0870) 418 8022 F (01929) 450423 E info@knollhouse.co.uk
T (International) +44 [0] (1929) 450450 W www.knollhouse.co.uk

This delightful hotel is situated on the finest stretch of Dorset heritage coastline surrounded by some of the prettiest countryside in the West and it is well worth a visit. It is within a National Trust Reserve and overlooks three miles of golden beach with first class swimming, fishing, boating and windsurfing. Knoll House is an independent country house hotel under the personal management of its family owners and is set in pine trees with the most attractive gardens where you can relax away from the cares of everyday life. The sporting facilities are numerous - tennis courts, a nine-hole par 3 golf course and outdoor heated level deck swimming pool. For relaxation there is a sauna, steam-room, Jacuzzi, plunge-pool and gym set in a marvellous health spa complex with fruit juice and coffee bar. Many of the bedrooms are arranged as suites, ideal for families. Log fires and an attractive cocktail bar add to the unique atmosphere of this extremely efficiently run hotel. The quality, choice and presentation of the menus is excellent. At lunchtime a superb hors d'oeuvres selection and buffet table laden with cold meats, pies and salads is a speciality, followed by delicious puddings and a good English cheese board. Young children are catered for in their own dining room and there are many and varied facilities to keep them amused all day. Sandbanks and Bournemouth are easily reached via the car ferry. Dorchester, Corfe Castle and the picturesque villages of Dorset are only a short drive away.

Dorset, Studland Bay

45

🛏 79 (inc 30 ⬜) 🐕 🔺 ⛷ 🏋 🔍 🍷 🐾 ♨ 🚣 📶 🐟 🎱 🍽 🔫 ♨ 🐕 (£4)

Traditional family country house hotel with outstanding views.

Rates Half board from £102 daily or full board (weekly) from £820 (April) to £1030 (August). Generous full board terms for five nights out of season.

Special Breaks Family Five' (two adults, one or two children under 13) - five nights full board in low season £930. Purbeck Five (single or twin rooms without private bathroom) five nights full board in low season £375 per person. September 14th-October 17th, two nights full board £208-£230 per person. Prices include VAT & service .

Other facilities Isle of Purbeck Golf Club (2 courses) 2 m; Childrens' dining room; Studland Riding Stables (1m); childrens' playground. Broadband wireless connectivity in the main lounges.

C Cards Mastercard & Visa accepted. Hotel open Easter-end October.

Directions
A351 to Corfe Castle, then B3351 through Studland. Hotel on left.

Nearby attractions
Brownsea Island, Poole Harbour, Jurassic Coast, Lulworth Cove.

Distances
Swanage 3, Bournemouth 7 (via ferry), London 113 (Heathrow two hours).

Dorset, Studland Bay

46

Springfield Country House Hotel & Leisure Club
Grange Road, Stoborough, Wareham, Dorset BH20 5AL
T (0870) 418 8025 F (01929) 551862 E enquiries@springfield-country-hotel.co.uk
T (International) +44 [0] (1929) 552177 W www.thespringfield.co.uk

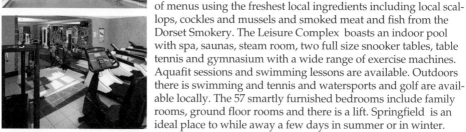

Springfield Country Hotel is a family run hotel set in six acres of beautiful landscaped gardens at the foot of the Purbeck Hills in the scenic Dorset countryside. The hotel is ideally suited for visiting such local attractions as Lulworth Cove, Durdle Door, Corfe Castle, Dorchester (Hardy's *Casterbridge*), the Army Tank Museum at Bovington, Poole and Swanage. There is a choice of two dining rooms and excellent facilities for private banquets, conferences and meetings. The Mill View restaurant offers a wide choice of menus using the freshest local ingredients including local scallops, cockles and mussels and smoked meat and fish from the Dorset Smokery. The Leisure Complex boasts an indoor pool with spa, saunas, steam room, two full size snooker tables, table tennis and gymnasium with a wide range of exercise machines. Aquafit sessions and swimming lessons are available. Outdoors there is swimming and tennis and watersports and golf are available locally. The 57 smartly furnished bedrooms include family rooms, ground floor rooms and there is a lift. Springfield is an ideal place to while away a few days in summer or in winter.

Country house in the heart of Dorset with all the facilities of a modern hotel.

Directions A351 Wareham by-pass twds Corfe Castle. Brown hotel sign on rt
Nearby attractions Lulworth Cove, Durdle Door, Corfe Castle, Bovington Army Tank Mus'm
Distances B'nemth 13, Dorchester 16, London 117

Rates Single room with breakfast from £85; double/twin from £120.
Meals Grange restaurant 3-cse tdh £24.50; alc, lunch & spec. diets avail; last orders 2130.
Leisure Breaks Min two-night stay inc tdh dinner & breakfast from £140 per couple per night.
Other activities Aerobics theatre. Fishing, golf, sailing & watersports nearby.

 & major credit cards accepted. Open all year.

Dorset, Wareham

The Priory Hotel

Church Green, Wareham, Dorset BH20 4ND

T (0870) 860 8500 F (01929) 554519 E reservations@theprioryhotel.co.uk
T (International) +44 [0] (1929) 551666 W www.theprioryhotel.co.uk

47

Tucked away in a quiet corner of Wareham, an idyllic and enviable location where peace and tranquility prevails, the Priory Hotel stands on the banks of the river Frome in over four acres of lovingly cultivated English cottage gardens with superb views of the river, the valley and the hills beyond. The *modern* building is less than 450 years old 'though the Priory's history goes back much further. For 500 years there were monks in residence and before that it was a convent. Luxury rooms, some of which open onto the river, are either in the main house or located in the hotel's Boathouse, with its own landscaped gardens. Boathouse rooms all have luxury spa/whirlpool baths. Lunch is normally served in the delightful Garden Room and in the summer *alfresco* in dappled shade whilst watching the boats go by. Afterwards perhaps a game of croquet on the lawn with afternoon tea or champagne and strawberries or simply a walk along the riverbank. Dinner is served in the Abbots Cellar Restaurant, an ambient setting in which to enjoy the elegant cuisine. Pre-dinner drinks and canapes can be enjoyed in the Cloisters Bar or Drawing Room.

🛏 18 (inc 🛏) 🚭 ☉ 🔟 ♪ ❋ 🕺 🎱 24 🅿 30

Historic hotel on the banks of the river Frome in four acres of garden.

Rates Single/double room with breakfast from £210.
Meals Abbots Cellar & Garden Room restaurants 3-cse tdh £38.50; alc lunch & spec. diets avail; last orders 2145; bfst fm 0730 (0830 Suns/Bank Hols).

Other activities Golf, riding, sea bathing, shooting nearby.

Major credit cards accepted. Open all year.

Directions
A351 Wareham fm Bournemouth. Hotel at sth'n end of town by parish church.

Nearby attractions
Corfe Castle, Brownsea Island, Poole Harbour, Jurassic Coast.

Distances
B'nemth 13, Dorchester 16, London 117

Dorset, Wareham

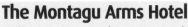

48

The Montagu Arms Hotel
Palace Lane, Bealieu, Hampshire SO42 7ZL

T (0870) 860 8501 F (01590) 612188 E reservations@montaguarmshotel.co.uk
T (International) +44 [0] (1590) 612324 W www.montaguarmshotel.co.uk

In the heart of Beaulieu village, albeit easily accessible, the Montagu Arms achieves an aura of total seclusion. Each room, named after a type of tree is individually decorated and furnished, some being suites. The conservatory makes an ideal place for drinks before dining in The Terrace, an oak-panelled AA ☺☺ restaurant overlooking the beautiful terraced gardens cascading with plants and shrubs. Local meat, game and seafood feature on the menu according to seasonal availability. Alternatively guests may choose the informal Brasserie known as *Monty's*. This is a lively oak panelled bar in keeping with the 17th century origins of the building. *Monty's* offers the best home cooked food, blending traditional British and European influences, with hand drawn beer available. Guests may upgrade to have complimentary access to the health club facilities at Senspa about five miles away, including use of swimming pool, jacuzzi, sauna and state of the art fitness suite. The hotel hosts private functions, conferences and weddings. Discounted green fees are available to residents at both Brockenhurst and Lyndhurst golf clubs.

Secluded hotel in the middle of the New Forest, known for its cuisine

🛏 22 ✳ ⚘ ❀ ⚕ ⚔ ⚘ ⚏ 10/30 🅿 80 WIFI 🐾

Directions M27 Junc 1/A337 to Lyndhurst, then B3056 to Beaulieu, left on B3054 twds Dibden Purlieu, hotel on rt

Nearby attractions
Exbury Garden, Beaulieu Motor Museum, Palace House & Abbey.

Distances
Lymington 7, Lyndhurst 8, London 100

Rates Single/double room with breakfast from £185. [Ad]
Meals Terrace Restaurants 3-cse tdh £42; also Monty's Bar & Brasserie; alc, lunch & spec. diets avail; last orders 2130; bfst fm 0700.
Other activities Golf, riding, fishing, sailing, sea bathing, shooting, watersports nearby. All residents also have access to the Health Club facilities - pool, jacuzzi, sauna, steam room & fitness suite - at Senspa nearby.

 & major credit cards accepted. Open all year.

Hampshire, Beaulieu

Careys Manor Hotel & Senspa

Lyndhurst Road, Brockenhurst, Hampshire SO42 7RH

T (0870) 860 8407 **F** (01590) 622799 **E** info@careysmanor.com
T (International) +44 [0] (1590) 623551 **W** www.careysmanor.com

49

Only 90 minutes from London and between Bournemouth and Southampton, this highly commended elegant Victorian hotel is an ideal place from which to explore the New Forest - perhaps by bicycle. Enjoying a relaxing short break and make use of the hotel's health club. Discover the luxury Thai Senspa offering indulgent spa treatments and state of the art hydrotherapy facilities. A range of spa breaks are available. The hotel is also an ideal place for conferences, meetings and team building events. Bedrooms in the old Manor House are traditional in design and unique in character, whilst rooms in the garden wing have either a terrace or a balcony with views over the well maintained landscaped gardens. In the AA ◎◎ fine dining Manor Restaurant, the menu is Classic British with French influences. A less formal alternative, *Blaireau's Bar & Brasserie*, is situated in the hotel grounds. The Zen Garden Restaurant serves a fusion of Eastern and Western dishes, freshly prepared by Thai chefs. Guests have full use of the health club facilities including the ozone treated swimming pool, jacuzzi, steam room and fitness suite.

🛏 79 ⚲ ♨ ♗ 🔟 ⚐ ⚒ 🎿 ♨ ⚗ 🕭 ⚍100 🅿 140 🐾

Luxurious hotel and oriental spa in the heart of the New Forest.

Rates Single room with breakfast from £139; double/twin from £178.
Meals Manor Restaurant; alc, lunch & spec. diets avail; last orders 2145.
Leisure Breaks 20% disc on b&b selective dates, subj to avail. 1-3 night spa breaks inc full board accom, lunch in Zen Garden Rest't, use of health cllub, Senspa facilities & treatments, from £165 per pers per nt.
Other activities Massage, treatments. Golf, riding and sailing nearby.

& major credit cards accepted. Open all year.

Directions
M3 Southampton, then M27 junc 1 A337 thru Lyndhurst. Careys at entrance to town.
Nearby attractions
Nat'l Motor Museum Beaulieu, Wilton House, Exbury Gardens, Broadlands.
Distances
Lymington 4, Southampton 15, London 99

Le Poussin at Whitley Ridge
Beaulieu Road, Brockenhurst, Hampshire SO42 7QL
T (0870) 418 8108 **F** (01590) 622856 **E** whitleyridge@lepoussin.co.uk
T (International) +44 [0] (1590) 622354 **W** www.whitleyridge.co.uk

Set in the heart of the New Forest in ten acres of open parkland, close to the river Lymington, stands Whitley Ridge, once a Royal Hunting Lodge. Le Poussin are proud to be in their second year at Whitley Ridge where their unbranded family run unique style has once again proved a success. The main focus of Le Poussin is food. They have held three AA ❀❀❀ for over ten years with the emphasis on the freshest local produce, seen in dishes such as local wild venison with New Forest haggis. All bedrooms are individually furnished and almost all offer stunning views over the grounds to the New Forest, where it is not uncommon to see a herd of deer grazing and buzzards circling in your airspace. With the constant green blanket of the forest enfolding you, peace and tranquility are top of the menu at Whitley Ridge. Public rooms are elegant and relaxing with roaring log fires on colder days. Some of the best woodland walks in the country start from the hotel. Superb horse riding and golf is also within easy reach. The hotel can arrange courtesy transport from Brockenhurst station as well as to *Simply Poussin*, our brasserie in the Village.

Small hotel with great cuisine on the edge of the New Forest.

🛏 14 ⚡ ✆ ⚘ ᎯᎯᎯ20 🅿 30

Directions From North turn left on B3055, signed Beaulieu, past Balmer Lawn hotel. Under rlwy br, hotel on left.

Nearby attractions
Nat'l Motor Museum Beaulieu, Exbury Gardens, Broadlands. Bucklers Hard

Distances
Lymington 4, Southampton 15, London 99

Rates Single room with breakfast from £90; double/twin from £110.
Meals 3-cse tdh dinner £39.50; alc, Sun lunch & spec. diets avail; last orders 2145.

Leisure Breaks Stay two nights and get the third free if you eat in our restaurant. Excludes Public Holidays.
Other activities Golf, riding nearby.

 & major credit cards accepted. Open all year.

Hampshire, Brockenhurst

Stanwell House Hotel & Bistro

15 High Street, Lymington, Hampshire SO41 7AA

T (0870) 860 8406 F (01590) 677756 E sales@stanwellhousehotel.co.uk
T (International) +44 [0] (1590) 677123 W www.stanwellhousehotel.co.uk

51

Every aspect of Stanwell House, be it décor, furnishings or materials is an expression of the owners' eclectic taste. Guests are presented with a vibrant hotel whose every surface and fabric bursts with fruity bejewelled shades of colour. Velvets and silks adorn windows and cover plump cushions. Burnished bare floorboards and York stone floors and a selection of junk shop finds, prints and antiques create a rich riot of images. Service is friendly and unobtrusive yet efficient in a gentle, relaxed, romantic and yet slightly decadent atmosphere. Dining is either in the candlelit Bistro or in the lofty conservatory which opens onto an attractive sheltered walled garden and patio - a good spot for afternoon tea. Each bedroom is different, from suites with roof terraces, through four-posters and Georgian rooms to the adjoining new 2-bedroom Elgar's Cottage, which can be let for self-catering. Stanwells clothing shop next door stocks up-to-the-minute designer leisure wear, accessories and shoes. This characterful hotel is ideal for a short break or as a base for the many activities in the area.

 29 (inc 🛏) 🚭 ☺ 🐕 🎚 50 🎣

Rates Single with breakfast from £85; double from £110.
Meals Stanwells Bistro; alc, lunch & spec. diets avail; last orders 2130.
Leisure Breaks Please check the website for special offers.

Other activities Riding, sailing, fishing, shooting nearby.

 & major credit cards accepted. Open all year.

Vibrant hotel in the heart of New Forest yachting centre.

Directions
Left off A 337 in Lymington signed station and Hythe. Hotel cnr High St/Captains Row

Nearby attractions
Broadlands, Beaulieu Motor Mus'm, Furzey Gdns, Cranborne Manor.

Distances
Lyndhurst 8, Bournem'th 16, London 92

Hampshire, Lymington

Chewton Glen - The Hotel, Health & Country Club
New Milton, Hampshire BH25 6QS
T (0870) 418 8028 **F** (01425) 272310 **E** reservations@chewtonglen.com
T (International) +44 [0] (1425) 275341 **W** www.chewtonglen.com

Look for a great team, a fine building situated close to the sea and on the edge of the New Forest , less than a two-hour drive from southwest London and you have found Chewton Glen. Offering consistently high standards and attention to detail in all areas, it is the only privately owned 5-red star hotel in the UK and has consistently set standards which others hotels can only aspire to. The high point of your stay will probably be dining in the spacious airy restaurant with views from many tables over the immaculate gardens. Preparation, presentation and service are of the highest standard, possibly equalled elsewhere, but certainly not surpassed. The hotel has 58 first class bedrooms including some on the ground floor overlooking the golf course, others a mix of traditional bedrooms and suites with balconies and terraces, all with views over the immaculate gardens. The hotel's 130 acres of woods, gardens and fields form a perfect setting for a myriad of activities. The spa facilities are top class. If asked to sum up my visit, I would say *"Ask and you shall get is the philosophy here."*

Luxury hotel, spa & country club between the New Forest and the sea

58 (AC) 🛏 100 P 100

Directions
A35 Lyndhurst to Christchurch Rd, left at Walkford, 'Ringwood Rd' to Chewton Fm Rd

Nearby attractions
Broadlands, Beaulieu Motor Mus'm, Furzey Gdns, Cranborne Manor.

Distances
Lymington 7, B'nemth 10, London 97

Rates Single/double room with breakfast from £290; junior suite from £445; suite from £545. Half board rate, inc tdh dinner from £445 2 people sharing.
Meals Tdh dinner £62.50; alc, lunch & spec. diets avail; last orders 2115.
Leisure Breaks Special spa breaks from £226 per person. Golf & tennis breaks available. Special offers throughout the year.
Other activities Riding, sailing, fishing, shooting nearby.

& major credit cards accepted. Open all year.

Hampshire, New Milton

The Priory Bay Hotel
Priory Drive, Seaview, Isle of Wight PO34 5BU

T (0870) 418 8030 F (01983) 616539 E enquiries@priorybay.co.uk
T (International) +44 [0] (1983) 613146 W www.priorybay.co.uk

53

This exclusive 70-acre estate was originally built by medieval monks and is now probably the finest hotel on the Isle of Wight. Its mixture of medieval, Tudor and Georgian buildings have been carefully restored into a unique Country House Hotel by the sea. Superior rooms are in the main building, whereas those in the converted barn outbuildings are more suitable for families. Self-catering cottages are also available. A nice touch, especially for the nautically inclined, is the provision upon retiring, of a printed weather forecast in bedrooms. Subject to weather conditions, you can arrive in style - the hotel will send its own launch to Portsmouth and land you on its own beach. It also has a civil wedding licence. Dinner in the spacious dining room will be the highlight of the day, local game and seafood as well as produce from the hotel's own garden being used where possible. Or in the summer you can dine at the beachside Priory Oyster restaurant. Cuisine is complemented by an exceptional wine list. To aid digestion, a summer stroll exploring the woodland and beach walks is recommended - an ideal end to a great day in a memorably relaxing setting.

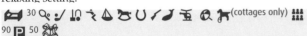

Secluded hotel with old and new wings set in a 70-acre estate.

Rates Single room with breakfast from £65; double/twin from £100.
Meals Tdh dinner AA ◎ £29.50; alc, lunch & spec. diets avail; last orders 2115
Leisure Breaks Reductions for 3-7 nights.
Other activities Beach walks, watersports nearby.

Directions
Take B3330 Ryde-St Helens Rd. Turn left in Nettlestone for Priory Bay.
Nearby attractions
Brading Downs, Osborne House, Isle of Wight Steam Railway.
Distances
Ryde 3, Bembridge 3, Cowes 9, London 77

 & major credit cards accepted. Open all year.

Isle of Wight, Seaview

The Hambrough

Hambrough Road, Ventnor, Isle of Wight PO38 1SQ

T (0870) 860 8509 **F** (01983) 857260 **E** info@thehambrough.com
T (International) +44 [0] (1983) 856333 **W** www.thehambrough.com

Style is the hallmark of this stunning new boutique hotel set high above the harbour at the southern end of Ventnor Bay, with stunning views of the coastline and scenic views of St Boniface Down to the rear. Two of the Hambrough's newly presented bedrooms are 'luxury' with sitting areas and balconies where guests can relax and sip a cocktail with the vista of colourful yachts drifting below. Décor is minimalist throughout. Bedrooms are contemporary with invitingly comfortable beds, flat screen TVs and DVD players - even an expresso machine. Bathrooms are a joy with underfloor heating and deluxe baths and showers. The relaxing bar is particularly welcoming for a morning coffee break, a light lunch, a sundowner or a nightcap after the superbly presented dinner in the AA ✿✿ restaurant. Chef Craig Atchison is a master of his craft, producing the most imaginative and inspired gourmet cuisine from the finest and freshest ingredients available from the market daily. Golf, sailing, riding and tennis can be arranged. Picnic hampers can be made up for those taking a coastal or down walk or a slow peaceful stroll through the calming Botanic Gardens nearby.

Smart boutique hotel with acclaimed restaurant, overlooking Ventnor Bay

🛏 7 (1 ☗ only) ⚜ 🗖 ⏣ 🎿 ⚏ 20

Directions From Cowes/Newport take A3020 twds Shanklin. After Sandford rt on B3327 to Ventnor.

Nearby attractions
Botanic Gardens, Blackgang Chine, Tropical Bird Pk, Appledurcombe Hse

Distances
Cowes 21, Newport 15, London 91

Rates Single/double room with breakfast from £95.
Meals Tdh 3-cse dinner £35; alc, lunch & spec diets available. Last orders 2130' bfst fm 0800.

Other activities Beach walks, watersports, sailing, fishing, squash, shooting, golf, tennis, riding all within five miles.

Visa, Mastercard, Switch, Maestro, Delta cards accepted. Open all year.

Isle of Wight, Ventnor

The Cotswold Lodge Hotel

66a Banbury Road, Oxford OX2 6JP

55

T (0870) 418 8032 F (01865) 512490 E sig@cotswoldgehotel.co.uk
T (International) +44 [0] (1983) 856333 W www.cotswoldlodgehotel.co.uk

The elegant 4-star Cotswold Lodge Hotel is a delightfully peaceful retreat, set in a conservation area only half a mile from the historic dreaming spires of Oxford city centre. Bedrooms are very comfortable - each floor having a different style and the 10 individually designed deluxe rooms and suites resemble those in a country manor. Downstairs the drawing room is smartly furnished with antiques. Magazines and flowers are in abundance. The Scholars Bar is the perfect meeting place for a light lunch or to relax with a drink in the evening. Cuisine in the hotel's restaurant *Sixty Six A*, refurbished in 2006, is under the supervision of head chef Garin Chapman and is international with well thought out dishes to suit every palate. The quality of food is exceptional: freshly baked bread, free-range eggs, specially made sausages, free range local poultry, fresh cod and lobster from Cornwall, wild salmon from Scotland and local lamb and game. The air-conditiond conference room has also been refurbished and has space for 90 delegates. The patio and courtyard are ideal for *al fresco* dining and drinks. The hotel is excellently placed for leisure breaks in Oxford or the Cotswolds and is highly recommended for both business and pleasure.

🛏 49 ♟ 90 🅿 50

Rates Single room with breakfast from £95; double fm £125; suite fm £175.
Meals Alc 3-cse dinner from £17.50; lunch & spec diets available. Last orders 2130.
Leisure Breaks Fri/Sat/Sun dinner (to value of £25 per head), b & b £225 per couple per night.
Other facilities Broadband in all bedrooms by 2005. Swimming pools, riding, golf nearby.

 & major credit cards accepted. Open all year.

Smart hotel within walking distance of Oxford city centre.

Directions
M40/A40 to Oxford, northern ring road then Banbury Rd sth to corner Norham Rd.

Nearby attractions
The Ashmolean, Bodleian Library, Blenheim Palace, Botanic Garden.

Distances
Banbury 23, Wycombe 26, London 56

Oxfordshire, Oxford

The Lamb at Hindon
High Street, Hindon, Wiltshire SP3 6DP
T (0870) 418 8166 **F** (01747) 820605 **E** nick@boisdale.co.uk
T (International) +44 [0] (1747) 820573 **W** www.boisdale.co.uk

The Lamb is situated in the attractive village of Hindon, just two miles from the A303 and dates back to the 12th century, when it was already a coaching inn. The new owners have refurbished the 14 bedrooms, (three have four poster beds) with warm decor and tartan carpets, yet retained the period feel of each. Each has Sky TV and LCD wide screen TVs. High standards are offered in a relaxed atmosphere in the bar and dining areas. Meals are well prepared and served. The emphasis is on market-fresh fish, game in season and well-chosen meat dishes. Ingredients are always fresh and sourced, where possible, from the best local or Scottish suppliers. Wines have been carefully selected, many of them from independent growers rarely seen in the UK. The Lamb, Whisky & Cigar Bar offers reputedly the largest choice of malts in Wiltshire as well as a good selection of Cuban cigars. The Lamb makes an ideal base for a romantic country break, for Wincanton races, for a shooting party or as a journey break en route to the South-West. Stonehenge, Salisbury and Shaftesbury are but a short drive away.

Former coaching inn in centre of picturesque Wiltshire village

🛏 14 ♟ 22 🅿 20-25

Directions
From East take M3/A303 til 6m after Deptford, left to Fonthill Bishop, rt 1m to Hindon

Nearby attractions
Stonehenge, Wilton, Longleat, Stourhead House & Gardens, Salisbury.

Distances
Shaftesbury 8, Salisbury 21, London 107

Rates Single room with breakfast from £70; double fm £99.

Meals Alc, tdh, lunch & spec. diets available. Last orders 2130; bfst fm 0730.

Other facilities Fishing, shooting, stalking, golf, riding nearby

 & major credit cards accepted. Open all year.

Wiltshire, Hindon

Signpost Guide 2007
London & South East

Fact File
Illustrated Guide to
Historic Houses and Gardens,
Attractions and Walks

London & South East

Fun-filled resorts along 257 miles of coastline, interesting harbours, glorious countryside, historic heritage, lovely gardens, hundreds of different places to visit and the capital's buzz and history - the South East has it all. With two of the country's main airports and the Channel tunnel, the South East is gateway for most of the country's 28 million annual overseas visitors.

GREATER LONDON

SURREY

KENT

WEST SUSSEX

EAST SUSSEX

Hotels guide

London	page 62
Kent	page 72
Surrey	page 79
East Sussex	page 83
West Sussex	page 94

Further information:
Visit London
6th floor, 2 More London Riverside,
London SE1 2RD
Tel: 0870 156 6366
www.visitlondon.com

Tourism South East
40 Chamberlayne Road,
Eastleigh, Hampshire SO5 5JH
Tel: 02380 625525
www.tourismse.com

Bodiam Castle

London

London's treasures are well chronicled. Most visitors prefer to stay in the West/Central Knightsbridge/Kensington areas which are handy for shopping, museums and quick access to the West End.

In the **Central/West End** area the most visited sights are the now public rooms of **Buckingham Palace**, the **National Gallery** in Trafalgar Square, **Tate Britain** on Millbank, **Westminster Abbey**, **Houses of Parliament** and **Cabinet War Rooms**. Westminster Abbey, nearly a thousand years old, has tombs of many English kings, queens, statesmen and writers. The **British Museum** in Bloomsbury houses one of the world's largest lections of antiquities, including the Magna Carta, the Elgin Marbles and the first edition of *Alice in Wonderland*. This entire area can be well viewed from **The London Eye** on the South Bank.

Further **East**, in the city of London, is **St Pauls Cathedral**, redesigned by Sir Christopher Wren. Nearby is the **Tower of London**, a medieval fortress dominated by the White Tower and dating from 1097. The Crown Jewels are kept here, guarded by the famous Beefeaters.

In **North Central** London are the **Planetarium** and **Madame Tussauds**, although the **London Dungeon**, near London Bridge Station, has recently overtaken Tussaud's Chamber of Horrors as childrens' favourite gruesome waxwork collection.

London's parks are its lungs. **St James**, the oldest, was founded by Henry VIII in 1532. **Hyde Park**, bordering Kensington, Mayfair and Marylebone, is the largest at 630 acres. **Regents Park**, with its zoo, lies north of Oxford Circus and was given to the nation by the Prince Regent.

To the **South east** of the capital, land has been reclaimed. **Canary Wharf** and the **Docklands** area provide an interesting study or urban renewal. On the south bank opposite Docklands are **Greenwich Observatory**, the **National Maritime Museum** and the **Millennium Dome**.

Kent

Kent is the Garden of England with hectares of hop growing fields and now over 70 vineyards, some open to visitors. The formidable **White Cliffs of Dover** have served as a bulwark against foreign invaders since time immemorial. Now they overlook some of the busiest shipping lanes in the world. The **Channel Tunnel** has replaced some ferries but hovercraft still ply between Dover/Folkestone and the French and Belgian coast.

Canterbury Cathedral

Kent's oldest city, **Canterbury**, is the centre of the Anglican faith, brought to Southern Britain by St Augustine landing in Sandwich Bay *(in AD596)* nearby. It is also the site of St Thomas a Becket's martyrdom. The flatland of **Romney Marsh** lies to the south, gradually reclaimed from the sea since Roman times. To the north is the **Weald of Kent** with its distinctive oast houses and orchards.

 Historic Houses Gardens and Parks

Boughton Monchelsea Place, Near Maidstone
Canterbury Cathedral
Chartwell, Westerham
Chiddingstone Castle, Edenbridge
Deal Castle
Dover Castle & Wartime Tunnels
Hever Castle & Gardens, Edenbridge
Leeds Castle & Gardens, Near Maidstone
Penshurst Place & Gardens, Near Tonbridge
Sissinghurst Garden, nr. Cranbrook

 Attractions

The Canterbury Tales, Canterbury
The Dickens Centre, Rochester
Dreamland Amusement Park, Margate
Eurotunnel Exhibition Centre, Folkestone
Howletts Zoo Park, nr Canterbury
Kent Battle of Britain Museum, Folkestone
Kent Garden Vineyard, Headcorn,
Knole, nr. Sevenoaks
Lullingstone Castle & Roman Villa, Nr. Swanley
Romney, Hythe & Dymchurch Model Railway

TOP 10 Walks and Nature Trails

Bewl Water Walks & Rides, Lamberhurst
Cobtree Manor Park Nature Trail
The Ecological Park, Elms Vale
Greensand Way: Chartwell > Mereworth > Ashford
Haysden Country Park Nature Trail
North Downs Way: Westerham to Chatham/Canterbury
Saxon Shore Way (north), Gravesend > Chatham > Whitstable > Sandwich
Saxon Shore Way (south), Rye > Folkestone > Sandwich
The Western Heights, Dover
White Cliffs Country Trail, var. walks around Kent

60

TOP 10 Historic Houses Gardens and Parks

Claremont Landscape Garden, Esher
Ham House, Richmond-upon-Thames
Hampton Court Palace, East Molesey
Kew Royal Botanic Gardens, Richmond
Loseley Park, Guildford
Painshill Landscape Garden, Cobham
Polesden Lacey, Gt Bookham, Nr. Dorking
RHS Garden, Wisley, Nr. Woking
The Savill Garden, Nr Egham
Winkworth Arboretum, Hascombe, Goldalming

TOP 10 Attractions

Birdworld, Nr. Franham
Brooklands Museum, Weybridge
Chessington World of Adventures
Devil's Punchbowl/Gibbet Hill, Godalming
Gatwick Zoo, Charlwood
Hyland House Museum, Guildford
Marble Hill House/Orleans House, Richmond
Public Record Office, Richmond
Thorpe Amusement Park, Egham
Wimbledon Lawn Tennis Museum

TOP 10 Walks and Nature Trails

Downs Link: Wonersh > Rudgwick
Greensand Way: Haslemere > Dorking > Limpsfield
Hampton Court & Bushy Park Walk
Mortlake > Richmond > Key Thames Circular Park
North Downs Way: Farnham to Westerham (Kent)
Stane Street: Epsom to Dorking
Sussex Border Path: Haslemere > Rudgwick > Gatwick
Virginia Water round walk
Wey South Park: Guildford to Goldalming
Windsor Great Park

Surrey

Hampton Court

Popular commuter county but nonetheless with large areas of beauty: **Ashdown Forest**, now more of a heath, covers 6400 acres of upland, with a large deer, badger and rare bird population.

The heights of **Box Hill** and **Leith Hill** rise above the **North Downs** to overlook large tracts of richly wooded countryside, containing a string of well protected villages. **The Devil's Punchbowl**, near Hindhead, is a two mile long sandstone valley, overlooked by the 900-ft Gibbet Hill. **Farnham**, in the west of the country, has Tudor and Georgian houses flanking the 12th century castle, but terrible traffic jams! **Aldershot** nearby is the home of the British Army.

County Town **Guildford** is a modern business and shopping centre with a modern cathedral and university. The North of the county borders Greater London and includes the 2400 - acre **Richmond Park**, where deer roam, **Hampton Court Palace** and **Kew Gardens**.

Richmond Park

Sussex

Battle Abbey

Beachy Head

Petworth

Brighton Pavilion

Administratively divided into East and West 35 years ago, **Sussex** is a much visited county for those wanting a short break from the metropolis.

Brighton, now a city, must be East Sussex' capital, with its culture, boutique hotels, marina, shops and general 'buzz'. It was the Regency summer capital of Britain and has the eccentric Pavilion as a monument to this era. Further west is the impressive **Arundel Castle**, seat of the Duke of Norfolk, and Chichester, with its famous drama festival and nearby popular marinas and Wittering sands. **Bognor Regis** was a favourite with the Prince of Wales, later Edward VIII.

Sussex has a plethora of historic houses and gardens and three of the historic cinque ports. **Rye** in particular, with its cobbled streets, transports the visitor back three centuries. The 1066 Story is told at **Battle**, near Hastings. Eastbourne has the impressive **Beachy Head** and **Seven Sisters** cliffs as backdrop.

 TOP 10 Historic Houses Gardens and Parks

Arundel Castle, Arundel
Batemans, Burwash, Etchingham
Battle Abbey, Abbey
Bodiam Castle, Nr Robertsbridge
Goodwood House, Chichester
Great Dixter House & Garden, Northiam, Rye
Merriments Gardens, Hurst Green
Petworth House, Petworth
The Royal Pavilion, Brighton
Uppark, South Harting

 TOP 10 Attractions

1066 Battle of Hastings, Battlefield & Abbey
Alfriston Old Clergy House & Wine Centre
Bluebell Railway, New Combe Bridge > Sheffield Park
Carr Taylor Vineyards, Hastings
Cowdray Park, Midhurst
Kent & E Sussex Railway. Bodiam to Tenterden
Leonardslee Lakes & Gardens, Lower Beeding
Parham House & Gardens, Pulborough
Pulborough Brooks RSPB Nature Reserve
Quarry Farm Rural Experience, Robertsbridge

 TOP 10 Walks and Nature Trails

1066 Walk – Battle to Bexhill
Burton Pond Nature Trail
Downs Link Way: Wonersh to Steyning
East Dean Round, Eastbourne
Horsted Keynes to Sheffield Park walk
Saxon Shore Way: Rye > Appledore > (Folkestone)
South Downs Way: South Harting > Ditchling > Eastbourne
Sutton: Barlavington to Bignor Hill Walk
Sussex Border Path: South Harting > E.Grinstead
Worth Way Walk: Worth Way > E. Grinstead

Searcys Roof Garden Rooms
30 Pavilion Road, London SW1X OHS
T (0870) 860 8408 **F** (020) 7823 8694 **E** rgr@searcys.co.uk
T (International) +44 [0] (20) 7584 4921 **W** www.30pavilionroad.co.uk

30 Pavilion Road, situated in the heart of Knightsbridge, has charm and character. Originally an old pumping station, it has been transformed into a tasteful hotel with a rooftop garden. There is a relaxed atmosphere and friendly staff with a high level of personal and attentive service. It is perfect for people seeking an alternative to large hotel chains. It is privately owned by the Searcy's Catering Company, who manage several restaurants in London and provide banquets, weddings and business functions in this, their London townhouse. For the convenience of those attending such events, they have converted the upstairs rooms into 10 bedrooms, also available to anyone seeking affordable accommodation in the centre of London. The rooms have recently been completely redecorated and refurbished, each being individually designed and with its own character. Country house furnishings add to the charm, with antiques, tasteful fabrics, large comfortable beds (some with canopies), and often a sitting alcove. A peaceful haven in the bustle of London and yet conveniently located for Knightsbridge, Hyde Park, museums and the theatre district.

Stylish accommodation in the heart of Knightsbridge.

10 AC ⊙ ✂ ৬ ⚓ ? **P** (NCP opposite) ⚌ 240 WIFI

Directions
From Sloane Street, turn into Basil Street, first on left is Pavilion Road.

Nearby attractions
Victoria & Albert, National History & Science Museums, Harrods, Peter Jones, Royal Albert Hall, Hyde Park.

Rates Single room, b&b from £110; double/twin room from £160.
Meals 24-hour room service.
Other facilities Lift.
Closed two weeks over Chistmas/New Year.

 Visa, Mastercard, Maestro accepted.

Ad

London, SW1

T (0870) 860 8481 F (020) 7225 0011 E reservations@capitalhotel.co.uk
T (International) +44 [0] (20) 7589 5171 W www.capitalhotel.co.uk

The Capital has the ambience and charm of a comfortable country home in the very centre of London. 35 years ago David Levin envisaged a grand hotel on a smaller, more intimate scale and created the Capital as a luxury townhouse with just 49 rooms. Every one is individually designed with specially commissioned fabrics and wallpaper, original paintings and objets d'art. The solid marble bathrooms have large tubs and the beds are specially made for the hotel with hand stitched mattresses by Savoir. Patronised by royalty, Heads of State and international celebrities, the atmosphere is serene, achieved by very personal service and attention to detail. Still family owned and run, the Capital is in the very heart of Knightsbridge, just yards from Harrods and an easy alk to Harvey Nichols, Peter Jones and other stores. The Capital Restaurant opened in 1974 and was one of the first in Britain to be awarded a Michelin star. In 2001 head chef Eric Chavot won his second star, which he retains to this day. Tea can be taken in the cosy sitting room.

🛏 49 AC 👬 ♨ 🍴 🔗 ☂ 🅿 12 WIFI

Country house hotel in the city with legendary cuisine and style

Rates Single room inc. breakfast from £224; double from £299; all prices + VAT & service.
Meals The Capital Restaurant 3-cse tdh £55; 3-cse lunch fm £29.50; diets catered for; last dinner orders 2245; bfst fm 0700.
Other facilities DVD players, satellite/SKY TV; airport pickup on request; modem points on request. Beauty salaon, jogging (Hyde Park), health club nearby.
& all major credit cards accepted. Open all year.

Directions
From Knightsbridge Tube Station (Sloane St exit), turn rt & rt again into Basil Street
Nearby attractions
Victoria & Albert, National History & Science Museums, Harrods, Peter Jones, Royal Albert Hall, Hyde Park.

Parkes Hotel

41 Beaufort Gardens, Knightsbridge, London SW3 1PW

T (0870) 418 8043 F (020) 7581 1999 E reception@parkeshotel.com
T (International) +44 [0] (20) 7581 9944 W www.parkeshotel.com

Parkes is a real gem - a beautiful, stylish townhouse hotel nestling in a quiet, tree-lined cul de sac only 100 metres from Harrods. The location is unbeatable and so are the friendly, professional staff who are on hand to look after you 24 hours a day. The whole property has recently been lovingly refurbished with no expense spared. The result is perfection - luxurious surroundings complete with every convenience that modern technology can provide and plenty of little extras designed to make your stay more comfortable. The property originally consisted of three town houses so no two rooms are quite the same - however they are of a uniformly high standard. Each marble bathroom has under floor heating and a fabulous power shower with 9" head. Bedrooms have wireless internet access, individual climate control, digital satellite TV, a DVD player, multiple phone lines and personal voicemail. You won't find larger rooms anywhere in London. The 17 beautiful suites each have their own compact kitchenettes. A free newspaper comes with your delicious breakfast. Once you've stayed at Parkes, you'll see why so many guests think of it as their London home.

London 'home from home' townhouse hotel.

🛏 33 (ac) inc 17 suites

Directions
From Knightsbridge Underground Sta, (Harrods exit) Beaufort Gdns is 4th street on the left walking down Brompton Road

Nearby attractions
Science, V & A, Natural History Museums, Harrods, Royal Albert Hall.

Rates Single room inc. buffet breakfast from £150; double from £199; junior suite from £300. All prices + VAT.

Other facilities Airport transfer on request. Gymnasium and riding in Hyde Park nearby. Breakfast room.

 & all major credit cards accepted. Open all year.

London, SW3

The Mayflower Hotel & Apartments

26-28 Trebovir Road, Earls Court, London SW5 9NJ

T (0870) 418 8037 **F** (020) 7370 0994 **E** info@mayflower-group.co.uk
T (Central Resvns) [0] (20) 7370 4934 **W** www.mayflowerhotel.co.uk

65

This well established independently run hotel is close to Earls Court Exhibition Centre, Olympia and the Underground, providing a fast link to the West End. There are many restaurants in the area, catering for every cuisine. The Mayflower is a sister hotel to Twenty Nevern Square (*see preceding page*) and has just completed an extensive refurbishment to bring it up to 4-star standard. With the introduction of a lounge/coffee bar, a smart new reception area and an enhanced breakfast room, guests will immediately feel at home. Each of the 48 rooms, which range from singles to siuites is individually themed with dark polished wooden floors, climate controls and ceiling fans are common to all. Four rooms have balconies. Marble bathrooms come with complimetary toiletries. Secure car parking can be arranged. The studios and apartments are for longer term occupation and come with daily maid service, fully equipped kitchen and bathrooms and entry phone system. We recommend The Mayflower as a homely place with friendly and attentive multi-lingual staff.

Refurbished Earls Court hotel and apartments representing excellent value

 48 + 35 appts 👓 ♀ 🅿 (charged)

Rates Single room inc breakfast from £65; double from £75; apartments from £84.
Special breaks Shopping, Conference, Valentines, Xmas and Honeymoon breaks available.
Other facilities Satellite TV, lift. No restaurant.

 & all major credit cards accepted. Open all year.

Directions
From Earls Court Underground Sta (west), right & right again into Trebovir Rd.

Nearby attractions
Earls Court Exhibition Centre, Olympia, Syon House, Kew Gardens

London, SW5

The Rockwell
181 Cromwell Road, London SW5 0SF
T (0870) 860 8508 **F** (020) 7244 2001 **E** enquiries@therockwell.com
T (International) [0] (20) 7244 2000 **W** www.therockwell.com

The Rockwell, opened in April 2006, is London's latest luxury hotel. Independently owned and managed, the emphasis is on understated contemporary chic, intimate charm and a high level of personal service. Its forty rooms create a relaxed atmosphere, whilst retaining their individual character. They combine English tradition with modern styling. Crafted in light oak, each is well soundproofed and has air-conditioning, an honesty bar, flat screen TV with satellite/SKY, fax-modem point and writing surface. Shower rooms are contemporary with clean lines, shaving mirrors and White Company toiletries. The distinctive mezzanine suites are split into two levels with separate sitting areas and bedrooms; the spacious garden rooms have private terraces. There is a comfortable lounge, small meeting room and modern restaurant, offering a good choice of *tables d'hôtes* at reasonable prices. Unusually for West London, there is a garden behind the restaurant where drinks and snacks can be enjoyed. Earls Court, Olympia, Harrods, the Royal Albert Hall are all on the Rockwell's doorstep, making it an excellent base for both business and leisure visitors, good value and very comfortable.

Stylish new hotel between Kensington and Earls Court

🛏 40 (🚭 only - inc 2 suites) ✂ ♿ 🖥 ⊙ ♨ 10 ♀ ♨ WIFI

Directions From Earls Court Underground Sta (Earls Ct Rd exit), turn left up to Cromwell Rd; hotel 100 yds on rt.

Nearby attractions
Earls Court Exhib. Centre, Olympia, Royal Albert Hall, Nat History Musm

Rates Single, room only from £110; double, room only from £160.
Meals One Eight One Restaurant, 3-cse tdh ca £35; alc, lunch & spec. diets avail; last orders 2230; bfst fm 0700.
Other facilities Satellite/Sky tv.

 & all major credit cards accepted. Open all year.

London, SW5

Twenty Nevern Square
20 Nevern Square, London SW5 9PD
T (0870) 418 8048 **F** (020) 7565 9444 **E** hotel@twentynevernsquare.co.uk
T (Central Resvns) [0] (20) 7370 4934 **W** www.twentynevernsquare.co.uk

67

Overlooking a quiet, tree-lined garden square, this is one of London's newest and, at the same time, most original and discreet boutique hotels. The mosaic patterned steps of the late 19th century mansion give a hint of the Eastern influences within, which are also apparent in the decor of the cosy ground floor lounge. The interior has been refurbished in exotic style. Most impressive are the carved oriental headboards and wardrobes and the silk curtains, found in, for example, The Grand Pasha Suite or the Chinese Room. The sleek marble bathrooms, too, imitate those found in designer hotels. The Far Eastern feel extends to the lounge and light, airy conservatory/ breakfast room, which is filled with wicker furniture and greenery. The hotel overlooks an elegant square, which seems worlds away. The hotel is close to Earls Court and Olympia Exhibition Centres and has easy access to the West End, Kensington, Chelsea and Knightsbridge. To stay in this distinctive townhouse hotel is an experience not to be missed.

 20 (inc 1 suite) ☺ ⚥ 🅿 (charged)

Earls Court hotel with public and bedrooms showing an Asian style

Rates Single room inc breakfast from £79; double £95 -160.
Meals No restaurant but Cafe Twenty provides tea/coffee 24 hours.
Other facilities Airport transfer on request. Gymnasium nearby. Open 24 hours.

Directions
From Earls Court Underground Sta (Warwick Rd exit), right & 2nd right into square. Hotel 30m on right hand side.

Nearby attractions
Earls Court Exhib. Centre, Olympia, Royal Albert Hall, Nat History Musm

 & all major credit cards accepted. Open all year.

London, SW5

68

Blakes Hotel

33 Roland Gardens, South Kensington, London SW7 3PF
T (0870) 860 8411 **F** (020) 7373 0442 **E** blakes@blakeshotels.com
T (International) +44 [0] (20) 7584 7586 **W** www.blakeshotels.com

Created by the British designer Anouska Hempel, Blakes Hotel has established itself as a unique model for fashionable small hotels around the world. It offers style and elegance with efficient and sensational service. Each of the 48 rooms is individually designed to provide the ideal blend of colour, texture and atmosphere. *Directors Double* rooms feature European king-size beds, French gilded swan beds or four-posters. Luxury suites feature European king-size beds or sumptuous four-posters. Some feature private balconies, mother of pearl inlaid furniture, gossamer nets, *trompe l'oeil* walls and stencilled floors. Decorative items from Versailles are just one of the design features. Stylish, elegant and opulent, Blakes Hotel offers a haven of privacy for its clients, which include stars of stage and screen, musicians and designers. The hotel is located in a quiet residential road, yet near to the shopping areas of Kensington and Chelsea. Being Grade II Listed, there is no lift but an excellent porter service. The restaurant enjoys an unrivalled reputation for the originality and content of its superb menu. The characterful Singapore Lounge and Blakes Bar are also on the ground floor.

Luxury designer-built hotel near South Kensington.

48 AC (inc 9 suites) 🔪 🕭 ☉ 🖵 ⚷ ☕ 🎭

Directions
From South Ken Underground Sta, walk down Old Brompton Rd, 5th street on left

Nearby attractions
Victoria & Albert, Natural History, Science Museums, Royal Albert Hall

Rates Single, room only from £175; double from £275.
Meals Blakes Restaurant; alc, lunch & spec. diets avail; last orders 2300; bfst fm 0630. Cont'l bfst + £17.50; English + £25.
Special Breaks Seasonal breaks available. Notice sent to people on mailing list six weeks before.
Other facilities Massage can be arranged. Airport pickup arranged (charged).

 & all major credit cards accepted. Open all year.

The Leonard Hotel & Apartments

15 Seymour Street, London W1H 7JW

T (0870) 860 8505 **F** (020) 7935 6700 **E** reservations@theleonard.com
T (International) [0] (20) 7935 2010 **W** www.theleonard.com

The Leonard Hotel is located off Portman Square, near to Marble Arch, Bond Street and the shops of Oxford Street. It comprises four elegant 18th-century townhouses converted to a luxury hotel with an intimate atmosphere and a very high level of comfort and service. For the energetic, there is a fitness room on the first floor and Hyde Park is a two-minute jog away. On a fine day the roof garden provides a quiet retreat for reading or relaxation. The 45 rooms and suites convey warmth and intimacy in an atmosphere of understated luxury, with marble bathrooms, modem points and wirelsss connectivity. For ultimate self-indulgence, enquire about the Grand Suite. There is also a function suite for private entertaining or meetings. 24-hour room service is available and the Cafe Bar, with its picture gallery, is also open 24 hours for residents and offers breakfast, lunch, afternoon tea and evening meals. There are five serviced apartments across the road. The Leonard is a very complete hotel and provides a supremely civilised haven of relaxation in the heart of London.

45 (inc 16 suites) 🚿 ⬆ 🖥 ☺ ✈ ✂ ♨ 30 ♀ ⚓ WIFI

Luxury hotel of rooms, suites and apartments in London's West End

Rates Single room inc breakfast from £110; double fm £170; suite fm £395
Meals Cafe Bar meals from £15.95; alc, lunch & spec diets avail; open 24 hrs
Leisure breaks Weekend single £99; double £125. Both inc VAT & breakfast.
Other facilities DVD players, satellite TV.

Directions Hotel one block north of and parallel to Oxford St, on cnr with Portman Street, Nearest Underground: Marble Arch

Nearby attractions
Hyde Park, Madame Tussauds,London Planetarium, Oxford St shops

 & all major credit cards accepted. Open all year.

London, W1

70

Miller's Residence
111a Westbourne Grove, London W2 4UW
T (0870) 418 8502 **F** (020) 7243 1064 **E** enquiries@millersuk.com
T (International) +44 [0] (20) 7243 1024 **W** www.millersuk.com

Owned by Martin Miller, founder of the eponymous Antiques Guide, the Residence is a world apart from the normal run of Bayswater/Notting Hill hotels. Its modest entrance (in Hereford Road) belies the style that hits you as you walk up the stairs. You pass murals of the Pope's Palace at Avignon on your way to the main reception room. Here complimentary drinks before dinner are served and breakfast is taken at a large table. It is bustling with genuine antiques, some of which may change with the seasons, and collectibles and curios of every sort. As well as being the heart of the building and from time to time doubling as Martin's office, the drawing room is also popular for private parties, photo shoots or small business meetings. On the second floor there are six spacious double rooms and two suites, all named after English poets and furnished and decorated in period style. *Byron meets Chatterton in Bohemian London.* Suites have a small kitchen, minibar and sitting area. Other guest services include ADSL Internet service, 24-hr computer access and a booking service for London theatres and restaurants.

Townhouse hotel in quiet square behind Notting Hill Gate & Hyde Park

8 (inc 2 suites) ✂ ☺ ♣ 12 WIFI

Directions
Fm Notting Hill Underground, walk up Pembridge Rd/Villas to Westburne Grove. Red door 1st street on rt - Hereford Road.
Nearby attractions
Kensington Palace, Hyde Park, Portobello Rd Market, Holland Park

Rates Double room with breakfast from £150; suite from £195. Rates include complimentary evening drinks.
Meals Breakfast only. (Communal table)
Other facilities Airport pickup on demand, SKY/Satellite TV some rooms. Gym etc can be arranged nearby. Theatre & Restaurant Booking Service.

 & all major credit cards accepted. Open all year.

New Linden Hotel

59 Leinster Square, London W2 4PS

T (0870) 418 8036 **F** (020) 7727 3156 **E** newlindenhotel@mayflower-group.co.uk
T (International) +44 [0] (20) 7221 4321 **W** www.hotelnewlinden.co.uk

The third hotel in the Mayflower Group (*see pages 65/67*), the New Linden is also new to Signpost, having undergone a major refurbishment to bring it up to the level of a top standard townhouse hotel. The displays of seasonal flowers outside welcome the visitor to the hotel, a recent winner of a *London in Bloom* award. There is the usual range of rooms of varying shapes and sizes, all attractively finished and comfortable with gleaming bathroom or shower areas. Broad darkwood headboards add an original touch. Two strikingly unusual family rooms in terms of size and layout sleep up to five and one of these is on split levels with Doric columns dividing the upper and lower sections. A spacious breakfast room in the basement serves an extensive continental buffet to guests. New Linden enjoys a quiet location in Leinster Square with Queensway and Bayswater underground stations both within five minutes' walk, and Paddington Station & the Heathrow Express 15 minutes' walk away. The area is cosmopolitan with a varied choice of restaurants and Whiteleys, the indoor shopping mall, close by.

 52 (inc 7 ⇔) ⊙ ⋔

Townhouse hotel in quiet square behind Notting Hill Gate & Hyde Park

Rates Single room with breakfast £69-79; double inc. breakfast £80-£120; family rooms £140.
Special breaks Discounted rates for Sun-Thurs specials, Valentines, Christmas, New year, Honeymoon.
Other facilities Satellite TV. Open all year.

Directions
From Bayswater Underground, walk left into Queensway, 2nd left Porchster Gdns.

Nearby attractions
Hyde Park/Kensington Gardens, Whiteleys, Oxford Street, Portobello Market, Notting Hill, Royal Albert Hall

 Visa, Mastercard, Switch, Solo accepted.

London, W2

The George Hotel & Brasserie

Stone Street, Cranbrook, Kent TN17 3HE

T (0870) 860 8412 **F** (01580) 715532 **E** reservations@thegeorgehotelkent.co.uk
T (International) +44 [0] (1580) 713348 **W** www.thegeorgehotelkent.co.uk

The George Hotel and Brasserie is one of Cranbrook's landmark buildings, dating back to the 14th century. Today it offers a delightful retreat from the bustle of the city and makes an ideal base for exploring Kent and Sussex. The hotel is a refreshing example of how striking period features can be supported with a modern, contemporary décor. The interior is sophisticated, whilst maintaining the attraction of candle lit tables and log fires. All bedrooms are individually designed, offering a unique choice of either period or contemporary style. All have luxury Egyptian cotton bedlinen, flat panel TVs + Sky, and Wireless Internet access. One features a hand carved four-poster bed and gold painted ceiling for a touch of decadent opulence. Bathrooms are equipped with fluffy white towels, bathrobes and Gilchrist & Soames toiletries. One features a jacuzzi bath for that ultimate spa effect. Every aspect of the hotel and brasserie is arranged around top quality and excellent service, with fine attention to detail. The AA ⍟ restaurant offers a regularly changing menu, using local produce where possible and with a well chosen wine selection.

Family owned inn of 14th century origin in Kentish market town.

🛏 12 ⍢ ☺ 🅿 12 WIFI

Directions Exit M20 junc 6 onto A229 for Cranbrook. Hotel on left side of Stone Street before it turns into High Street.

Nearby attractions
Sissinghurst, Bedgebury Nat'l Pinetum, Leeds Castle, Bodiam Castle.

Distances
Maidstone 15, Hastings 19, London 53

Rates Single room with breakfast from £65; double from £80.

Meals The Dining Room, The Brasserie, Bar Red. Tdh dinner £25; alc, lunch & spec. diets avail; last orders 2130; bfst fm 0730.

& all major credit cards accepted. Open all year exc. 25/26 December.

Walletts' Court Country House Hotel, Restaurant & Spa

Westcliffe, St Margaret's Bay, Dover, Kent CT15 6EW

T (0870) 418 8055 F (01304) 853430 E wc@wallettscourt.com
T (International) +44 [0] (1304) 852424 W www.wallettscourt.com

73

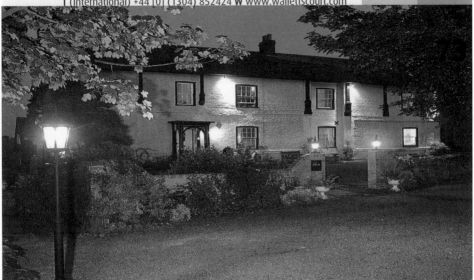

This lovely old country manor house set in beautiful grounds is located just outside St. Margaret's, opposite a Norman church and both sites date back to the Domesday Book. Most of the present Manor is Elizabethan, and today Walletts'Court testifies to the Oakley Family philosophy of making a home of the place they discovered 27 years ago. The Conservatory is a breakfast room with views across the North Downs. The 17th century beamed, candlelit restaurant is an award-winning gourmets' paradise, which offers deliciously robust and hearty cuisine with menus changing regularly to incorporate fresh seasonal ingredients. The bedrooms are divided between the main house and converted barns whose comfortably furnished rooms are named according to original usage such as *Dairy* or *Stable*. There are four luxury bedrooms: the *William Pitt*, the *Sir Edward de Burgh*, the *Lord Aylmer* rooms and *Crèvecoeur's Tower*. The Spa consists of the *Retreat in the Wood* for aromatherapy and relaxation and a Romanesque indoor pool, sauna, hydrotherapy spa and steam room. Walletts Court today is popular equally with business travellers, for a weekend break or as a stopover point for those crossing the Channel.

🛏 16 🍽 🥂 ⏱ 🔍 🎿 🚭 🅿 🎽 55

Family owned hotel with renowned restaurant and spa.

Rates Single room inc breakfast from £109; double from £129.

Meals 3-cse tdh dinner £40 in AA ⊙⊙ restaurant; alc & spec diets avail; last orders 2100.

Leisure Breaks Two nights, dinner b & b for two people £199 per person.

Other facilities Golf 6m, sea 1m.

Visa, Mastercard & Switch accepted. Open all year.

Directions
A258 Deal rd out of Dover, 1st rt to St Margarets Bay, hotel on right.

Nearby attractions
Dover Castle, Deal Castle, Walmer Castle, Crabble Corn Mill Dover.

Distances
Dover 3, Folkestone 7, London 74.

Kent, Dover

Hotel Relish

4 Augusta Gardens, Folkestone, Kent CT20 2RR

T (0870) 418 8053 **F** (01303) 850958 **E** reservations@hotelrelish.co.uk
T (International) +44 [0] (1303) 850952 **W** www.hotelrelish.co.uk

The canopy sheltering your approach to the new cutting edge Hotel Relish is reminiscent of Park Avenue, New York. The reception area is equally different - no formal desk just a simple glass table and an opulent sofa. Hospitality is paramount at Relish - you are given a complimentary glass of beer or wine when checking in; alternatively delightful fresh coffee and a homemade cake before being taken to your super-comfortable and contemporary room. Crisp white bed linen on your Hypnos bed and large bath towels as you step from your power shower (or bath) will cocoon you in comfort. Organic toiletries of the highest quality will have soothed and relaxed you. Other features are long sloping mirrors in most rooms, DVDs, modem points, Broadband and a wireless network. An extensive DVD library means that you never need leave your room. The drawing room has a roaring log fire in winter. The dining room looks out on the terrace (where breakfast is taken in summer) leading into private leafy gardens. The newly opened Relish is a testament to the good taste, enthusiasm and hard work of its two young owners who are bound to continue to attract both business and pleasure visitors to this prospering part of Kent.

Folkestone's newest hotel with state-of-the art comfort & facilities

🛏 10 (inc 2 suites) ☺ 🚫 🐕

Directions
Town centre then A259 twds Sandgate, left at Bouverie Rd W, 1st rt into Trinity Gdns

Nearby attractions
Battle of Britain Mus, Dover Castle, Port Lympne Zoo, Metropole Gallery.

Distances
Dover 7, Canterbury 16, London 88.

Rates Single room inc breakfast from £55; double from £79.
Meals Dinner not available but breakfast served from 0730. Tea/coffee and wine/beer available. Folkestone's finest restaurants within walking distance.

Other facilities Golf, watersports, sailing, tennis 3m, sea 1/2m.

Visa, Mastercard & Switch accepted. Open all year.

Kent, Folkestone

Sandgate Hotel

8/9 Wellington Terrace, Sandgate, Folkestone, Kent CT20 3DY

T (0870) 418 8056 **F** (01303) 220496 **E** info@sandgatehotel.com
T (International) +44 [0] (1303) 220444 **W** www.sandgatehotel.com

75

Part of a 19th century terrace, Sandgate Hotel stands opposite a pebble beach, just a stroll from the antiquarian shops and busy bistros of Sandgate Village, near Folkestone and Dover. The new owners have renovated and injected a new, more contemporary, feel to this beautiful old building whilst retaining its comfortable, peaceful atmosphere. This includes all 11 bedrooms, most of which have stunning sea views and some the aded advantage of period balconies. The beautifully renovated main bar with its glorious twin fireplaces offers sweeping sea views. Here you can grab a delicious meal at lunchtime or dine in the evening admiring the stunning sunsets and maybe meeting some of the area's celebrities. Downstairs the Wellington Bar is open mostly at weekends and offers a range of entertainments. Both bar and main restaurant, with their floodlit terraces, refect the hotel's tasteful, contemporary style.The dining room was full when we stayed, as word of their excellent cuisine has spread quickly. Our dinner was superb: an entrée of pan seared scallops, followed by grilled John Dory, with lemon tart and orange sorbet as dessert. Friendly staff and welcoming owners will enhance your stay here by the sea.

Seafront hotel near the Eurotunnel terminal and Dover's ferry ports.

🛏 11 ♟♟ 15

Directions
On seafront on A259 Folkestone-Hythe road.

Nearby attractions
Battle of Britain Mus, Dover Castle, Port Lympne Zoo, Rotunda Theme Park

Distances
Dover 9, Canterbury 18, London 90.

Rates Single room inc cont'l breakfast from £55; double from £75.
Meals 3-cse alc dinner fm £25; lunch & spec diets avail; last orders 2200; bfst fm 0700.

Other facilities Golf, watersports, sailing, tennis nearby, sea opposite hotel.

Visa, Mastercard, Diners & Switch accepted. Open all year.

Kent, Folkestone

76

Who'd a Thought It

Headcorn Road, Grafty Green, Nr. Maidstone ME17 2AR

T (0870) 860 8503 **F** (01622) 858078 **E** joe@whodathoughtit.com
T (International) +44 [0] (1622) 858951 **W** www.whodathoughtit.com

Who'd a Thought It indeed? Tucked away in the tiny hamlet of Grafty Green in Kent is a 16th century inn which describes itself as a *Champagne & Oyster Bar with Rooms*. It offers a fine dining restaurant and a less formal brasserie. As well as fresh, local seafood, Mediterranean, Indian and Oriental dishes are specialities. The à la carte menu offers Beluga and Sevruga caviar (at £65 & £45 respectively for 30 grammes). The extensive wine list includes more than 60 different champagnes. Our inspector enjoyed the Ruinart Rose champagne by the glass and the recent award of the prestigious *Trophée Gosset Celibris* confirms Who'd-A's status as a leading European champagne outlet. Enthusiastic proprietor Joe Mallett has created a very individual, relaxed and comfortable country dining and staying experience. Rooms are furnished contemporarily, some with hot tubs, some with jacuzzis. The setting, in the heart of the north Downs, is complemented by picturesque, well tended gardens. Finding Who'd A Thought It is not easy but the pilgrimage is worth it for the stylish accommodation, fine wining & dining experience and the unspoiled location.

Champagne & oyster bar, with rooms, tucked away in the Downs

🛏 8 (inc 2 🏠) ⚔ 🐕 🅿 ♨ 30

Directions
M20/A20 to Lenham, follow brown bed signs to Grafty Green, hotel on rt

Nearby attractions
Leeds Castle, Canterbury Cathedral, Sissinghurst Castle, Blue Water

Distances
Ashford 12, Maidstone 12, London 41

Rates Single room inc breakfast from £45; double from £60.
Meals Alc dinner; lunch & special diets available. Last orders 2130; bfst - continental only in rooms

Other facilities DVD/Satellite/SKY TV in rooms. Golf, fishing, riding, shooting, tennis nearby.

 & major credit cards accepted. Open all year.

Kent, Nr. Maidstone

Coast Road, Littlestone, New Romney, Kent TN28 8QY
T (0870) 418 8063 **F** (01797) 367156 **E** info@signpost.co.uk/romneybay
T (International) +44 [0] (1797) 364747 **W** www.signpost.co.uk/romneybay

Built in the 1920s for the American actress Hedda Hopper and designed by Sir Clough Williams-Ellis *(see Portmeirion, in the Wales section of this guide)*, Romney Bay House was acquired in 2003 by Clinton and Lisa Lovell, who are most welcoming hosts. The hotel is situated along a private road on a totally unspoiled stretch of coastline with spectacular sea views. The drawing room overlooks the terrace with the sea beyond and the first floor look-out room has a library, board games and a telescope! The ten bedrooms, including two four-posters, are exceptionally well appointed with cheerful antique furniture. In the grounds there is a croquet lawn with two golf courses immediately behind the hotel. Bicycles can be hired and other games are available. The popular restaurant serves a four-course dinner using the freshest local produce, complemented by a select but excellent wine list. Cream teas are also a speciality. The natural wildness of Romney Marsh and the proximity of the rolling Kent countryside and the historic Cinque Ports make this an ideal spot for a few days' relaxation.

 10 (inc 2 🛏) ⚗ 🛏 🛁 ℚ *Rest. closed Sun Mon*

Coastal 'folly' built in the 1920s, now a secluded comfortable hotel

Rates Single room inc breakfast from £60; double from £90.
Meals 4-cse set dinner £37.50 served at 2000; diets available.
Winter Breaks November-March, Mon-Thurs nights 2 nts+ = 25% discount (exc Bank Hols, Easter etc).
Other facilities Golf nearby; sea opposite hotel.

& major credit cards accepted. Open all year exc. one week over Xmas.

Directions
Take Littlestone turning in New Romney, left at seafront & follow ummade-up road
Nearby attractions
Romney, Hythe & Dimchurch railwy, Port Lympne Zoo, Dungeness Bird Res.
Distances
Folkestone 12, Rye 15, London 75.

Kent, New Romney

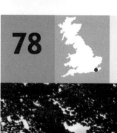

Little Silver Country Hotel

Ashford Road, St Michaels, Tenterden TN30 6SP

T (0870) 860 8413 **F** (01233) 850647 **E** enquiries@little-silver.co.uk
T (International) +44 [0] (1223) 850321 **W** www.littl-silver.co.uk

Little Silver Country Hotel is an elegant Tudor-style house set within its own landscaped gardens in the lovely Weald of Kent. It retains all the warmth and charm of its origins, whilst providing a range of 21st century comforts. The cosy 40-ft long oak beamed lounge has blazing log fires in winter. Breakfast, light lunches and tea are served in the Victorian-style conservatory overlooking the spectacular gardens. These include well kept lawns, graceful statuary, herbaceous borders, a pond & waterfall and a Kentish lych-gate. Some of the 16 traditionally furnished bedrooms have four-poster beds; suites have luxury bathrooms with jacuzzis. The well appointed restaurant offers a good selection of dishes concentrating on local ingredients. The octagonal Kent Hall in the garden, built in the style of a Kentish oast-house, makes a unique wedding venue. This picturesque hotel is well placed for visiting the many National Trust gardens, houses and castles in the area with the medieval town of Rye and the city of Canterbury within easy reach. The M20 and Ashford International Station, with high speed rail links to Europe, are also nearby.

Tudor style hotel in pretty gardens set in the Weald of Kent

16 AC (inc 2 suites) ❀ ✂ & ✗ ♨ 100 🐎

Directions
M20 Junc 9 Ashfod, take A28 for Tenterden. St Michaels at outskirts, hotel on rt.

Nearby attractions
Kent & E. Ssx Railway, Leeds Castle, Sissinghurst, Canterbury, Scotney Cas

Distances
Ashford 9, Maidstone 19, London 57

Rates Single room inc breakfast from £60; double £95-135; suites from £150
Meals Oaks Restaurant alc, lunch & spec. diets available; last orders 2100. Bfst fm 0730. [Ad]
Special Breaks 'Take a Break' from £62 pr pers per nt, dinner, b&b min 2 nts
Other facilities Golf, jacuzzi, indoor pool, sauna, health suite nearby.

 & all major credit cards accepted. Open all year.

Kent, Tenterden

Cedar House Hotel

Mill Road, Cobham, Surrey KT11 3AL

T (0870) 860 8504 **F** (01932) 862023 **E** info@maison-max.com
T (International) +44 [0] (1932) 863424 **W** www.cedarhousehotel.com

79

Cedar House was a great discovery! As we drove into its pebbled courtyard and parked by the forsythia covered old kitchen wall, we knew this would make a pleasant home-from-home for a few days. Inside the owners have carefully restored the Grade II listed 1450s house by unveiling many original features. Built during the reign of Henry VI, it is situated on the banks of the river Mole, with views towards the North Downs. All 12 bedrooms have been renovated in great style, with Queen size beds and antiques in every room. The Gallery Restaurant has a magnificent timbered ceiling, inglenook fireplace and minstrels' gallery, making it a popular venue for special anniversaries and wedding receptions. The superb food is another reason for visiting this delightful hotel. Cuisine is new English style, using fresh vegetables and daily delivered fresh meat, complimented by a wine list which is an eclectic mix from the new and old worlds. An elegant location where personal service meets individual guest needs. Cedar House is handy for Epsom Racecourse, Chessington World of Adventures and is convenienetly situated for the M25 and the motorway network.

🛏 12 (inc 1 🚭) ✗ ✈ 🕭 ☉ 🐓 ♨ 20 Ⓟ WIFI

Charming small hotel of 15th century origins overlooking river Mole.

Rates Single room inc breakfast from £75; double from £110.
Meals Tdh 3-cse dinner £32.50; bar meals & diets available; last orders 2100; bfst fm 0630.

Directions
On left on A245 Cobham-Stoke d'Abernon road

Nearby attractions
Epsom Racecourse, Claremont Ldscpe Gdn, Chessington World of Adventures

Distances
Cobham & Stoke d'A 1, Cen London 18

& all major credit cards accepted. Open all year

Surrey, Cobham

80

The Richmond Gate Hotel

Richmond Hill, Richmond-upon-Thames, Surrey TW10 6RP

T (0870) 418 8059 **F** (020) 8332 0354 **E** res.richmondgate@foliohotels.com
T (International) +44 [0] (20) 8940 0061 **W** www.foliohotels.com

This former Georgian country house stands on the crest of Richmond Hill, close to the Royal Park and Richmond Terrace with its commanding views over the river Thames. The 68 stylishly furnished en suite bedrooms, many with air-conditioning, combine every comfort of the present with the elegance of the past and include several luxury four-poster rooms and suites. Exceptional and imaginative cuisine, complemented by an extensive wine list , is served in the sophisticated surroundings of the award winning AA ◎◎ *Gates on the Park* restaurant. Weddings, business meetings and private dining events can be arranged in a variety of elegant function rooms, including the stunning conservatory which looks out onto a beautiful Victorian walled garden, ideal for barbecues and drinks receptions. Guests have free membership during their stay to *Cedars Health & Leisure Club* which is accessed through the hotel and includes a 20m indoor pool, 6-metre spa, sauna, steam room, aerobics studio, cardio-vascular and resistance gyms, and a health & beauty suite. Richmond is only seven miles from Central London via regular mainline trains to Waterloo or via the District Line tube and only seven miles from Heathrow Airport. Mainline and underground train stations are a ten-minute walk away.

Georgian country house overlooking Richmond Park

🛏 68 (+ 🛏 for 4) 🍴 ♣ 🖊 🥂 📦 🍵 📠 ☉ ♨ 50 WIFI 🐕

Directions From Central London A316 to Richmond, left A307 twds Kingston, left again Richmond Hill.
Nearby attractions
Marble Hill Hse, Ham House, Hampton Court, Twickenham RFU Ground
Distances
Central London 7, M3 motorway 5.

Rates Single/double/twin inc breakfast from £160. [Ad]
Meals 3-cse tdh dinner £31; alc, lunch & diets available; last orders 2115.
Leisure Breaks Special weekend breaks and special offers are available throughout the year.
Other facilities Aerobics studio, BT Wireless connectivity in all areas.

[AMERICAN EXPRESS] & all major credit cards accepted. Open all year.

Surrey, Richmond-upon-Thames

The Richmond Hill Hotel

81

Richmond Hill, Richmond-upon-Thames, Surrey TW10 6RW

T (0870) 418 8060 **F** (020) 8940 5424 **E** res.richmondhill@foliohotels.com

T (International) [0] (20) 8940 2247 **W** www.foliohotels.com

Richmond Hill Hotel is majestically situated on the crest of Richmond Hill in the charming town of Richmond-upon-Thames. Fashionable boutique style shops and art galleries line Richmond Hill leading up to the famous Richmond Terrace with its commanding views of the river Thames. The Richmond Hill Hotel has 138 bedrooms, all well presented incuding magnificent suites and balconied rooms, the majority with air conditioning. All the hotel's recently upgraded meeting rooms have AC, natural daylight, wireless broadband connectivity and offer much flexibility. The newly refurbished Pembrokes Restaurant is part of the Grade II listed building and its classical architectural features have been retained after the extensive redesign, whilst contemporary touches have been introduced. Pembrokes offers all day dining, seven days a week with a modern European menu, mixing brasserie favourites with classic light bites to create a more refined lunchtime and evening menu. The onsite Cedars Health & Leisure Club is the perfect place to relax by the poolside. Residents have complimentary use of the leisure facilities during their stay.

🛏 138 🍴 ♣ 🖊 ⛳ 🍷 🏊 ☉ 16 👥 220 WIFI

Rates Single inc. breakfast from £65; double/twin from £130.

Meals Alc dinner fm £25; alc, lunch & diets available; last orders 2130.

Leisure Breaks Special weekend breaks and offers are available throughout the year. Please see website for details.

Other facilities Aerobics studio, BT Wireless connectivity, air conditoning.

 & all major credit cards exc Diners accepted. Open all year.

Three former Georgian terraced houses, now a stylish hotel.

Directions From Central London A316 to Richmond, left A307 twds Kingston, left again Richmond Hill.

Nearby attractions

Marble Hill Hse, Ham House, Hampton Court, Twickenham RFU Ground

Distances

Central London 7, M3 motorway J1-5m

Surrey, Richmond-upon-Thames

The Bingham
61-63 Petersham Road, Richmond-upon-Thames TW10 6UP
T (0870) 418 8058 **F** (020) 8948 8737 **E** reservations@binghamhotel.co.uk
T (International) +44 [0] (20) 8940 0902 **W** www.binghamhotel.co.uk

The Bingham is unique - an eclectic mix of old and new. Originally built as two Georgian riverside townhouses in 1740, the Bingham has recently been refurbished in a classic contemporary chic style. As you enter from the busy main road, the river views and the hotel's garden to the rear create a wonderful sense of tranquillity. Privately owned since 1984, there is an intimate and relaxed atmosphere, which keeps guests coming back year after year. Loyal staff offer great personal and friendly service. The AA ⊛ Restaurant, serves modern French & British cuisine. There is a decked balcony for *al fresco* dining - an unrivalled spot for watching the sun set over the Thames. The magnificent bar, with ornate chandelier and open fireplace, offers a good range of drinks, from cocktails to chocolate beer, if that is your fancy. The 23 bedrooms are being transformed into 15 doubles and suites, due for completion in 2007. Most rooms have river views and some have four-poster beds, ideal for a night of romance or for a special occasion. The Bingham is a very popular venue for weddings and business meetings. Its location is ideal, just a few minutes from the town centre.

Gracious historic hotel with Thames views.

🛏 23 AC (inc 2 ♨) ✗ ♟ 40 🐾

Directions
From Central London A316 to Richmond, then left A307 twds Kingston. Hotel on lft

Nearby attractions
Marble Hill Hse, Ham House, Hampton Court, Twickenham RFU Ground

Distances
Central London 8, M3 motorway 5.

Rates Single/double room inc breakfast from £180.
Meals Bingham Restaurant 3-cse tdh £20+; alc, lunch & diets available; last orders 2200.
Special Breaks Contact the hoel or see website for special offers.
Other facilities Gym, golf, jogging track, watersports, tennis, swimming pools, riding nearby (daily membership fee £10)

& all credit cards accepted. Open all year.

Surrey, Richmond-upon-Thames

Deans Place Hotel

Seaford Road, Alfriston, Polegate, East Sussex BN26 5TW

T (0870) 860 8415 **F** (01323) 870918 **E** mail@deansplacehotel.co.uk
T (International) +44 [0] (1323) 870248 **W** www.deansplacehotel.co.uk

83

Situated on the edge of one of England's prettiest villages, Deans Place is a privately owned traditional country house hotel set in four acres of gardens with the South Downs as a backdrop. Bedrooms include four-posters, executives, doubles, twins and singles. The hotel is surrounded by well-tended gardens and open meadows. Harcourts Restaurant offers traditional English and Continental cuisine, complimented by an excellent wine list. Enjoy the warmth of the The Friston Bar - this intimate lounge is warmed by the glow of open fires. In the summer, one can dine *al fresco* on the terrace of the hotel. Deans Place offers a variety of leisure pursuits with a heated outdoor swimming pool, putting green and croquet on the beautifully manicured lawn. Close by attractions include the award-winning Drusilla's Zoo, a fun day out for the whole family just two miles from the hotel, Brighton with its many attractions, Eastbourne and Tunbridge Wells. The English Wine Centre, in the nearby Cuckmere Valley offers tasting from various local vineyards. The hotel is also a favourite for opera lovers visiting Glyndebourne just seven miles away.

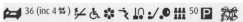 36 (inc 4 ≋) ✄ 🐾 ⚘ ⚘ 🍴 ✦/✦ ⊞ 50 **P** 🎾

Comfortable country house hotel nestling in the South Downs

Rates Single room inc breakfast from £71; double from £88.
Meals Harcourts Restaurant. Alc, lunch & diets available; last orders 2130; bfst fm 0730
Leisure Breaks Special leisure rates for two-night breaks.

Other facilities Golf, sea bathing nearby.

 & major credit cards accepted. Open all year

Directions
A27 Eastbound fm Lewes 7m rt at rdbt at Berwick to Alfriston 1m.

Nearby attractions
Drusilla's Zoo, Glyndebourne, Firle Place, Glynde Place, Old Clergy Hse

Distances
Lewes 10, Brighton 17, London 66.

East Sussex, Alfriston

Powder Mills Hotel
Powdermill Lane, Battle, East Sussex TN33 0SP
T (0870) 418 8054 **F** (01424) 774540 **E** powdc@aol.com
T (International) +44 [0] (1424) 775511 **W** www.powdermillshotel.com

The Powder Mills is situated in 150 acres of beautiful parkland, woods and lakes. Built in 1792, the hotel is situated close to the historic town of Battle and adjoins the famous battlefield of 1066. Privately owned, the Powder Mills has been skilfully converted into a fascinating country house hotel. The AA ☺ ☺ Orangery Restaurant with its colonial-style wicker seating, marble floor and Greek statues serves Classical English and French cuisine for lunch and dinner every day. In summer months meals can be taken *al fresco* on the terrace.There is a range of 40 individually decorated en suite bedrooms and junior suites in keeping with the style of the house. One is the Wellington Suite, where the great man once stayed and another is the Four Poster Room - allegedly haunted by a mysterious lady in white. The hotel is ideally located for exploring Kent and Sussex, with the Channel Tunnel just one hour's drive away. There are wonderful gardens, old towns and castles to visit nearby including Bodiam Castle, Sissinghurst and Bateman's and numerous antique shops in the neighbouring villages.

Stunning 18th century country house hotel nestling in 150 acres

🛏 40 (inc 6 suites) 🍴 🧍 🐾 🐕 ♨ 350 🅿 80 🎿

Directions
Take A2100 Hastings Rd from Battle, just before Railway Stn, turn rt Powdermill La

Nearby attractions
Battle Abbey, Bodiam Castle, Great Dixter House, Pevensey,Sissinghurst

Distances
Hastings 6, Brighton 34, London 56.

Rates Single room inc breakfast from £95; double from £125.
Meals Alc dinner £30; lunch & diets available; last orders 2100; bfst fm 0730
Leisure Breaks 2 nights+ breaks available from £80 per person per night, tdh dinner, b & b.
Other facilities Golf 3 miles.

 & major credit cards accepted. Open all year

East Sussex, Battle

Blanch House

17 Atlingworth Street, Brighton, East Sussex BN2 1PL

T (0870) 418 8062 **F** (01273) 689813 **E** info@blanchhouse.co.uk
T (International) +44 [0] (1273) 603504 **W** www.blanchhouse.co.uk

Opened in 2000 by husband and wife team Chris Edwardes and Amanda Blanch, Blanch House is at the forefront of the new Designer Hotel wave to have hit Brighton in recent years. Amanda gives each bedroom a unique style of its own; *Alice,* with its mirrors and magical feel; the exotic *Moroccan & India Rooms,* and *Boogie Nights* and *Snowstorm* that touch of retro. *Renaissance, Harlequin, Orchid and Sakura* all rich and opulent and the three largest rooms *Galaxy Promises, Perrier Jouet Suite* (crystal lined deep green velvet drapes) and *Decadence* - rich in damask, wall tapestries and with a beautiful roll-top bath. Each room comes with Trevi power showers, fogarty goose and duck down duvets and pillows, Relyon beds, flat screen TVs and a DVD player (with a free library at reception). Award-winning dining is in the basement, decorated by ever-changing contemporary Brighton artists. The ground floor cocktail bar area is intimate and stylish and serves an eclectic mix of drinks. Pampering treatments such as reflexology, Indian head massage, facials & manicures can also be arranged. The perfect place to get away from it all, Blanch House is centrally located near Brighton Pier and a stone's throw from the sea.

 12 (inc 3 suites)   20

Chic boutique hotel which sets standards not only for Brighton, but for the whole South of England

Rates Single/double room inc breakfast from £90.
Meals 3-cse tdh dinner £25-30 per head; 3-cse £16 per head; diets catered for; last orders 2200.
Other facilities Pampering treatment, flat screen TVs & DVD players, DVD & CD library, isdn lines.
Special breaks Special tasting menu evenings and other events. Check website for details.
& all major credit cards accepted. Open all year

Directions
Left at Old Steine rdbt opp Brighton Pier, along Marine Pde, 1st left, rt then rt again
Nearby attractions
Royal Pavilion, The Lanes, Sealife Centre, Preston Manor, Booth Museum
Distances Lewes 8, Arundel 20, London 53

East Sussex, Brighton & Hove

86 Neo Hotel

19 Oriental Place, Brighton, East Sussex BN1 2LL
T (0870) 860 8416 **F** (01273) 711105 **E** info@neohotel.com
T (International) +44 [0] (1273) 711104 **W** www.neohotel.com

Neo Hotel is a chic stylish hotel situated conveniently close to Brighton seafront and within a 10-minute walk of the bustling city centre. Known for its original and elegant décor, all rooms are highly individual and feature designer wallpapers, TV & DVD and wireless internet access. The hotel has 9 unique rooms, a cool cocktail bar and a charming breakfast/dining room. The hotel is a Grade II listed building, all bedrooms are en suite, and beautiful satin kimonos are provided. Bathrooms have slick black mosaic tiles, cone shaped basins and large polished chrome shower heads. All are stocked with an aromatherapy all in one hair-and-body-wash in soothing ginger and clary sage and products by L'Occitane. Breakfast is what the Neo does best with its fabulous fluffy blueberry pancakes and *Full English* with roasted vine tomatoes and Sussex pork sausages. The hotel's warm sophisticated vibe lends itself equally well to romantic breaks, wedding receptions or informal corporate meetings. Placing great emphasis on the personal touch, its friendly staff pay huge attention to detail and provide a great atmosphere for guests. An absolute gem!

Stylish townhouse small hotel between Brighton & Hove

🛏 9 ☺ ✂ ♨ 20

Directions Right at Old Steine rdbt opp main pier, along seafront 5 mins, past West Pier, turn rt up Oriental Place.

Nearby attractions
Royal Pavilion, The Lanes, Sealife Centre, Preston Manor, Booth Museum

Distances
Worthing 10, Arundel 18, London 54.

Rates Single room inc. breakfast from £55; double from £95.
Meals Breakfast 0800-0930; 0900-1030 weekends.

Other facilities Massage and beauty therapy treatments.

 & major credit cards accepted. Open all year exc. Dec 21-28.

East Sussex, Brighton & Hove

Best Western Lansdowne Hotel

87

King Edward's Parade, Eastbourne, East Sussex BN21 4EE

T (0870) 418 8049 **F** (01323) 739721 **E** reception@lansdowne-hotel.co.uk
T (International) +44 [0] (1323) 725174 **W** www.bw-lansdownehotel.co.uk

Best Western Lansdowne Hotel commands a fine view over Eastbourne's beach to the sea beyond. Owned by the same family since 1912, this hotel has the true hallmark of hospitality and comfort. Bedrooms are elegantly furnished with many overlooking the sea-front. Three years ago nine superior seafront rooms were opened, each formed by combining two former smaller rooms. These have been refurbished in great style. There is a choice of elegant lounges, all looking across the Western Lawns, as well as several refreshment venues, from the attractive Regency Bar to the stylish Devonshire Restaurant serving fixed price menus of traditional English cuisine. A comprehensive bar and lounge menu is available at lunch and supper time. Traditional Sunday lunch is served and a 4-course dinner every evening in the restaurant. Conferences and seminars are well provided for in a selection of rooms. Two snooker rooms, table tennis, darts and a pool table provide further relaxation. A good centre from which to tour Eastbourne's attractions and the South Coast.

AA★★★ Visit Britain Silver Award. AA Courtesy & Care Award 1992.
RAC Merit Awards for Hospitality, Service & Comfort 1995/6/7/8/2000.

101 (inc 2 & 10) (£5) 5x 375 P 22

Imposing Eastbourne hotel with views to Beachy Head.

Rates Single room inc breakfast from £50; double from £92.

Meals 4-cse tdh dinner £21.95; alc, lunch & diets available; last orders 2030; bfst fm 0700.

Leisure Breaks Available I Nov-30 April (exc. Xmas/NY/Easter) £61.50 pp per n't dinner, b & b (min 2 nts). **Weekend & Weekday Breaks**. Special Sun-Thurs or Mon-Fri offer: Last night of stay, only dinner charged for - rm & bfst free. Valid till 31.5.07

Other facilities Satellite TV, Golf (arr'ts on 13 local courses), watersports, sailing, tennis, riding nearby. Duplicate/social bridge weekends thr't year. & all major credit cards accepted. Sky Sports TV in public rm. Open all yr

Directions
Head for Arndale Centre/Station, then to seafront. Turn rt Grand Parade/King Eds Pa

Nearby attractions
Beachy Head & Seven Sisters, Battle Abbey, Michelham Priory, Drusillas Zoo

Distances
Newhaven 12, Hastings 20, London 63

Beauport Park Hotel & Health Club
Battle Road, Hastings, East Sussex TN38 8EA
T (0870) 418 8050 **F** (01424) 852465 **E** reservations@beauportparkhotel.co.uk
T (International) +44 [0] (1424) 851222 **W** www.beauportparkhotel.co.uk

This fine house was built in 1719 and remodelled by a former Governor of Quebec who named it Beauport after his summer home in Canada. It is unspoiled by its transition from residence to first class hotel and guests will particularly enjoy the three most attractive features - seclusion, the stylish elegance of the interior and the extensive range of leisure facilities including indoor pool, gym, sauna and coffee shop. Set at the end of a winding drive in 33 acres of tranquil parkland, it is a perfect example of a Georgian country house. The tastefully modernised lounge and bar areas are warmed by open log fires, and the candlelit restaurant, renowned for its cuisine, overlooks the formal Italian and sunken gardens. In 1999 a Victorian conservatory was added and a new Brasserie opened in 2000. The bedrooms too are furnished to a high standard. Beauport is close to the Channel ports and the many attractions of this beautiful part of Britain. Yet in these historic surroundings anyone seeking either peace and quiet or a more active holiday need look no further than this lovely hotel.

Georgian country house set in 33 acres of parkland.

25 (inc 7) 180. 3 x 70

Directions
Off A2100 Hastings-Battle Road, by golf club.

Nearby attractions
Battle Abbey, Carr Taylor vineyards, Bodiam Castle, Gt Dixter gardens.

Distances
Rye 11, Brighton 37, Lewes 29, London 65

Rates Single room inc breakfast from £95; double from £130.
Meals 3-cse tdh dinner £30; alc, lunch & diets available; last orders 2130.
Leisure Breaks Min 2 night short breaks available all year. A four-poster room, dinner, b & b, starts at £95 per night.
Other facilities Coffee shop.

& all major credit cards accepted. Open all year.

Newick Park Hotel & Country Estate

Newick, Nr Lewes, East Sussex BN8 4SB

T (0870) 418 8045 **F** (01825) 723969 **E** bookings@newickpark.co.uk
T (International) +44 [0] (1825) 723633 **W** www.newickpark.co.uk

89

Newick Park is a beautiful Georgian grade II Listed country house set in 250 acres of landscaped gardens and parkland, with glorious views over the Longford river and lake towards the South Downs. Although near to main routes, it is 'off the beaten track' and visitors enjoy total peace and tranquillity when staying. The oldest part of the house dates from the 16th century and was an ironmaster's home, the extensive Dell gardens behind the house being the site of his excavations. Rust coloured chalybeate springs still pop up at the bottom of the lake as evidence of this once thriving trade. The Victorian Dell Gardens contain many shrubs and rhodondendrons, together with giant leaved gunnera and a rare collection of Royal Ferns. Snowdrops, bluebells and daffodils provide sheets of colour in the Spring. Inside many bedrooms have king-size beds and reception rooms are exceptionally comfortable with the aura of a private house with no reception desk. Indeed the house can be hired for exclusive use and is popular as a wedding venue. AA ☺ ☺ cuisine is served in the elegant dining room and caps the experience of staying in one of the most comfortable small hotels in the South-East of England.

🛏 16 (inc 3 suites) ✂ ⚘ ✓ 🍴 ⚲ ♋ 🔟 ♪ 🐴(some rooms) ✓ 🅿100+
2x 🏃 80 🎿

Gracious country estate set in 250 acres of gardens and parkland.

Rates Double/twin room inc breakfast from £165.
Meals 3-cse alc dinner £35; lunch & diets available; last orders 2100; bfst from 0730.
Other facilities Golf, riding 5 miles. Tank driving and quad biking on estate.

Directions
From A272 in Newick village turn south twds church and follow signs to Newick Pk
Nearby attractions
Hever Castle, Sheffield Park Gdns, Glyndebourne, Penshurst Place.
Distances
Lewes 5, Haywards Heath 8, London 46

 Visa, Mastercard & Switch accepted. Open all year exc at New Year.

East Sussex, Newick

Flackley Ash Hotel
Peasmarsh, Nr Rye, East Sussex TN31 6YH
T (0870) 418 8051 F (01797) 230510 E enquiries@flackleyashhotel.co.uk
T (International) +44 [0] (1797) 230651 W www.flackleyashhotel.co.uk

This is one of Sussex' most charming small country house hotels. Rye is only a few miles away with its many historic buildings including the 15th century church, the Ypres Tower, the famous Landgate and Henry James' Georgian residence, Lamb House. Local activities are many and varied, with antique shops, potteries, local crafts and boutiques and a market on Thursdays. The fellow *Cinque Port*, Winchelsea, is nearby as is Camber Sands, with its beautiful beaches and safe bathing. In addition there are famous castles, abbeys and gardens to visit. The hotel has an indoor swimming pool and leisure complex, with a new hydro-pool, gym, steam room, saunas, aromatherapy and beauticians, sun terrace and putting lawns. This Georgian house offers a warm and friendly atmosphere and comfortable bedrooms, newly refurbished with sumptuous Sandereson fabrics. Dining by candlelight in our conservatory or overlooking the hotel's gardens, the restaurant boasts daily changing menus using the finest local produce. Staff are friendly, helpful and profssional. This beautiful privately owned hotel is run by the Betteridge family, who ensure quality accommodation to business and leisure traveller alike.

Georgian country house near the historic town of Rye.

45 · 120 WIFI

Directions
On A268 Hawkhurst-Rye road. From the north, hotel on left in village of Peasmarsh.

Nearby attractions
Rye, Great Dixter, Sissinghurst and Pashley Manor Gdns, Bodiam Castle

Distances
Rye 3, Hastings 11, Dover 36, London 60

Rates Room & breakfast from £74 per pers sharing.
Meals 3-cse tdh dinner £30; alc, lunch & diets available; last orders 2130.
Getaway Breaks Min 2 nights, dinner, b & b £93-118 per pers. per night.
Perfect Choice - 7 nights, dinner, b & b £483-£700 per person.
Other facilities Aromatherapy, massage, manicures, facials in beauty salon; 5 acres of gardens & grounds; children's tree tops; wireless

 & all major credit cards accepted. Open all year

East Sussex, Peasmarsh

Rye Lodge Hotel

Hilder's Cliff, Rye, East Sussex TN31 7LD
T (0870) 418 8052 **F** (01797) 223585 **E** info@ryelodge.co.uk
T (International) +44 [0] (1797) 223838 **W** www.ryelodge.co.uk

Rye - Ancient Town of the Cinque Ports. No town in England evokes the atmosphere of medieval times better than Rye with the charm and character of its cobbled streets, picturesque period houses, historic buildings and ancient fortifications. Situated on the East Cliff overlooking the estuary and Romney Marshes, yet within yards of the High Street of this beautifully preserved ancient town, stands Rye Lodge, acclaimed and acknowledged as one of the finest small luxury hotels in Southeast England. Much thought has gone into the décor, furnishing and equipping of the bedrooms and public rooms, creating an oasis of tranquillity and comfort for guests. The Terrace Restaurant is elegant, candlelit and its fine cellar houses some rare vintages. The hotel is centrally located, so that all antique shops, art galleries etc are within walking distance. This delightful privately owned hotel is run by the de Courcy family. It offers a degree of comfort and personal service rarely found in hotels these days and only achieved by experienced hoteliers through hard work and dedication to their art.

20 P 20

Family owned hotel overlooking Romney Marshes and the estuary

Rates Single occupanvy inc breakfast £75-£110; double £100-£200. Ad
Meals 3-cse alc & tdh dinner £29.50; special diets available; last orders 2100
Leisure Breaks Midweek short breaks - any 2 nights, dinner, b & b £69.50-£119.50 per pers per night.
Mini Holidays - 4 nights+, dinner, b & b £64.50-£104.50 per pers per night.
Other facilities Aromotherapy steam cabinet.

American Express Diners, Mastercard,Visa, Switch, Delta cards accepted. Open all year.

Directions
Follow town centre signs; go under Landgate Arch. Hotel 100 yds on right.

Nearby attractions
Great Dixter, Battle Abbey, Bodiam Castle, Camber Sands, Sissinghurst.

Distances
Hastings 11, Ashford 20, London 63.

…tels whose prices are followed by Ad accept the Signpost Advantage Card, which entitles holders either to a 10% …count from the room (only) rate or to an upgrade, according to availability. See back of this book for app'n form.

The Brickwall Hotel

The Green, Sedlescombe, Battle, East Sussex TN33 0QA
T (0870) 860 8506 **F** (01424) 870785 **E** info@brickwallhotel.com
T (International) +44 [0] (1424) 870253 **W** www.brickwallhotel.com

The Brickwall Hotel stands overlooking the village green of the pretty East Sussex village of Sedlescombe. Originally built in 1597 for the local ironmaster, the hotel combines the original charm of Tudor times with the comforts of the 21st century. A feature of the hotel is the large number of ground floor rooms, many looking out onto a sheltered walled garden; also the heated outdoor swimming pool. There is a spacious residents' lounge, an oak panelled lounge bar and a large beamed dining room. Golf is available at the nearby Aldershaw Golf Course at special rates to guests of the Brickwall and tennis courts can be rented by the hour in the village. The Cinque Ports of Rye and Winchelsea are within an easy drive as are such Sussex Weald landmarks as Battle Abbey, Bodiam and Pevensey Castles. Great Dixter garden is nearby n there are several vineyards, childrens' farms and bird sanctuaries to be visited. The beach at Camber Sands is some ten miles away. The Brickwall is a peaceful spot for a break with plenty to see and do in the area.

Timbered cottage hotel with pretty gardens and an outdoor pool

25 (inc 2) 2x 30/80 **P** 40

Directions From London A21 to Robertsbridge, then third left to Sedlescombe, hotel at top of village green.

Nearby attractions
Bodiam Cas, Camber Sands, Pevensey Cas, Sissinghurst, Battle Abbey.

Distances
Battle 3, Hastings 7, Rye 10, London 63

Rates Single with breakfast from £65; double from £92.
Meals 3-cse tdh dinner from £26; lunch & special diets available; last orders 2100. Breakfast from 0730.
Leisure Breaks Mini-breaks run all year round. Prices from £130 per person for a 2-night stay, dinner, b&b; stay a 3rd night and pay only £35 for meals - accommodation free. **Other Facilities** Tennis, golf, beach, riding nearby.

East Sussex, Sedlescombe

Crossways Hotel

Wilmington, Polegate, East Sussex BN26 5SG

T (0870) 860 8419 F (01323) 487811 E stay@crosswayshotel.co.uk
T (International) +44 [0] (1323) 482455 W www.crosswayshotel.co.uk

93

Crossways Hotel is a small Georgian period house with a well kept garden. Resident proprietors David Stott and Clive James, with their small team of helpers, have created a warm and peaceful ambience within this lovely old building. Guest rooms are individually styled and have every modern comfort and facility. Crossways nestles under the South Downs close to the *Long Man of Wilmington* - a 226 sq ft figure cut into the downland chalk. The origin of the figure remains a mystery but is believed to date back to Neolithic times. The village of Wilmington also has the substantial remains of a 13th century Benedictine Priory. Crossways offers comfortable reasonably priced accommodation, conveniently located for the South Coast resorts of Brighton and Eastbourne, Lewes, the many houses and gardens open in the area and for Glyndebourne Opera House. Several *Areas of Outstanding Natural Beauty* are in the vicinity. The monthly changing menu features meat, fish and vegetables from the region, prepared with flair and imagination. The restaurant is popular with locals and has a very good wine list. During our stay, we enjoyed a classic New Zealand *Sauvignon Blanc*, called *Cloudy Bay*.

Friendly small hotel nestling in the South Downs

Rates Single with breakfast from £65; double from £99.
Meals 3-cse tdh dinner £35.95; special diets available; last orders 2030. Breakfast from 0730.
Leisure Breaks Special Gourmet Breaks available - dinner, b & b, from £79 per person per night.
Other facilities Gym, golf, fishing, sea bathing, tennis, riding all within 5 miles

Directions
Wilmington is on the A27 btwn Berwick and Polegate. Hotel on north side of road.
Nearby attractions Glyndebourne Opera House, Clergy House Alfriston, Michelham Priory, Drusillas Zoo Park,
Distances
Lewes 9, Eastbourne 6, London 63.

 & all major credit cards exc Diners accepted. Closed 24 Dec-24 Jan.

East Sussex, Wilmington

The Millstream Hotel & Restaurant

Bosham Lane, Bosham, Chichester, West Sussex PO18 8HL
T (0870) 860 8420 **F** (01243) 573459 **E** info@millstream-hotel.co.uk
T (International) +44 [0] (1243) 573234 **W** www.millstream-hotel.co.uk

The Millstream is situated in the heart of old Bosham, an historic village with a fine Saxon church on the shores of Chichester Harbour. It combines the elegance of a small English country house with the character and charm of an 18th century malthouse cottage. Each bedroom is different and there are two suites across the bridge in the thatched *Waterside Cottage.* The AA ® restaurant overlooks the gardens, and is renowned for its execellent cuisine. It offers a varied selection of English and Continental dishes, prepared with the best available fresh produce and complemented by a list of fine wines from an established cellar. The bar offers a cosy fireside setting in which to relax. The charming sitting room, with its deep cushioned armchairs, grand piano, bowls of freshly cut flowers and tranquil atmosphere, is the ideal place to meet up with friends over afternoon tea or an apéritif, play cards or just laze away with a good novel or magazine. At one point the garden is bisected by the eponymous millstream which flows past the new Gazebo. Bosham is an ideal centre from which to explore this area of outstanding natural beauty and historical interest.

Restored 18thC malthouse and English cottages 300 yds from the sea

🛏 35 (inc 3 suites) ✗ ♿ ☺ (WIFI) 🕭 ⚲ ♨ 20 🐾

Directions
Leave A259 Southborne-Chichester rd at Broadbridge. Hotel 1m down on rt b4 ⚥

Nearby attractions
Fishbourne Roman Palace, Westdean Gdns, Chichester Festival Theatre.

Distances
Chichester 3, Portsmouth 18, London 69

Rates Single, with breakfast from £79; double from £138.
Meals 3-cse tdh dinner £30; lunch & spec. diets available; last orders 2115. Breakfast from 0730.
Leisure Breaks Bosham Breaks - 2 nights, dinner, b & b from £79 pppnight; third night (Sunday or Thursday) from £55.
Other facilities Golf, sailing, squash, riding, watersports nearby.

& all major credit cards accepted. Open all year.

West Sussex, Nr. Chichester

Gravetye Manor

Nr. East Grinstead, West Sussex RH19 4LJ

T (0870) 860 8421 F (01342) 810080 E info@gravetyemanor.co.uk
T (International) +44 [0] (1342) 810567 W www.gravetyemanor.co.uk

95

Dating from 1598, Gravetye Manor is one of the finest country houses in the UK. Peter Herbert arrived here in 1958. Captivated by the house and its William Robinson designed garden, he injected his own exceptional hotel keeping and restaurant experience into this rural spot. Time has enabled projects such as the restoration of the kitchen garden to come to fruition and miraculously the 1000-acre oasis of forest in which Gravetye sits has resisted encroachment, 'though only 30 miles from Hyde Park Corner. In April 2004 General Manager Andrew Russell and Chef de Cuisine Mark Raffan, both of whom had worked for the Herbert family for over 17 years, purchased the hotel. They both have great affection for this Elizabethan house and garden and continue to promote the philosophy of country house hospitality as well as maintaining and nurturing the historically important gardens. There are only 18 bedrooms, each elegantly furnished but with all modern comforts. Public rooms are cosy and restful. The intimate oak panelled restaurant has AA ☺☺☺ for cuisine and a wine list of over 600 bins - one of the finest cellars in the UK. One of the original country house hotels of the South-East .

🛏 18 ✿ ♧ ♪ 🔊 ♀ 🅿 30 ♔ 12 🐕 🎴

Classic, elegant distinctive country house hotel in 35 acre gardens

Rates Single, room only, from £100; double, room only from £170.
Meals 3-cse tdh dinner £38; alc, lunch & spec. diets available; last orders 2130. Breakfast from 0800.
Leisure Breaks Midweek Breaks Sun-Thurs Nov-March 2007: £245 per person sharing for 2 nights accomm, tdh dinner, b & b.
Other facilities Gym, golf, sauna, riding all within ten miles.

Directions
M23 exit 10 onto A264 E Grinstead. After 2m rt on B2028 thru Turners Hill; hotel on lft
Nearby attractions
Hever Castle, Chartwell, Wakehurst Place, Nymans Gdns, Sheffield Park
Distances
E Grinstead 4, Gatwick 12, London 52.

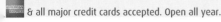

& all major credit cards accepted. Open all year.

96

Chequers Hotel
Old Rectory Lane, Pulborough, West Sussex RH20 1AD
T (0870) 418 8201 F (01798) 892715 E chequers@btinternet.com
T (International) +44 [0] (1798) 872486 W www.the-chequers-hotel.com

Now under new ownership, the Chequers featured in one of the earliest Signpost guides and there is a framed page from the 1939 edition in the hall as one enters this friendly, small hotel. It has eight bedrooms, some in the 16th century part and others in the later extension. They range from twins and doubles to a family room and a four poster. The Chequers delivers a family-run standard of service, including a collection and pickup service by arrangement. There are two licensed lounges. Dining is either here or in the linensed restaurant or in the airy brasserie/conservatory. This opens onto the small garden, where drinks, coffee and Sussex cream teas can be enjoyed. Both restaurants use, wherever possible, local products and suppliers. The hotel overlooks the Arun Valley to the South Downs beyond. Chequers is close to Petworth House & Park, Parham House & Gardens and Arundel Castle. It is convenient for Goodwood and Fontwell horseracing and Cowdray Park polo. An RSPB Nature Reserve is nearby and the South Downs Way passes close to the hotel.

Historic small hotel overlooking the Arun valley.

🛏 10 ✂ ☺ 🅿 16 ♨ 25 🐎

Directions
A24 Horsham to A29 thru' Billingshurst. On entering Pulborough Rectory La on left b4 ✠

Nearby attractions
RSPB Pulborough Brooks, Petworth Hse, Parham House, Arundel Cas.

Distances
Arundel 8, Chichester 16, London 45.

Rates Single room with breakfast from £60; double from £95.
Meals Alc & spec. diets available. Breakfast from 0730.

Other facilities Fishing, golf, sailing, watersports, shooting & riding nearby.

Visa & Mastercard accepted. Open all year.

West Sussex, Pulborough

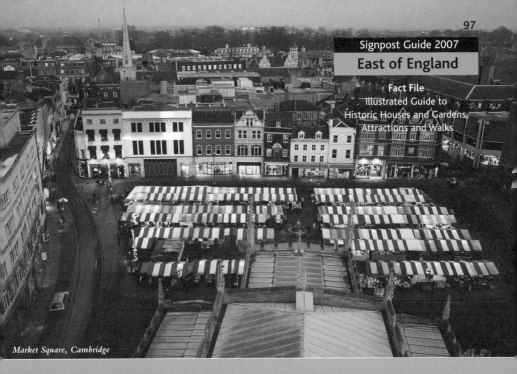

Market Square, Cambridge

Fact File
Illustrated Guide to
Historic Houses and Gardens,
Attractions and Walks

East of England

Norfolk claims to have more sunshine than any
other area of the country. Recently the North
Norfolk Coast has become fashionable but the
Norfolk Broads and Suffolk Coast have always been
popular with yachtsmen. High-tech Cambridge is an
expanding city with good communications while
Hertfordshire and Essex have excellent transport
links into the capital as well their own enclaves of
beauty and seclusion.

Hotels guide	
Bedfordshire	page 102
Cambridgeshire	page 104
Hertfordshire	page 105
Norfolk	page 107
Suffolk	page 112

Further information:
East of England Tourist Board
Toppesfield Hall, Hadleigh,
Suffolk IP7 5DN
Tel: 01473 822922

www.eetb.org.uk

Orford

Queen's College, Cambridge

Bedfordshire and Hertfordshire

Woburn Abbey

Principal attraction in **Bedfordshire** is Woburn Abbey, the still inhabited home of the Dukes of Bedford, which stands in a 3000-acre park and is now part of Europe's largest drive-through Game Reserve. The 18th century mansion's 14 state apartments are open to the public and the art collection includes works by Rembrandt, Holbein and Velasquez. Nearby is **Whipsnade Zoo**, where 2000 animals roam a 500-acre park.

Luton Hoo is a fine Robert Adam designed house in a 1200-acre Capability Brown designed park. South Bedfordshire's Chiltern landscape gives way to the fertile plains of East Anglia north of Bedford.

Shaw's Corner, Ayot St. Lawrence

Hatfield House

Hertfordshire too has its fair share of stately homes, with **Hatfield House**, built from 1707 by Robert Cecil, first Earl of Salisbury, leading the way. Nearby **Knebworth House** is the venue for several summer concerts and events. Roman walls, mosaic floors and part of an amphitheatre are still visible at **Verulanium, St Albans.**

Much Hadham, where the Bishops of London used to have their country seat, is a showpiece village. Britain's first 20th century new towns were built in this northern commuter belt at **Welwyn Garden City**, **Letchworth** and later **Stevenage**. Welwyn in particular retains a certain *art deco* attraction.

Cambridgeshire and Essex

King's College, Cambridge

Cambridge is a city of colleges, each founded for the personal glorification of the founder as an act of piety. The city's winding streets are lined with old houses, colleges and churches, while the gently flowing Cam provides a serene backdrop to the architectural wonders. **Kings College Chapel**, started by Henry VI in 1446 should not be missed. The **Fitzwilliam Museum** is one of Europe's treasure houses, with antiquities from Rome, Greece and Rome. Outside the city the Technology Park leads the world in computer science and research. **Peterborough** has a fine Norman cathedral with three soaring arches whilst Ely has had an abbey on its cathedral site since AD 670.

Western Essex borders London and has fast trains to Liverpool Street. Further East the **Blackwater** and **Crouch** estuaries provide havens for yachts and pleasure craft.

Some of its loveliest countryside is on the Suffolk Border around **Dedham Vale**, where Constable and Turner painted. County town **Colchester** was founded by the Romans and its massive castle keep, built in 1067 on the site of the Roman Temple of Claudius, houses a collection of Roman antiquities.
At the Western end of the county, Stansted Airport continues to expand and roads East are being upgraded accordingly.

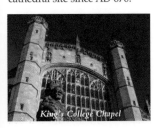
King's College Chapel

Constable's Mill

 TOP 10 Historic Houses Gardens and Parks

Anglesey Abbey, Nr. Cambridge
Audley End House & Gardens, Saffron Walden, Essex
Copped Hall, Nr Epping, Essex
Docwra's Manor Garden, Shepreth, Cambs
Elton Hall, Nr Peterborough, Cambs
Ely Cathedral, Ely, Cambs
Hinchingbrooke House, Huntingdon
Layer Marney Tower, Nr. Colchester
Peterborough Cathedral, Cambs
University of Cambridge Botanic Garden

 TOP 10 Attractions

Abberton Reservoir Nature Reserve, Nr. Colchester
Cambridge & County Folk Museum
Cromwell Museum, Huntingdon
Fitzwilliam Museum, Cambridge
Imperial War Museum & Aircraft Collection, Duxford, Cambs
Oliver Cromwell's House, Ely, Cambs
Priory Vineyards, Little Dunmow, Essex
Scott Polar Research Institute, Cambridge
Southend Sea Life Centre, Essex
Wimpole Hall & Home Farm, Nr Royston, Cambs

TOP 10 Walks and Nature Trails

Bishop's Way, north of Ely, Cambs
Devil's Dyke, from north of Feach to south of Stechworth, Cambs
Essex Way: Hainault > Dedham
Grafham Water Circular, Cambs
Harcamlow Way: Chipping Ongar > Linton
Hemingford Abbots > Hemingford Grey > St Ives > Wyton
St Peters Way: Chipping Ongar > Bradwell-on-Sea, Essex
Three Forests Way: Chingford > Chipping Ongar, Essex
Walton-on-the-Naze > Cormorant Creek, Essex
Wivenhoe > Wivenhoe Sta > Alresford Creek, Essex

100

Norfolk

 TOP 10 Historic Houses Gardens and Parks

Blickling Hall, Aylsham,
  Nr. Norwich
Felbrigg Hall, Nr. Cromer
Holkham Hall, Wells-next-the-Sea
Houghtion Hall, Nr. Kings Lynn
Mannington Hall & Gardens,
  Nr. Norwich
Norfolk Lavender Ltd, Heacham
Oxburgh Hall & Gardens,
  Nr. Swaffham
Plantation Garden, Norwich
Sandringham, Nr. Kings Lynn

TOP 10 Attractions

Ancient House Museum, Thetford
Brideswell & Church Museums,
  Norwich
Bure Valley Railway
  Aylsham > Wroxham
Maritime Museum, Great Yarmouth
Norwich Castle Museum
Old Gaol House & Museum,
  Kings Lynn
RAF Air Defence Museum,
  Norwich
Shrine of Our Lady of Walsingham
Thursford Steam Collection,
  Nr. Fakenham
Wymondham Abbey

 TOP 10 Walks and Nature Trails

Alderford Common > Upgate
  Swannington, Nr Norwich
Angles Way:
  Knettishall > Lowestoft
Bure Valley: Coltishall > Belaugh
  Railway Line, Nr. Norwich
Knettishall Heath Country Park
Ludham Marshes > River Thurne.
  Nr. Cromer
Marriotts Way: Norwich > Aylsham
Norfolk Coast Path:
  Holme next the Sea > Cromer
Peddars Way: Knettishall Heath >
  Holme next the Sea
Peter Scott Walk.
  Kings Lynn > Sutton Bridge
Weavers Way:
  Cromer > Aylsham > Gt Yarmouth

Sandringham

Cromer

Norfolk Broads

Norfolk is not as flat as Noel Coward would have it, as any cyclist will tell you. Nevertheless cycling or walking is a good way to see the county.

In the **West** the county is thickly afforested - **Thetford Forest** is said to be the oldest in England. In the **East** it is criss-crossed by waterways and lakes known as **The Broads** - apparently the remains of medieval man's peat diggings!

The county town of Norfolk and unofficial capital of East Anglia is **Norwich**, a finely planned city whose cathedral walls are decorated with biblical scenes dating from 1046. In addition there are 30

medieval churches in central Norwich alone and many interesting streets and shops to explore. Near **Kings Lynn** in the north west of the county is **Sandringham**, the royal palace bought by Queen Victoria for the then Prince of Wales.

The **North Norfolk** coast has become known as '*Chelsea-on-Sea*' and good restaurants and hostelries abound from **Hunstanton** in the West to **Cromer** in the East. House prices in this area now rival those in the home counties.

Felbrigg Hall

Suffolk

Aldeburgh

Suffolk is famous for its winding lanes and pastel painted thatched cottages. This is a rich county, from the time when wool was the money crop of Middle England. See the great churches of **Lavenham**, **Sudbury** and **Long Melford**.

Suffolk's coast, with its inlets and estuaries is popular with yachtsmen. **Framlingham Castle**, near Aldeburgh, stands intact since the 13th century. **Aldeburgh** itself is the home of the Benjamin Britten Music Festival at Snape.

The hills and valleys on the Suffolk-Essex border open up to magnificent skies, captured in paintings by Constable, Turner and Gainsborough. The Heart of Constable Country is **Nayland** and **Dedham Vale**.

Helmingham

County Town **Ipswich** now has a buzzing waterfront and the ports of **Harwich** and **Felixstowe** are now well connected to the Midlands via the improved A14.

Framlingham Castle

TOP 10 Historic Houses Gardens and Parks

Blakenham Woodland Garden, Nr. Ipswich
Framlingham Castle
Haughley Park, Nr. Stowmarket
Helmingham Hall, Nr. Stowmarket
Hengrave Hall, Bury St Edmunds
Ickworth House, Bury St Edmunds
Kentwell Hall, Long Melford
Melford Hall, Long Melford
Orford Castle, Nr. Woodbridge
Somerleyton Hall & Gardens, Lowestoft

TOP 10 Attractions

Bressingham Gardens & Steam Locomotive Collection, Nr Diss
Christchurch Mansion Museum, Ipswich
Dunwich Underwater Exploration Exhibition, Orford
Gainsborough's House, Sudbury
Museum of East Anglian Life, Stowmarket
National Horseracing Museum, Newmarket
Pakenham Watermill & Windmill, Ixworth
The Priory & Little Hall, Lavenham
St Edmondsbury Manor House Museum, Bury St Edmunds
Sizewell Visitors Centre, Sizewell B Power Station

TOP 10 Walks and Nature Trails

Alton Water Bird Sanctuary Circular Walk, Nr. Ipswich
Angles Way: Harleston > Gt Yarmouth
Blakenham Woodland Garden Walk, Nr. Ipswich
The Constable Trail, Dedham Vale
Dunwich > Eastbridge > Kenton Hills > Sizewell Walk
Orford &The Gull/Butley River Path
Painters Way: Sudbury > Manningtree
Stour Valley Path: Long Melford > Kentwell Hall >Glemsford >Liston
Suffolk Coast Path: Bawdsley Quay > Lowestoft
Suffolk Way: Flatford > Lavenham

102 The Mill House Hotel & Riverside Restaurant

Mill Road, Sharnbrook, Bedford, Bedfordshire MK44 1NP
T (0870) 860 8507 **F** (01234) 783921 **E** enquiries@millhouse-riverside.co.uk
T (International) +44 [0] (1234) 781678 **W** www.millhouse-riverside.co.uk

Between the A1 and the M1, on the banks of the Great Ouse, is the Mill House, a restaurant with rooms, which is carving itself quite a reputation in the Bedford area. It has recently been bought by the Noel family, who also own Barnsdale Lodge (*see Leicestershire section of this guide*) and who have injected their own smart/casual style into this small, relaxed hotel. The Riverside Restaurant prepares quality dishes using locally sourced materials wherever possible, including vegetables from the market garden next door. The terrace and marquee can cater for larger functions such as weddings and al fresco dinners. The hotel also organises a range of leisure activities, such as art classes, yoga, pilates and bespoke cookery demonstrations. Bedrooms are bright and cheerful with ISDN lines and luxury en suite facilities. On the doorstep is the Bedford Autodrome, the Glenn Miller Museum at Twinwoods and the thriving amateur Mill Theatre. The Mill House is 15 minutes from the historic market town of Bedford and from the growing centre of Rushden and is ideal for those on business or pleasure in the area.

Quiet Restaurant with Rooms on the banks of the Great Ouse

 10 ⚄ ♿ ☎☉ ♨♨♨ 40 🅿 30

Directions
A6 from Bedford. Turn left at first Sharmbrook roundabout, hotel 200 m on left.

Nearby attractions
Bedford (Thurleigh) Autodrome, Glenn Miller Museum, Bromham Mill

Distances
Rushden 7, Bedford 6, London 56

Rates Single room wth breakfast from £70; double inc. bfst from £85.
Meals 3-cse tdh dinner £25; lunch £17.50. Sun lunch fm £15.50. Last orders 2145.
Leisure Breaks Stay Friday & Saturday and get 50% off Thurs or Sun accom.
Other facilities Golf, clay shooting, riding, autosport nearby.

 & all major credit cards accepted. Open all year.

Bedfordshire, Nr. Bedford

The Inn at Woburn
George Street, Woburn, Bedfordshire MK17 9PX
T (0870) 418 8071 **F** (01525) 290432 **E** enquiries@theinnatwoburn.com
T (International) +44 [0] (1525) 290441 **W** www.theinnatwoburn.com

103

We are pleased to welcome The Inn at Woburn, (formerly *The Bedford Arms*) back into Signpost after its considerable refurbishment. The original building has been extended in keeping with its Georgian origins and in 2001 outbuildings were converted to provide seven smart new *cottage*s including three suites. The reception area has been extended and there are now three dining areas. The Tavistock Bar has been upgraded and has cartoons from the collection of the 13th Duke of Bedford on its walls. It still retains its local appeal. Olivier's restaurant, under the supervision of chef de cuisine Olivier Bertho, provides a superb menu of contemporary English and Continental cuisine and has proved a magnet for discerning diners in the area. The overall result is one of the best hotels in the area, appealing both to visitors to Woburn Abbey and to business travellers. The attractive village, with its antique and craft shops, retains its quiet character but is convenient for Milton Keynes, Dunstable and Luton. The Inn can book tee-times on Woburn Golf Course, just up the road, and obtain entrance tickets for the Abbey and Safari Park. Special Golf and Safari Breaks are available.

🛏 58 ⤢ ♿ ✓ 🖥 🍴 ☉ ⚏ 90 🅿 80

Modernised coaching Inn which has been caring for travellers for 300 years

Rates Single room wth breakfast from £120; double inc bfst from £145. Cottage suite from £195 b & b.
Leisure Breaks Woburn Safari Breaks: Family of 4 one night stay inc. entry to Safari Park £280. 2-night break inc family room accomm + £60 twds dinner each nt £465. Woburn Golf Breaks: 2 nights b & b + £20 twds lunch or dinner one day per head + one round of golf - one golfer £265/2 golfers £215 each.
Other facilities Squash, swimming, leisure centre, riding 5m; sailing/shooting 10m & all major credit cards accepted. Open all year.

Directions
J12 or 13 M1, into Woburn, left. Inn is at X-roads George St/Park St. Parking off Park St
Nearby attractions
Woburn Abbey & Safari Park, Whipsnade Zoo, Woburn Golf/Country Club
Distances
Milton Keynes 6, Bedford 13, London 43

Bedfordshire, Woburn

Arundel House Hotel
Chesterton Road, Cambridge CB4 3AN
T (0870) 418 8072 **F** (01223) 367221 **E** info@arundelhousehotels.co.uk
T (International) +44 [0] (1223) 367701 **W** www.arundelhousehotels.co.uk

The Arundel House Hotel occupies one of the finest sites in the City of Cambridge, overlooking the River Cam and open parkland. It is only a short walk across the park known as Jesus Green to the city centre with its wealth of historic buildings. The hotel is well known for its bar, restaurant and conservatory. The bright, cheerful colours in the bar, coupled with its comfortable sofas and armchairs, leather bound books, beautiful fireplaces and its magnificent Victorian-style bar, carved out of solid American red oak, combine to create a warm and refreshing atmosphere, ideal for a pre-lunch or -dinner drink, or just to relax in. The restaurant, which is equally sumptuous has a reputation for providing some of the best food in the area at very modest prices. All tastes are catered for, thanks to the several different menus on offer, all featuring a wide range of imaginative dishes, freshly prepared in the hotel's award winning kitchen. As an alternative to the restaurant, there is a Victorian style conservatory, providing a luscious green environment. This is open all day and offers a wide range of different options from cooked meals to cream teas, all of which can also be served in the hotel's secluded garden on fine days.

Elegant Victorian terrace overlooking river, within walking distance of city

🛏 103 🍴 🛏 50 🅿 70

Directions
Nthbnd M11 exit J13, turn rt to mini 0, turn left & str't over at lts. Hotel 300m on left.

Nearby attractions
Historic University Colleges, Botanic Gardens, Fitzwilliam Museum.

Distances
Newmarket 13, Stansted 26, London 55

Rates Single room inc. breakfast from £75; double inc bfst from £95.

Meals 3-cse tdh lunch or dinner £20.75/2-cse £16.95; alc, vegetarian, conservatory & childrens' menus also available. Last orders 2130 restaurant/2200 conserv.

Leisure Breaks 2 nights dinner, b & b £139 per person sharing. Singles £134.

Accreditations AA★★★ 79%

 Visa, Mastercard, Diners cards accepted. Open all year.

Cambridgeshire, Cambridge

Pendley Manor Hotel

Cow Lane, Tring, Hertfordshire HP23 5QY

T (0870) 860 8425 **F** (01442) 890687 **E** sales.pmanor@btconnect.com
T (International) +44 [0] (1442) 891891 **W** www.pendley-manor.co.uk

105

Pendley Manor stands in 35 acres of rolling Hertfordshire countryside, quiet and self-contained, yet less than one hour's drive
from Central London. This splendid late Victorian manor was
refurbished and re-opened as an hotel in 1989. It boasts a number
of gracious, large rooms and a spectacular hall, with a suspended
staircase and gallery. My favourite bedroom was No 220 on the
second floor. Outside peacocks roam amongst ancient cedar trees
in the landscaped gardens. Pendley's sporting and leisure facilities are second to none, with a heated swimming pool, gymnasium, jacuzzi and Clarins Spa. Treatments include aromatherapy,
hydrotherapy, reflexology, facials, massage and holistic therapies,
as well as special *Indulgence Days*. Outside tennis, buggy riding,
laser shooting, archery and hot air balloon rides are available.
Once arrived at this 'resort', there is really no need to leave. You
can imagine it is a popular spot to 'tie the knot' or to have a business conference or special dinner. The AA ® Oak Restaurant
serves English and French cuisine to a high standard. Private
dining and prestigious meetings can be held in the Verney Room.

 73 (inc 34 🛏) 🥄 ♿ ☉ 🍴 🛝 ⚲ ✒ 🍸 🐕 🏊 ☂ 🎬 🐎 🔍 ◎
🍷 🎱 ⚒ 🐟 ♟ 👥 250 🅿 350 🎿

**Late Victorian manor set in 35
acres of wooded parkland**

Rates Single room wth breakfast from £130; double inc bfst from £140. [Ad]
Meals 3-cse tdh dinner ca £31; alc, lunch & spec. diets available. Last orders
2130 ; bfst from 0700.
Leisure Breaks Spa Break, b & b + full use of leisure facilities + one treatment each £190 per couple per night; inc dinner £230 per couple.
Other Facilities Massage. Golf, laser shooting, ballooning, riding, squash,
airport pickup can be arranged.
& all major credit cards accepted. Open all year.

Directions
Leave A41 at Tring exit. Rt at roundabout
(Tring town is to left). Cow Lane is fst on lft
Nearby attractions
Whipsnade Zoo, Woburn Safari Park,
Roald Dahl Museum, Verulanium.
Distances
Berkhamsted 6, Aylesbury 7, London 38

Hertfordshire, Tring

Redcoats Farmhouse Hotel
Redcoats Green, Nr. Hitchin, Hertfordshire SG4 7JR
T (0870) 418 8073 **F** (01438) 723322 **E** sales@redcoats.co.uk
T (International) +44 [0] (1438) 729500 **W** www.redcoats.co.uk

Near the village of Little Wymondley, set amidst rolling Hertfordshire countryside, yet only a few minutes from the A1, lies the 15th century Redcoats Farmhouse. It has been in the Butterfield family for generations and in 1971 Peter and his sister Jackie Gainsford converted the building into an hotel. Today it retains its relaxed and easy going country atmosphere. Bedrooms are either in the main house, some with crooked floors and all with exposed beams or in the converted stables. Last year two rooms in the old house were converted into a luxury suite, called *Bobbie's Room*, named after a favourite aunt whose room it used to be many years ago. The dining room and the conservatory serve outstanding cuisine that has won an AA ❀ for the past three years. The à la carte menu changes every month or two, making best seasonal use of local products. A daily menu is available from Sunday to Friday and may include such dishes as fresh sardines and char grilled lamb rump on rosemary mash. Breakfast, winner of a special AA award, is equally memorable with devilled kidneys and kedgeree often on the menu. Two self-catering cottages are available to rent, long or short term.

Family owned small hotel in rolling countryside, 1¹/₂ miles from the A1(M) 🛏 13 (+ 2 sc cotages) ☺ 🐎 ♨ 20 🐴

Directions
From A1(M) exit 8 Stevenage, take unclass rd to Little Wymondley, then left at rndabt

Nearby attractions
Knebworth House, Woburn Abbey, Hatfield Hse, Shuttleworth Acrft Coll

Distances
A1(M)1¹/₂, Hitchin 3, Hatfld 10, London 32

Rates Single room wth breakfast from £76; double from £107.
Meals Last dinner orders 2130. Two intimate private dining rooms.
Leisure Breaks Two nights from £290 per couple, dinner, b & b and free entrance into either Knebworth House or Hatfield House
Other Facilities Tennis 1m, golf 1 ¹/₂ m. Closed Dec 26-Jan 3.

 Visa, Mastercard, Switch accepted.

Hertfordshire, Redcoats Green

The White Horse
Brancaster Staithe, Norfolk PE31 8BY
T (0870) 860 8511 **F** (01485) 210930 **E** reception@whitehorsebrancaster.co.uk
T (International) +44 [0] (1485) 210262 **W** www.whitehorsebrancaster.co.uk

107

The White Horse has been licensed as a public house since 1836 although the original building was replaced in 1934. In 1999 it was extended and completely renovated by owners Cliff and Tina Nye. The Inn has since become a national and local award winning establishment offering a friendly welcome at its fabulous location on the unspoiled North Norfolk coast. There are 15 stylish bedrooms, eight ground floor, redecorated in 2006, with their own terraces and seven in the main building, including the *Room at the Top*, which has a telescope to take in the amazing coastal views. Dine in the conservatory restaurant where the daily changing menu boasts local produce in abundance - oysters, crabs, mussels, locally smoked fish as well as lamb, pork and steaks. Chef's home made breads and ice creams are also firm favourites. The White Horse is a glorious base for those who enjoy birdwatching, walking, sailing, golf or a day out on the coast's glorious beaches. You can hire a cycle to visit one of the county's many stately homes or the lavender fields at Heacham. This part of Norfolk is a paradise, whatever time of year you choose to visit.

 15 (inc 8 grd fl) (£5 p nt, grd fl rms) P 40 WIFI

Popular restaurant with modern bedrooms on the North Norfolk coast

Rates Single room wth breakfast from £65; double from £90.
Meals Tdh dinner from £24.50; alc, lunch & diets avail; lst orders 2100; bfst fm 0830.
Leisure Breaks Special breaks, Sun-Thurs dinner, b & b, min two nights, two sharing £66 pr prson per night.
Other Facilities Beach, golf, tennis, sailing, birdwatching nearby.

 & major credit cards accepted. Open all year.

Directions
A 149 Kings Lynn to Hunstanton, Brancaster Staithe after Brancaster; hotel on left.
Nearby attractions
Holkham Hall, Heacham Lavender Fields, Sandringham, Titchwell Bird Res
Distances
Hunstanton 8, Kings Lynn 24, London 115

Norfolk, Brancaster Staithe

The Kings Head Hotel

108

Great Bircham, King's Lynn, Norfolk PE31 6RJ

T (0870) 418 8066 **F** (01485) 578635 **E** welcome@the-kings-head-bircham.co.uk
T (International) +44 [0] (1485) 578265 **W** www.the-kings-head-bircham.co.uk

Set in the heart of North Norfolk, the Kings Head is a real gem - a Victorian hotel that has undergone a major refurbishment with breathtaking results. Spacious bedrooms, each with king size beds, have been individually styled with every attention to detail and offer many welcoming touches: fresh flowers, a decanter of port, minibar, home made biscuits, as well as a playstation, flat screen TV and internet wireless connection. Bathrooms are opulent, well lit with wide power showerheads and bathrobes, and toiletries made locally by The Natural Soap Company. The award winning restaurant is presided over by head chef Ben Handley, who uses local produce in season wherever possible. There is a sensible selection of wines by the glass and our dinner was superbly presented. Breakfast was an equal treat with home made muesli and jams. The hotel has a conference/private dining room for up to 20 people, a sitting room and a friendly bar area. It also makes a great wedding venue. Close by is the Bircham Windmill, great walking and bicycling countryside and the nearby beaches at Brancaster, Thornham and Hunstanton.

Contemporarily converted and extended hotel in heart of rural Norfolk

🛏 9 ⚙ ♿ ☉ 🖥 🐾 🅿 30 ⚌ 20 🐎

Directions From King's Lynn A148 twds Fakenham. After 5m left on B1153 Brancaster Rd. Kings Head on left after 5m.

Nearby attractions
Houghton Hall, Sandringham, Norfolk Lavender, Titchwell Bird Reserve

Distances
King's Lynn 12, Fakenham 10, London 108

Rates Single room wth breakfast from £69.50; double from £125. Ad
Meals Lunch 12-2pm; dinner 7-9 pm. Spec. diets available.
Leisure Breaks Sun-Thurs dinner, b & b breaks from £165 per room per night
Other Facilities Tennis, indoor pool, gym, squash, golf courses, horseracing, sailing, fishing, beaches all within 8 miles.

Visa, Mastercard, Switch cards accepted. Open all year.

Norfolk, Great Bircham

Beechwood Hotel

Cromer Road, North Walsham, Norfolk NR28 0HD

T (0870) 860 8427 **F** (01692) 407284 **E** enquiries@beechwood-hotel.co.uk
T (International) +44 [0] (1692) 403231 **W** www.beechwood-hotel.co.uk

109

I always enjoy my visits to the Beechwood, largely due to the infectious enthusiasm of its owners, Don & Lindsay. Don is busy with advice in the dining-room, chatting to Duke and Dustman alike and Lindsay works front-of-house and in the bar. Unsurprisingly they won the Visit Britain *Excellence in England* Small Hotel of the Year award in 2003 and this has spurred them into opening a smart 7-bedroom extension, where all beds are four-posters or half testers and bathrooms are state-of-the-art. Cuisine is presided over by chef Steven Norgate and has been recognised by two AA 🏵🏵. I had the duck with celeriac rösti , which was memorable. Sheringham lobster, Cromer crab, Thornham oysters and Morston mussels all feature when in season. Do leave room for one of their to-die-for desserts. The Beechwood used to be known as *'The Doctor's House'* and Agatha Christie stayed there regularly. Today it caters for discerning leisure and business travellers who wish to sample Norfolk hospitality at its best. The coast at Cromer and Mundesley is nearby as well as the Norfolk Broads and Norwich. A ⚡ Hotel.

🛏 17 (inc 8 🏚) ⚡ ♿ ☉ ✻ ♫ 🐴 (£8 per nt fee)

Georgian country house hotel in pleasant gardens

Rates Single room wth breakfast from £70; double from £90.
Meals Tdh 3-cse dinner £34; Sunday lunch & spec. diets avail; last orders 2100; bfst fm 0730.
Leisure Breaks Available all year: dinner, b & b from £60 per person per night. min 2 nt stay. Complimentary Sundays - please enquire.
Other Facilities Golf, riding, fishing nearby.

Major credit cards accepted. Open all year.

Directions
From Norwich B1150 go under rlwy br, left at 1st traff lts, rt at next. Hotel 150m on lft

Nearby attractions
Blickling Hall, East Ruston Gdns, NorfolkBroads, Norwich, Sandringham

Distances
Cromer 8, Norwich 12, London 120.

The Old Rectory
103 Yarmouth Road, Norwich, Norfolk NR7 0HF
T (0870) 418 8080 **F** (01603) 300772 **E** enquiries@oldrectorynorwich.com
T (International) +44 [0] (1603) 700772 **W** www.oldrectorynorwich.com

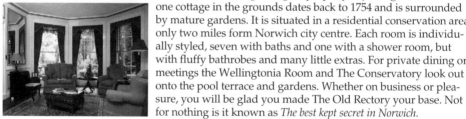

Chris & Sally Entwistle are very much hands-on hosts, the kind of whom Signpost is proud. When we stayed, Chris made all the guests feel at home while Sally was busy front-of-house the following morning. Chris recommended a short walk around the Yare close to the hotel - a good way to work up an appetite for our shredded duck with chilli peppers salad, followed by marinated local pork tenderloin, which was cooked by James Perry, and we subsequently enjoyed the AA ◎ ◎ cuisine in the elegant dining room. This charming Georgian property of just eight bedrooms + one cottage in the grounds dates back to 1754 and is surrounded by mature gardens. It is situated in a residential conservation area only two miles form Norwich city centre. Each room is individually styled, seven with baths and one with a shower room, but with fluffy bathrobes and many little extras. For private dining or meetings the Wellingtonia Room and The Conservatory look out onto the pool terrace and gardens. Whether on business or pleasure, you will be glad you made The Old Rectory your base. Not for nothing is it known as *The best kept secret in Norwich.*

Charming old rectory on the outskirts of Norwich.

🛏 8 🍴 ⌕ ⚓ 🏛 18

Directions
From A47 southern by-pass onto A1042 Yarmouth Rd twds city centre, left at mini-rdbt onto A1242. Hotel on rt 100 meters.

Nearby attractions
Norwich Cathedral, Castle Museum & Art Gallery, Whitlingham Cntry Pk

Distances Norwich 2, London 111.

Rates Single room with bkfst from £80; double from £110; deluxe dble fm £130.
Meals Tdh 3-cse dinner fm £23; spec. diets avail; last orders 2030; bfst fm 0715.
Leisure Breaks Short break rate from £68 per person per nt Tues-Sat inc, based on 2 sharing a twin/dble min 2-night stay. Price includes dinner, b & b.
Other Facilities Golf, sailing, indoor pool nearby.

AMERICAN EXPRESS & major credit cards accepted. Open all year exc. Christmas & New Year.

Norfolk, Norwich

Broom Hall Country Hotel

Richmond Road, Saham Toney, Thetford, Norfolk IP25 7EX

T (0870) 418 8086 **F** (01953) 885325 **E** enquiries@broomhallhotel.co.uk
T (International) +44 [0] (1953) 882125 **W** www.broomhallhotel.co.uk

111

Broom Hall is a family-run Victorian country house set in 15 acres of garden and parkland in the peaceful West Norfolk countryside. The traditional English gardens are laid out with mixed and herbaceous borders and mature trees. Bedrooms are spacious and airy with pretty bedspreads and most have views over the grounds. A feature of the reception rooms are ornate moulded ceilings. Traditional home cooked food is prepared by the head chef in Swallowtails Restaurant using fresh local produce where possible. They pride themselves also on their mouth-watering home made desserts. Home made cream teas are another treat. There is an indoor heated swimming pool. Small conferences can be arranged at the hotel and the whole house can be hired for a special occasion. Five cheerful new ground floor rooms have been added in the converted stable block, two of which are suitable for disabled access. Within easy driving distance are Sandringham, Blickling Hall, Thetford Forest Park and the trans-Norfolk Peddars Way.

Victorian country house set within 15 acres of mature garden & parkland.

Rates Single room with breakfast from £70; double from £95.
Meals 3-cse tdh dinner £18.50-£22; lunch & bar snacks avail; last orders 2030.
Leisure Breaks Winter Breaks available Oct-mid-March, 2 days dinner, b & b £240 per room/3 days £360. Weekly rates available on request.
Other Facilities Fishing, golf, riding, cycling, walking, shooting nearby.

Major credit cards accepted. Open all year exc. Dec 26-Jan 2.

Directions
From London A11 to Thetford, then A1075
E Dereham Rd to Watton, left onto B1077.
Nearby attractions
Ancient House Mus, Gooderstone Watr
Gdns, Thetford Fs't Pk, Sandringham
Distances
Swaffham 6, Thetford 12, London 93.

Norfolk, Thetford

Brudenell Hotel
The Parade, Aldeburgh, Suffolk IP15 5BU
T (0870) 418 8084 F (01728) 454082 E info@brudenellhotel.co.uk
T (International) +44 [0] (1728) 452071 W www.brudenellhotel.co.uk

Walking along the southern seafront of the picturesque Suffolk town of Aldeburgh, past the fishermens' huts and the pretty pastel coloured houses, you will come to the Brudenell Hotel. Literally a pebble's throw from the beach, the views out to sea are spectacular. You will enter a stylish hall, pass the open plan panoramic restaurant, and take the lift to one of the hotel's light, airy bedrooms, many of which overlook the sea or the river Alde. The emphasis in the hotel's AA☺☺ restaurant is on flexibility and informality. The menu offers a variety of dishes using local produce, which is complemented by a selected wine list. With seafood and grills a speciality, the Brudenell concentrates on wonderful food, simply prepared. With its New England style décor, panoramic views, friendly staff and mouthwatering food and drink, which can be taken *al fresco* on the terrace in the summer months, the Brudenell is a place you will want to return to. The hotel can arrange for guests to play golf or tennis at the nearby Thorpeness Hotel & Golf Club. Aldeburgh is the ideal base for a host of outdoor activities, Snape Maltings Concert Hall, RSPB & National Trust reserves.

Contemporary beachside hotel on Suffolk's sailing and golf coast.

🛏 42 ☺ & ℚ 🐾 (£5 per day) 🅿 16 WIFI

Directions A12/A1094 to Aldeburgh, into town centre, turn right to south of town. Hotel on left on seafront.

Nearby attractions
Snape Maltings, Orford Castle, Helmingham Hall, Framlingham Castle.

Distances
Ipswich 25, Norwich 41, London 74.

Rates Single room with breakfast from £68; double from £106.
Meals Tdh dinner £26.50; alc, lunch & spec diets avail; last orders 2145(summer)/ 2130 winter.
Leisure Breaks Short breaks available throughout the year, from £55 per person per night sharing, dinner, b & b, min two night stay.
Other Facilities Fishing, golf, riding, tennis, bicycle hire, shooting nearby.

 & major credit cards accepted. Open all year.

Suffolk, Aldeburgh

Waveney House Hotel

Puddingmoor, Beccles, Suffolk NR34 9PL

T (0870) 860 8480 **F** (01502) 470370 **E** enquiries@waveneyhousehotel.co.uk
T (International) +44 [0] (1502) 712270 **W** www.waveneyhousehotel.co.uk

113

The Waveney House Hotel has just undergone a major refurbishment to make it the equal of any hotel in East Anglia. It sits on the river Waveney in the market town of Beccles. The hotel has 12 luxury bedrooms, each individually decorated and with top floor rooms having exposed beams. The function room caters for 150-200 guests and is the perfect venue for conferences, private parties and weddings, the location making an ideal backdrop for photographs. The Staithe Restaurant overlooks the river and cuisine is based on traditional and Mediterranean flavours using local produce where possible, including herbs from the hotel's own garden. There is a good range of ten house wines. Beccles used to be a flourishing seaport in Saxon times. It has well preserved Georgian houses and the famous St Michaels's Church and 14th century belltower. Nelson's parents were married in this church. The waterside is fringed with picturesque moorings and boathouses. Beccles borders the Norfolk Broads and guests can hire a small craft to follow the river as far as the Geldeston Locks.

 30 WIFI 3x 70-220

Waterside hotel, recently refurbished, by the Norfolk Broads

Rates Single room with breakfast from £83.50; double from £98.50.
Meals Staithe Restaurant tdh; alc, lunch & spec diets avail; last orders 2100; bfst from 0700.

Directions Into town centre from North. Turn right at town hall, signed St Michaels Church, into Puddingmoor. Hotel on rt.

Other Facilities Fishing, birdwatching, gardens, indoor pool, walking nearby.

Nearby attractions
Somerleyton Hall/Gdns. Oulton Broad, Raveningham Gdns, E Anglia Trans Mus

Distances
Bungay 7, Lowestoft 9, London 114.

 & major credit cards accepted. Open all year.

Suffolk, Beccles

The Angel Hotel

3 Angel Hill, Bury St Edmunds, Suffolk IP33 1LT
T (0870) 418 8173 **F** (01284) 714001 **E** staying@theangel.co.uk
T (International) +44 [0] 1284 714000 **W** www.theangel.co.uk

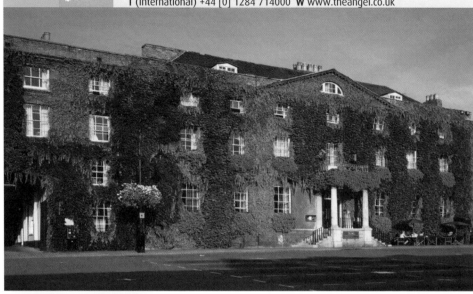

The Angel is a beautiful historic coaching inn dating back to 1452, situated in the centre of Bury St Edmunds, opposite the Abbey, dominating one of the prettiest squares in England. For over 400 years Royal visitors, actors and writers have stayed at The Angel. Charles Dickens wrote part of the Pickwick Papers whilst in residence. Its warm relaxed atmosphere is enhanced by an interesting collection of antiques, art and photographs and an open fire burns in the lounge. The hotel offers a range of bedroom styles, including traditional four-posters, suites and family rooms as well as new contemporarily designed rooms. Most are air-conditioned. WIFI high speed internet access is also available throughout the hotel. The Angel Eatery provides a stylish and comfortable atmosphere in which to enjoy the hotel's award winning food. There is a brasserie-style menu and an eclectic choice of superb wines from around the world, over 30 of which are available by the glass. The air-conditioned St Edmunds Business centre is self-contained and there are two further meeting rooms, ideal for smaller meetings or private parties.

Historic former coaching inn, now a centre of sophistication and style

76 (inc 10 suites) ⚡ ♿ 🔼 ⊙ (+WIFI) 🍴 ♨ 100 **P** 50 🐾

Directions From A14 Bury central exit, follow signs town centre to Northgate St, turn right into Angel Hill, hotel on right.

Rates Single room with breakfast from £77; double from £127.
Meals Dinner, lunch & spec diets avail; last orders 2130; bfst fm 0700.

Nearby attractions
Theatre Royal, Newmarket Racecourse, Kentwell Hall, Bury Abbey, Ickworth Hs

Leisure Breaks 1. Angel Break £290 for two people, two nts, b & b inc £52 dinner allowance. 2. Special Sunday night rate - £85 for 2 sharing b&b.

Distances
Ipswich 33, Cambridge 27, London 79.

 & major credit cards accepted. Open all year.

Suffolk, Bury St Edmunds

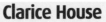

Clarice House

Horringer Court, Horringer Road, Bury St Edmunds, Suffolk IP29 5PH
T (0870) 418 8083 **F** (01284) 716120 **E** bury@claricehouse.co.uk
T (International) +44 [0] (1284) 705550 **W** www.claricehouse.co.uk

Clarice House is a residential spa set within a neo-Jacobean mansion in 20 acres of grounds. The 13 superbly furnished bedrooms each have their own individual style and character. The restaurant offers a wide menu of delicious dishes, with a vegetarian option and a *detox* menu plan if desired. The Spa itself is 21st century state-of-the-art at its most appealing. The swimming pool uses a unique filtration system. Spa baths, steam and sauna rooms lead off it. The gymnasium has an advanced computer system, *Fitlinxx*, which gives guests a virtual training partner. The dance studio offers classes including the all-new Studio Cycling, Monanae, and Power Yoga as well as more traditional classes in Pilates, Step Aerobics and Callanetics. Treatments include Ayurvedic Stone Therapy, Reiki, Collagen and Reflexology and CACI and there is a hair salon and sunbeds. You will feel truly rejuvenated after a stay at Clarice House - a world of relaxation and well-being. It is near historic Bury St Edmunds and Ickworth and convenient for Newmarket and Ipswich.

🛏 13 🍴 ♿ 🗄 📶 ⚲ 🎿 🏊 🍽 🏔 **P** 90

State-of-the-art spa with comfortable rooms in Jacobean manor house

Rates Single room with breakfast from £55; double from £85.
Meals Papillon Restaurant; alc, lunch & spec diets avail; last orders 2045.
Spa Breaks including accommodation, all meals, beauty treatment, use of lesiure facilities from £145 per person per night.
Other Facilities Fishing, golf, riding, shooting nearby.

Directions
From West leave A45 at Bury West exit, signs Ickworth, join A143, hotel on right.
Nearby attractions
Ickworth House, Bury Abbey & Theatre Royal, Nat Horseracing Mus, Newmkt.
Distances
Bury St Eds 2, Newmarket 14, London 74

& major credit cards accepted. Open all year exc Dec 25/26 & Jan 1.

Suffolk, Bury St Edmunds

Ravenwood Hall Hotel
Rougham, Bury St Edmunds, Suffolk IP30 9JA
T (0870) 860 8512 **F** (01359) 270788 **E** enquiries@ravenwoodhall.co.uk
T (International) +44 [0] (1359) 270345 **W** www.ravenwoodhall.co.uk

Ravenwood Hall has been here since Tudor times and today its carved oak structure and rare 16th century wall paintings carry a whiff of Tudor charm. Nestled within seven acres of it own lawns and woodland, Ravenwood offers tranquillity and seclusion. Bedrooms are either in the main building or in an adjoining mews which is near *The Pavilion*. This used to be the cricket pavilion for a nearby school but has been rebuilt at Ravenwood. It overlooks its own private garden and pond and makes an ideal venue for a wedding reception or private meeting. Ravenwood has a wide range of leisure facilities, including swimming pool, croquet and riding, the owner being a keen horseman. The Restaurant with its Tudor fireplace uses home preserved fruits and vegetables, with meats and fish smoked on the premises and locally produced seasonal foods to produce a menu that is both adventurous and classical, featuring long forgotten English recipes. Ravenwood is set in the heart of Suffolk, just three miles from the historic market town of Bury St Edmunds and near the medieval wool towns of Lavenham and Long Melford, ideally placed for Suffolk's coastline and for racing at Newmarket.

Hotel of Tudor origin in extensive grounds in central Suffolk

🛏 14 (inc 2 🚲) ❀ ♙ ⚡ ⚟ ♿ ☉ 🐎 ♪ 🎣 ✒ ♨ 200 🅿 150 🐾

Directions
A14 eastbound from Bury, take Junc 45 turn-off twds Rougham. Hotel on left.

Nearby attractions
Kentwell Hall, Long Melford; Greene King Brewery Tour; Bury Abbey, Lavenham.

Distances
Bury St Eds 3, Ipswich 27, London 77

Rates Single room with breakfast from £87.50; double from £113.50.
Meals Tdh 3-cse dinner £25.75; alc, lunch & spec diets avail; last orders 2130.
Leisure Breaks £296 per couple for 2 nights sharing, dinner, b & b, min two night stay. Sunday special dinner, b&b two persons £99 per room.
Other Facilities Children's menu, toys/high chairs/pygmy goats and geese. Fishing, health club, riding, squash, tennis nearby.

 & major credit cards accepted. Open all year.

Suffolk, Bury St Edmunds

Hintlesham Hall
Hintlesham, Ipswich, Suffolk IP8 3NS

T (0870) 418 8082 F (01473) 652463 E reservations@hintleshamhall.com
T (International) +44 [0] (1473) 652334 W www.hintleshamhall.com

117

Hintlesham Hall is like the Jewel in the Crown - one of the loveliest hotels in England, superbly situated in over 175 acres of unspoiled Suffolk countryside - a beautiful building steeped in history. The hotel's magnificent Georgian façade, Elizabethan red brick chimney stacks, splendid carved oak staircase built in the Stuart period and wonderful plasterwork on the ceiling of the Carolean room, are just some of its architectural delights. The bedrooms vary from Georgian to timbered Tudor, all different and each enhanced by elegant fabrics, antiques and works of art, and some with four-posters. Dining at Hintlesham is always a treat. Cuisine in the three dining rooms is under the supervision of Head Chef Alan Ford, and the 300-bin wine list includes a good range of New World vintages. Hintlesham has an associated 18-hole championship golf course and a refurbished Leisure Club with state of the art gym and health & beauty suite. Guests can wander in the attractive gardens or enjoy the excellent array of beauty treatments and massages on offer. Constable country is on the doorstep with Cambridge and Newmarket nearby. An excellent spot for a relaxing break, whether on business or pleasure.

33 (inc 3 suites) 🛏 🍴 🎿 ⚗ 🏊 🚲 🚶 💆 ⚕ ✓ ♿ 80 🎱 🅿 100+ 🐕

Georgian 'stately hotel' with golf course & state-of-the-art leisure club

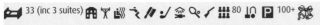

Rates Single room with breakfast from £110; double from £135.
Meals Tdh dinner £30; alc, lunch & spec diets avail; last orders 2130.
Leisure Breaks Sun-Thurs from £175 per couple per night sharing, dinner, b & b, min two night stay. Fri/Sat from £210 per couple per night.
Other Facilities Fishing & riding five miles. Airport pickup by arrangement.

Ad*

Directions
from A12/A45 west of Ipswich, take A 1071 Sudbury road for 4m; hotel on right
Nearby attractions
Dedham Vale (Constable Cntry), Helmingham Hall, Lavenham, Framlingham
Distances
Ipswich 5, Colchester 18, London 74

& major credit cards accepted. Open all year.   (* = Sun-Thurs only)

Suffolk, Ipswich

Salthouse Harbour Hotel

1 Neptune Quay, Ipswich, Suffolk IP4 1AX

T (0870) 418 8179 **F** (01473) 226927 **E** staying@salthouseharbour.co.uk
T (International) +44 [0] (1473) 226789 **W** www.salthouseharbour.co.uk

The Salthouse Harbour Hotel represents the best of tradition, coupled with contemporary interior design. It offers a high standard of professionalism and personalised attention in a town centre setting with striking views across the marina and beyond. Bedrooms are spacious with carved headboards, crisp linen, squashy duvets, SKY TV, DVDs and WIFI Internet access. Bathrooms have walk-in power showers, fluffy towels and bathrobes, gleaming chrome and deep tubs. All rooms have some harbour view, with the penthouse suite at the top of the hotel looking directly over the marina, with its constantly changing panoply of yachts. The Brasserie serves British and Mediterranean dishes presented by young, friendly staff in informal surroundings. There is always plenty of seafood on the menu as well as a selection of Seasonal Specials on the blackboard - all reasonably priced and accompanied by an eclectic wine list. There is private parking, a lift and a meeting room. Public areas are appealingly decorated with paintings by contemporary artists from the UK, China, France, USA, Japan and the Ukraine. Truly a cosmopolitan meeting place.

Converted warehouse, now the chic fulcrum of Ipswich waterfront

🛏 43 ✂ ♿ ☉ ⌹ 🔼 ♨ 20 🅿 30 🐾

Directions Fm A14 take A1156 TownCtr/ Docks, follow one-way Star Lane past Suffolk olk College into Key St, left @Old Customs Ho

Nearby attractions
Christchurch Mansion, Framlingham Castle, Sutton Hoo, Snape Maltings

Distances
Bury St Eds 30, Norwich 55, London 76

Rates Single/double room with breakfast from £100.
Meals Alc 3-cse ca. £30; lunch & spec diets avail; last orders 2200; bfst fm 0700.
Leisure Breaks Salthouse Break: 2 nights, b & b two people £290 inc. £46 to spend in Brasserie. Sunday Special rate £99 b&b two people sharing.
Other Facilities Gym, sauna, solarium within $1/4$ mile.

 & all major credit cards accepted. Open all year.

The Swan Hotel

119

High Street, Lavenham, Sudbury, Suffolk CO10 9QA
T (0870) 860 8429 **F** (01787) 248286 **E** info@theswanatlavenham.co.uk
T (International) +44 [0] (1787) 247477 **W** www.theswanatlavenham.co.uk

The Swan at Lavenham is one of England's oldest inns, dating back to 1436. It provides some of Suffolk's most elegant accommodation - no wonder Claudia Schiffer spent the first night of her honeymoon there! Medieval wall paintings were uncovered some years ago and formed an influence on the new decorative style. Natural fabrics, including linen curtains and bedspreads, and wool rich upholstery and carpets, befitting Lavenham's heritage, have been used throughout. One wall in the bar area is covered in the signatures of local Second World War servicemen and re-unions are still held here. All 51 bedrooms are enchantingly furnished with linen sheets, feather pillows, rich fabrics and antique furniture. The most striking room is the Constable Suite, a mezzanine retreat for that away-from-it -all break. AA ☺☺ cuisine is served in either the Gallery Restaurant or in the less formal brasserie, the Garden Bar Restaurant. The chefs work hard with local suppliers to produce immensely flavoured, yet unpretentious fare. Lavenham has one of the most famous Suffolk churches and other beautifully preserved half-timbered buildings.

 49 (inc 4 & 2 🛏)   🐕 (charged) 🖥 ♨ 40 **P** 62 🎣

Quintessental Old English Inn in historic Suffolk market town

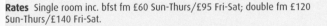

Rates Single room inc. bfst fm £60 Sun-Thurs/£95 Fri-Sat; double fm £120 Sun-Thurs/£140 Fri-Sat.

Directions On A1141 Bury St Edmunds-Hadleigh road. The Swan is in middle of Lavenham, where main road turns left.

Meals Alc, lunch & spec diets avail; last orders 2130; bfst fm 0700.
Leisure Breaks Midweek winter breaks available. See our website for details
Other Facilities Iron+board, CD players/Sky TV in rooms.

Nearby attractions
Long Melford, Kentwell Hall, Framlingham Cas, Ickworth House, Dedham Vale

Distances
Bury St Eds 13, Norwich 34, London 76

 & all major credit cards accepted. Open all year.

Suffolk, Lavenham

The Black Lion Hotel

Church Walk, The Green, Long Melford, Suffolk CO10 9DN
T (0870) 860 8513 **F** (01787) 374557 **E** enquiries@blacklionhotel.net
T (International) +44 [0] (1787) 312356 **W** www.blacklionhotel.net

The Black Lion has enjoyed a commanding position overlooking Long Melford for centuries, with its back to the church. In 2000 it was acquired and redeveloped by Craig Jarvis, who also owns the Ravenwood Hall (*see previous pages*). The result has been an outstanding success. The ten bedrooms have been upgraded in bold colours and furnished with antiques. One of the most sought after is the corner bridal suite looking over the green and towards the turrets of Melford Hall. When we lunched there off fresh Suffolk scallops in the summer, service was efficient and charmingly served. The room was full of contented diners, including a birthday party. The Black Lion is just a few minutes' walk from some of Suffolk's finest antique shops and the fine Tudor mansion of Kentwell Hall is just around the corner. Whether on business in Sudbury or Bury St Edmunds or taking a leisure break to visit Suffolk's stately homes and Constable Country, if a quiet retreat into history with the best of modern dining and individual service is what you are looking for, then the Black Lion is for you.

Charming small hotel overlooking the green in Long Melford.

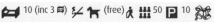
10 (inc 3) (free) 50 P 10

Directions From Sudbury take A134 Bury rd, after 1m left on B1064 then rt to Long Melford. Hotel on corner of A1092

Nearby attractions
Kentwell Hall, Melford Hall NT, Bury St Ed's, Lavenham, Newmarket Racec'se.

Distances
Sudbury 5, Bury St Eds 15, London 74

Rates Single room with breakfast from £90; double from £123.50.
Meals 3-cse tdh AA ☺ dinner £25; alc, lunch & spec. diets avail; last orders 2130; bfst fm 0730. Special child friendly menus available.
Leisure Breaks Black Lion short breaks (min. two nights), 2 nts dinner, b & b two people £309 per room. Sunday special, dinner, b&b £99 per room.
Other Facilities Health club, riding, squash, shooting, antique shops nearby

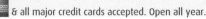
& all major credit cards accepted. Open all year.

The Swan
Market Place, Southwold, Suffolk IP18 6EG
T (0870) 418 8079 **F** (01502) 724800 **E** swan.hotel@adnams.co.uk
T (International) +44 [0] (1502) 722186 **W** www.signpost.co.uk/swansouthwold

121

The Swan has occupied its present site since the 14th century. Following the Great Fire of 1659, it was rebuilt in time to provide refreshments for bell-ringers pealing out the restoration of Charles II in 1660. In 1880 the owner at the time substantially remodelled the hotel and built himself a fine house next door, now the Town Hall. Subsequent alterations of great character were made in 1938 and in more recent times the Swan has been fully restored and refurbished in a most comfortable and attractive style. There are 25 bedrooms in the main building and a further 17 clustered round the old bowling green in the garden. The public rooms have the traditional character of an English country house, enhanced by fine furniture, carved 18thC door-frames and mantelpieces, prints, paintings and photographs connected with the history of Southwold. The dining room has a daily changing table d'hôte menu and is complemented by a fine wine list. In 2003 The Swan acquired some neighbouring rooms which have been made into sumptuous Junior Suites with names like The *Admiral's* (which has a telescope!) and *Mr Crisp's*.

 42 ♦♦♦ 45 **P** 40

Rates Single room with breakfast from £83; double from £146.
Meals Tdh dinner £35; alc, lunch & spec diets avail; last orders 2130.
Leisure Breaks Midweek breaks Sun-Fri available Oct-April £88 per pers per night inc bfst, 3-cse dinner, newspaper, early morning tea & VAT.
Other Facilities Croquet, golf, fishing, riding, sailing & boating, tennis nearby

Major credit cards accepted. Open all year.

Comfortable inn of character, the historical fulcrum of Southwold

Directions
A12 from Ipswich onto A1095 twds town centre. Inn on left in market place.
Nearby attractions
Helmingham Hall, Framlingham Castle Bungay Otter Trust, South Elmham Hall
Distances
Ipswich 34, Norwich 34, London 108

Suffolk, Southwold

Signpost Guide 2007
Heart of England
Fact File
Illustrated Guide to
Historic Houses & Gardens,
Attractions and Walks

Guiting Power

Heart of England

The Heart of England: a name that defines this lovely part of the country so much better than its geographical name: The Midlands. Like a heart it has many arteries and compartments, from the March counties of Shropshire and Herefordshire through the West Midlands, birthplace of the Industrial revolution, via the light industrial East Midlands out to the Lincolnshire Wolds.

Cheltenham

Burghley

Hotels guide

Further information:
Heart of England Tourism
Larkhill Road, Worcester,
Worcestershire WR5 2EZ
Tel: 01905 761100
www.hetb.co.uk

Derbyshire

Cycling Path

Bolsover Castle, Bolsover
Calke Abbey Park & Gardens, Ticknall
Chatsworth House & Garden, Baslow
Eyam Hall, Eyam
Haddon Hall, Herts
Hardwick Hall, Chesterfield
Kedleston Hall, Nr. Derby
Lea Gardens, Matlock
Melbourne Hall, & Gardens, Melbourne
Renishaw Hall, Nr. Sheffield
Tissington Hall, Nr. Ashbourne

TOP 10 Attractions

American World of Adventures, Ilkeston
Arkwright's Cromford Mill, Matlock
Blue John Museum, Ollernshaw Collection, Castleton
Buxton Pavilion Gardens & Country Park
Cauldwell's Mill & Craft Centre, Rowsley
Donnington Car Collection, Castle Donnington
Gullivers Kingdom Adventure Park, Matlock
Heights of Abraham, Matlock
Royal Crown Derby Museum & Factory, Derby
Sudbury Hall & NT Museum of Childhood, Ashbourne

'There is no finer county in England than Derbyshire. To sit in the shade on a fine day and look upon verdure is the most perfect refreshment' - JANE AUSTEN.

'I assure you there are things in Derbyshire as noble as in Greece or Switzerland.' – LORD BYRON.

Derbyshire, home of the UK's first National Park, the **Peak District**, has been popular with home grown holidaymakers for more than 200 years. It is convenient for **Sheffield** and **Manchester** and right in the middle of the country, well served by road and rail connections.

Chatsworth

It forms the beginning of the **Pennine Chain** and its reservoirs and hills are second to none in beauty. It is excellent walking, riding and bicycling country and the **Buxton** Festival, increasingly a pan-arts occasion, has achieved international recognition. The 17th-century Palladian Chatsworth, seat of the Duke of Devonshire, is one of the most visited houses and gardens in the country.

TOP 10 Walks and Nature Trails

Aston-on-Trent >Trent & Mersey Canal > Shardlow > River Derwent, Nr Derby
Carsington Water, Ashbourne
Gullivers Kingdom, Matlock Edge
Longhshaw Estate, Hathersage
Lower Lea Valley Walk. Ware > Stanborough Lakes, Herts
Midshires Way. Stockport > Buxton > Sandiacre
Nine Ladies and Robin Hood's Stride, from Winster.
Pennine Way, starts near Glossop
Tissington Trail. Buxton to Ashbourne
Vale of Edale > Mam Tor > Castleton > Hope

The Peak District

Gloucestershire

Burford

The **Cotswolds** is one of the most visited parts of the UK with its landscapes of rolling hills and stone cottages. Many of its villages have twinned names like **Lower & Upper Slaughter, Little & Great Rissington, Temple Guiting** and **Guiting Power**.

Gloucester Cathedral

The magnificent churches at **Fairford**, **Cirencester** and **Chipping Campden** were built with the patronage of rich wool merchants, which brought the area its prosperity. Some of Britain's most celebrated country house hotels are in this area, which was the birthplace of the Signpost guide 70 years ago.

Bourton-on-the-Water

Hidcote

Cheltenham is the Centre for the Cotswolds and now hosts a respected annual Literary Festival as well as a Music Festival and of course the National Hunt Gold Cup every March. Its stately colonnades and Regency terraces bring back the aura of a less hurried age. County town **Gloucester**, with its cathedral of Norman origins, co-hosts with **Hereford** and **Worcester** the Three Choirs Festival in rotation every three years.

Hereford and Worcester

Symonds Yat

Herefordshire's ruined castles in the border country and Iron Age and Roman hill-forts recall a turbulent battle-scarred past. **Offa's Dyke**, constructed by King Offa of Mercia in the 8th century marks to this day the border with Wales. Today the landscape is peaceful, with comfortable small towns and villages and Hereford cattle grazing in pastures beside apple orchards and hop gardens.

Hereford Cathedral

Hereford, co-venue of the Three Choirs Festival, has an 11th century cathedral and the Mappa Mundi. In the West, the **Wye** meanders through meadows and valleys, past **Hay-on-Wye**, now best known for its annual Book Festival and plethora of second hand bookshops, with over one million titles on sale.

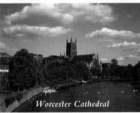
Worcester Cathedral

Worcestershire borders the West Midlands complex and serves as a dormitory area for many Birmingham workers. **Worcester** too has a famous cathedral, cricket ground, and 15th century Commandery, now a Civil war museum. **Great Malvern**, still a Spa town, is famous as the birthplace of Sir Edward Elgar, who drew much of his inspiration from the countryside around. The annual Malvern Festival celebrates him and George Bernard Shaw, whose plays were first premiered there.

Evesham is the centre of the fruit growing area and **Droitwich** still has briny water in its spa baths, in which visitors can float.

TOP 10 **Historic Houses Gardens and Parks**

Eastnor Castle,
  Nr. Ledbury, Herefords
Goodrich Castle,
  Ross-on-Wye, Herefords
Hagley Hall, Nr Stourbridge, Worcs
Hampton Court, Leominster,
  Herefords
Hanbury Hall,
  Nr. Droitwich, Worcs
Hartlebury Castle,
  Kidderminster, Worcs
Hergest Croft Gardens,
  Kington, Herefords.
Hill Court Gardens,
  Nr. Ross-on-Wye
Queenswood Country Park,
  Nr. Leominster
Spetchley Park Gardens, Worcester

TOP 10 **Attractions**

Avoncroft Museum of Buildings,
  Bromsgrove, Worcs
Cotswold Teddy Bear Museum,
  Broadway, Worcs
Droitwich Spa Brine Baths, Worcs
Elgar's Birthplace, Lower
Broadheath, Worcs
Hereford Cathedral
  & Mappa Mundi
Severn Valley Railway.
  Bewdley to Bridgnorth
Twyford Country Centre,
  Evesham, Worcs
West Midlands Safari Park,
  Bewdley, Worcs
Worcester Cathedral
Worcester Royal Porcelain Museum

TOP 10 **Walks and Nature Trails**

City of Hereford Guided Walks
Croft Garden Centre, Nr. Leominster
Herefordshire Beacon &
  Midsummer Hill from Hollybush
How Caple > Brockhampton >
  Fownhope, Herefordshire
Malvern Hills Walks & Trails
Kingsford Country Park, Wolverley
The North Worcestershire Path
Offa's Dyke Path.
  Hay-on-Wye to Knighton
Symonds Yat Forest Trail,
  SW of Ross-on-Wye
The Worcestershire Way.

126

Birmingham, Warkwickshire & W. Midlands

Mailbox, Birmingham

Shakespeare's Birthplace

The Industrial revolution of the 19th century led to the growth of **Birmingham** into Britain's second city - *the city of a thousand trades.* Its prosperity was based on factories, hundreds of small workshops and a network of canals, all of which helped in the production of everything from needles and chocolate to steam engines and bridges. Grand public buildings expressed a sense of civic pride. Nowadays the city has one of the best concert halls in Europe, an International Airport & Exhibition Centre and is learning through its entrepreneurial spirit, to adjust after the gradual erosion of its car and components industries.

Birmingham City Museum & Gallery

Warwickshire's most visited town is **Stratford-upon-Avon**, the bard's birthplace, with three theatres playing Shakespeare and other

dramatists' work. It is also a well preserved Tudor town on the banks of the Avon. The city of **Warwick** is dominated by its 14th century castle (alas the furniture has gone) and its museums. Many family activities are staged at the castle throughout the year. **Meriden**, near the city of Coventry, claims to be the centre of England.

The **West Midlands** is an urban area, criss-crossed by motorways, and still representing the powerhouse of Central Britain. **Coventry**, its main city, rose like a Phoenix from the Ashes after the last war and its 1962 cathedral stands next to the ruins of the former 14th century edifice. **Wolverhampton** has been called *Capital of the Black Country*, made famous through its ironwork. **Walsall**, birthplace of Jerome K Jerome, has three museums. **Sutton Coldfield** and **Solihull**, sometimes known as Birmingham's Hampstead and Wimbledon, have proud civic traditions.

Leicestershire, Northamptonshire, Lincolnshire & Nottinghamshire

Belvoir Castle

Lace Centre, Nottingham

Rutland Water

Leicestershire's uplands are home to some of the country's best known hunts and her pastures also fuel one of the county's main exports: Stilton Cheese. **Leicester** itself is a cathedral city with a 2000-year history, now host to a modern university and light industry. **Belvoir Castle** in the East dominates its vale and. **Rockingham** was built by William the Conqueror.

Althrop

Northamptonshire too has its share of stately homes. County Town **Northampton** is famous for its shoe making, celebrated in the Central Museum and Art Gallery. **Silverstone** in the South of the county is home to the British Grand Prix. **Althorp** was birthplace and is now the resting place of the late Princess of Wales.

Nottingham's castle dates from 1674 and its university is reputedly the most sought after in England. Its Lace Centre illustrates the source of much of its wealth. Today diggers and builders are testament to the city's continued expansion. To the north the remains of **Sherwood Forest** provide a welcome breathing space.

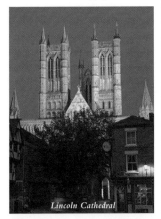
Lincoln Cathedral

Lincolnshire is said to produce one eighth of what is eaten on British tables and its wide open meadows are testament to this. Gothic triple-towered **Lincoln Cathedral** is visible from the Fens from miles around, whilst **Burghley** in the South hosts annual Horse Trials and is a top tourist attraction.

TOP 10 Historic Houses Gardens and Parks

Althorp, Nr. Northanpton
Belvoir Castle, Nr Grantham, Leics
Boughton House, Kettering, N'thants
Burghley House, Stamford, Lincs
Cottesbrooke Hall, Creaton, Northants
Deene Park, Corby, Northants
Grimsthorpe Castle, Park & Grounds, Bourne, Lincs
Lamport Hall, Lamport, Northampton
Rockingham Castle, Nr Market Harborough, Leics
Stanford Hall, Lutterworth, Leics

TOP 10 Attractions

Billing Aquadrome, Northampton
Bosworth Battlefield Visitor Centre & Country Park, Leics
Central Museum & Art Gallery, Northampton
Guildhall & Jewry Wall Museum, Leicester
Lace Centre & Costume Museum, Nottingham
Lincoln Cathedral, Lincoln
Nottingham Castle, Nottingham
Silverstone Circuit, Nr. Towcester
Sulgrave Manor, Nr. Brackley, Northants
Wickstead Amusement Park, Nr. Kettering

TOP 10 Walks and Nature Trails

Barnwell Country Park, Oundle, Northants
Beacon Hill Country Park, Woodhouse Eaves, Leics
Brigstock Country Park, Kettering, Northants
Harringworth Viaduct > Turtle Bridge > Seaton, Rutland
Melton Mowbray C'ntry Park, Leics
Pitsford Water Circuit, Brixworth, Northants
Rutland Water Circuit, Oakham, Rutland
Sherwood Pines Country Park, Edmonstowe, Notts
Weedon > Nether Heyford > Bugbrooke, Northants
Wolds Walk: Tetford > Worlaby > Farforth > Oxcombe > Tetford,Lincs

Historic Houses Gardens and Parks

Shropshire and Staffordshire

Attingham Park, Nr. Shrewsbury
Biddulph Grange Garden,
Stoke-on-Trent, Staffs
Boscobel House & The Royal Oak,
Bishops Wood, Shrops
The Dorothy Clive Garden,
Market Drayton, Shrops
Hodnet Hall Gardens,
Market Drayton, Shrops
Ludlow Castle, Ludlow, Shrops
Oakley Hall, Market Drayton, Shrops
Shrewsbury Castle & Quest, Shrops
Shugborough, Stafford
Weston Park, Nr. Shifnal, Shrops

 Attractions

Alton Towers, Alton, Staffs
Childhood & Costume Museum,
Bridgnorth, Shrops
**Drayton Manor Family Theme
Park & Zoo,** Tamworth, Staffs
Greanaway Bank Country Park,
Biddulph, Staffs
Ironbridge Gorge Museums, Shrops
Lectotum Wall Roman Site,
Nr. Lichfield, Staffs
Lichfield Cathedral, Staffs
Moseley Old Hall,
Nr. Wolverhampton
Stafford Castle & Visitors Centre,
Stafford
Stoke-on-Trent china factory tours

 Walks and Nature Trails

Broadway Tower Country Park,
Shrops
Cardingmill Valley,
Long Mynd, Shrops
Clee Hills,
Cleobury Mortimer, Shrops
Codsall Nature Trail, Staffs
Deep Hayes Country Park,
Longsdon, Staffs
Gradbach Wood & The Roaches,
Leek, Staffs
Historic Hawkstone Park & Follies,
Weston-under-Redcastle, Shrops
Manifold Valley,
Nr. Waterhouses, Staffs
Offas Dyke Path,
by Clun Forest, Shrops
The Staffordshire Way.
Cannock Chase > Leek

Ironbridge

Shropshire is another March county that saw much conflict between English and Welsh, hostilities between warring tribes and invading Romans. The **Wrekin** and **Stretton Hills** were created by volcanoes and in the south the **Long Mynd** rises to 1700 ft and has panoramic views of much of the Severn plain. **Ironbridge**, near the present day Telford, is said to be where the Industrial Revolution started in Britain.

Weston Park

County town **Shrewsbury** was an historic fortress town built in a loop of the river **Severn**, whereas **Ludlow**, with its 11th century castle, is now one of the gastronomic high spots of Britain, with no less than five Michelin-starred eateries! AE Housman is buried in its churchyard.

Alton Towers

Staffordshire, squeezed between the **Black Country** to the south and **Manchester** to the north is home to the **Potteries,** a union of six towns made famous by Wedgwood, Spode and other ceramic designers. **Lichfield** has a magnificent three-spired 13th century cathedral and was birthplace of Samuel Johnson.

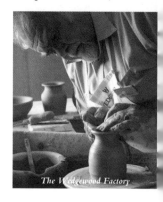

The Wedgewood Factory

colliersrobertbarry.co.uk

Signpost's recommended agent for hotel sales and valuations

... because we sell pubs and hotels, and lots of them

Please contact your nearest office:

London 020 7344 6644	**Glasgow** 0141 226 1055	**Plymouth** 01752 664 499
Birmingham 0121 265 7525	**Leeds** 0113 200 1888	**Reading** 0118 970 4646
Cirencester 01285 852 852	**Manchester** 0161 831 3333	**Southampton** 023 8063 6333
Edinburgh 0131 240 7575	**Norwich** 01603 759 605	**International** 020 7344 6666

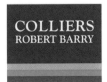

COLLIERS
ROBERT BARRY

The Izaak Walton Hotel
Dovedale, Ashbourne, Derbyshire DE6 2AY
T (0870) 418 8090 **F** (01335) 350539 **E** reception@izaakwaltonhotel.com
T (International) +44 [0] (1335) 350555 **W** www.izaakwaltonhotel.com

The Izaak Walton Hotel is situated just above the river Dove in the idyllic hills of Dovedale. Originally built as a farmhouse in the 17th century, the hotel retains much of its original charm. There are magnificent views of Thorpe Cloud and the surrounding scenery from all the public rooms and from many bedrooms. The Dovedale Bar, adorned with fishing memorabilia, is most welcoming with an open stone fireplace. Generous salads and snacks are served here at lunchtime. The AA rosetted Haddon Restaurant serves both traditional and modern dishes in a candle-lit atmosphere in the evenings, adding to the romance. High peaks swoop down dramatically to the river Dove below the hotel and gently rolling fields surround it. There are four rods (four miles) on the river available to residents. The Izaak Walton also arranges Spring Birdwatching Breaks and can arrange for guests to play at Ashbourne Golf Club. It is the perfect location for a restful holiday and is well placed for visiting Haddon Hall, Chatsworth and the many attractions of Derbyshire.

Famous fishing hotel in the cradle of the Peak District

Directions
A515 Buxton rd out of Ashbourne. 1st left through Thorpe on rd to Ilam. Hotel on rt.

Nearby attractions
Chatsworth, Haddon Hall, Hardwick Hall, Alton Towers, Tissington Trail.

Distances
Ashbourne 5, Derby 14, London 144

Rates Single room with breakfast from £110; double from £137.
Meals 3-cse tdh dinner £28; lunch & diets available; last orders 2130.
Leisure Breaks Weekend Breaks (May-Oct) 2-nights, dinner, b & b fm £85 per pers per nt; Sunday bonus - from £45 per pers. Midweek Breaks (May-Oct) 2 night stay Sun-Thurs dinner, b & b fm £72.50 pppn. Winter Warmer Breaks: From £80 pppn dinner, b & b two sharing. (Exc Xmas/New Year/ Easter). **Other Facilities** Golf nearby.

 & all major credit cards accepted. Open all year.

Riverside House Hotel
Ashford-in-the-Water, Nr. Bakewell, Derbyshire DE45 1QF
T (0870) 418 8091 **F** (01629) 812873 **E** riversidehouse@enta.net
T (International) +44 [0] (1629) 814275 **W** www.riversidehousehotel.co.uk

131

The Riverside is owned by the Thornton family (whose excellent chocolates are in each bedroom). It nestles by the river Wye in a quiet cul-de-sac with the beauties of the Peak District National Park on all sides and several classic stately homes: Chatsworth, Haddon Hall and Hardwick Hall near at hand. The country house, Georgian in origin, stands in mature gardens in this quaint unspoiled village of stone houses between Bakewell and Buxton, a wonderful spot for those seeking peace and quiet. Oak panelling and crackling log fires in cooler weather welcome the visitor who is then shown to one of the individually decorated and named bedrooms, some of which have four-posters. 2006 saw the conversion/merging of three former bedrooms into the deluxe Hawthorn and Mulberry rooms. One has a free-standing antique bath and both have new flat screen slimline TVs which double as mirrors. The two AA 🌸🌸 restaurant has an excellent local reputation for seasonally available game and fish from the neighbouring river. There is a separate meeting/dining room for that important private party or small wedding. Rated 82% AA.

🛏 14 🍴 🕊 🕴 🛎 20 🅿 30 🐾

Quiet riverside hotel with luxurious bedrooms and fine dining

Rates Single room with breakfast from £95; double from £115.
Meals 3-cse alc dinner £44.95; lunch & diets available; last orders 2130.
Leisure Breaks 2-day inclusive break, dinner b & b from £200 per person.
Other activities Riding, walking, shooting nearby.

[Ad] **Directions**
Turn off A6 at Ashford A6020. First left in village, strt on past church, hotel at end rd

Nearby attractions
Chatsworth, Haddon Hall, Hardwick Hall, Alton Towers, Tissington Trail.

Distances
Matlock 9, Buxton 10, London 186.

 & all major credit cards accepted. Open all year.

Dannah Farm Country House

Bowmans Lane, Shottle, Nr. Belper, Derbyshire DE56 2DR
T (0870) 860 8514 **F** (01773) 550590 **E** slack@dannah.co.uk
T (International) +44 [0] (1773) 550273 **W** www.dannah.co.uk

Dannah Farm is a little bit different - an 18th century farmhouse, still part of a working farm, with superb award winning accommodation, set amidst the beautiful Derbyshire countryside on the Chatsworth estates at Shottle. Nestling just below Alport Heights with its panoramic views over the surrounding six counties, the discerning guest will find something a little out of the ordinary at Dannah Farm. The newly recreated Feature Rooms definitely have the WOW factor. From the *Studio Hideaway* with private sitting room and spiral staircase leading to the romantic beamed bedroom above, with its own fantastic Canadian Spa outdoor tub set on a private terrace, to the *Ecclesbourne* with six foot sleigh bed, dressing room, luxurious bathroom with double spa bath, wet room, and, tucked away, a private sauna! Dannah is fully licensed and dinner is available by prior arrangement. Breakfast is a special treat, with free range eggs, home made bread and superb local produce. An outstanding spot for a romantic weekend, an important business meeting away from it all, or to celebrate a special occasion. Discover sheer unadulterated luxury in the Derbyshire Dales.

Luxurious accommodation in the heart of the Derbyshire Dales

9 (inc 4 stes & 3 🖵) 🥄 🗘 ☉ 🎄 🕏 🐕 🕍 ♨ 12 **P** 20 🐾

Directions Take turning for Shottle off the A517 Ashbourne-Belper road, straight on thru village n'thb'nd, branch rt down Bowmans La

Nearby attractions
Chatsworth House, Kedleston Hall, Dovedale , Alton Towers, Carsington Wtr

Distances
Belper 3, Derby/Ashbourne 10, London 143

Rates Single with breakfast from £75; double from £110. 　[Ad]
Meals Tdh dinner 3-cse £24.50; spec. diets available. Last orders 1915; bfst fm 0730.
Leisure Breaks See website for details.
Accreditations AA★★★★★ guest accommodation.
Other Facilities Fishing, golf, sailing, squash, shooting, watersports nearby.

Major credit cards accepted. Open all year exc. 24-26 Dec.

Derbyshire, Belper

Makeney Hall Hotel

Makeney, Milford, Nr. Belper, Derbyshire DE56 0RS

T (0870) 860 8431 **F** (01332) 842777 **E** makeneyhall@foliohotels.com
T (International) +44 [0] (1332) 842999 **W** www.foliohotels.com/makeneyhall

133

Magnificent Victorian country mansion, just eight miles from Derby, set in six acres of beautifully landscaped gardens with views over the Amber Valley. These tranquil surroundings make it a popular spot for wedding receptions, meetings, conferences and other special occasions. With some of the most beautiful parts of the country on the doorstep, it is the perfect spot for a leisurely break in the Derbyshire Dales. Bedrooms are spacious and high-ceilinged; many are being refurbished, with the Milford Wing (ground floor courtyard rooms) already completed. Flat screen TVs are now in most rooms. Dining is either in *Lavinia's*, the oak-panelled dining room, or in the Conservatory with its stunning views. Cuisine is mainly *English Modern* based, wherever possible, around seasonal ingredients. The Cocktail Bar also has a good bar menu. Many walking trails are nearby as is the Peak District - home to some of the country's finest stately homes including Chatsworth, Haddon Hall and Kedleston. This year a new conference/reception suite, The Derwent, was opened in the hotel's grounds.

Victorian country mansion offering a warm welcome in a grand setting

🛏 46 ⚲ ⛰ 🍴 🐾 (£5 per day fee) ♨ 180 🅿 200 🏊 WIFI

Directions
From A6 Derby south, turn off after br in Milford @ King William Pub. Hotel 250 yds on rt

Nearby attractions
Chatsworth, American Adventure, Kedleston Hall, Alton Towers, Carsington Wtr

Distances
Belper 2, Derby 6, M1 J25 14, London 141

Rates Single with breakfast from £45; double from £104; dinner, b & b £70 per person per night.

Meals Tdh & alc dining; lunch & spec. diets available. Last orders 2130; bfst fm 0700.

Leisure Breaks Stay Friday & Saturday nights and get Sunday for 50%. Stay five nights for the price of four.

 & all major credit cards accepted. Open all year.

Derbyshire, Belper

Biggin Hall

Biggin-by-Hartington, Nr. Buxton, Derbyshire SK17 0DH
T (0870) 860 8094 **F** (01298) 84681 **E** enquiries@bigginhall.co.uk
T (International) +44 [0] (1298) 84451 **W** www.bigginhall.co.uk

Biggin Hall is an historic old hall of 17th century origin, situated 1000 ft above sea level in the Peak District National Park. The Hall is Grade II* listed and stands in its own grounds of some eight acres. There are eight bedrooms furnished with antiques in the main house (inc. one 4-poster) and a further 12 en suite in converted old stone buildings in the grounds: the Courtyard, The Bothy and the Lodge. Dinner is a daily changing menu of traditional home cooking with the emphasis on local ingredients and free range wholefoods. Guests have a choice of two sitting rooms and will feel very much at home in this exceptionally welcoming, comfortable house. Host James Moffett is a great walker and will be able to recommend itineraries and traffic-free cycle trails. There are several historic houses nearby: Haddon Hall, Chatsworth and Kedleston Hall. Also close by are important archeological sites including Arkwrights Mill, Cromford Canal, Ecton Hill lead and copper mines and Magpie lead mine - Britain's deepest. Packed lunches can be arranged and there is even stabling for those who wish to bring their own horse or pony.

Jacobean hall of special architectural interest, now a small hotel

🛏 20 ♿ ⚘🚭 🐕(in bothy/annex only) ♟ 20 🅿 20

Directions
A515 Buxton rd from Ashbourne. After 8m take **2nd** turn to Biggin, strt on 1m, hotel on rt

Nearby attractions
Chatsworth, Haddon Hall, Hardwick Hall, Alton Towers, Tissington Trail.

Distances
Ashbourne 9, Buxton 10, London 153

Rates Double/twin room with breakfast from £70(apartments)/£80 (main house & bothy).Dinner, b & b from £47 per pers per nt (midweek low season) to £75 pppn weekend high season.

Meals Tdh dinner £19.50 at 7 pm. Packed lunches available.

Leisure Breaks Ice-breaker specials - 2 nights midweek from £94 per person dinner b & b + packed lunch & glühwein.

Other activities Cycling, fishing nearby.

 & all major credit cards accepted. Open all year.

Derbyshire, Biggin by Hartington

Donington Manor Hotel

1 High Street, Castle Donington, Derbyshire DE74 2PP
T (0870) 860 8515 **F** (01332) 850330 **E** stay@doningtonmanorhotel.co.uk
T (International) +44 [0] (1332) 810253 **W** www.doningtonmanorhotel.co.uk

135

Built in 1794 as a coaching inn on the Nottingham-Ashby road, Donington Manor sits in the centre of Castle Donington on the Derbyshire/Leicestershire border, just five minutes from East Midlands Airport and the M1. Bedrooms come in all shapes and sizes and to suit all pockets: modest for the business guest on a limited budget but sleek and contemporary or Georgian and high-ceilinged for that weekend away or special occasion. All have modern amenities and WIFI access. The dining room, restored to its former glory with cornices and a Georgian fireplace, is under the supervision of chef Jeff Cadden. Both lunch and dinner here are remarkably good value. Dinner might start with grilled field mushrooms with a brie, herb and mustatrd crust, progress through grilled fillets of red mullet with black olive potatoes and basil pesto to a hot butterscotch sponge pudding with ice cream. Its position makes The Manor a popular choice for weddings and it also has a large separate-entrance conference room. It is handy for the race circuit & museum, airport, motorway network and cities of Derby and Nottingham.

🛏 32 🍴 ♿ ☺ (+WIFI) 🚭 🧍 🐕 5x ♟ 120 🅿 20 ⚙

Georgian coaching hotel in centre of quiet village, near M1 & airport

Rates Single room with breakfast from £75; double from £115.
Meals Adam Restaurant 3-cse tdh £24.50; lunch 3-cses £10.50; spec. diets available; last orders 2145; bfst fm 0700.

[Ad]

Other activities Motor circuit, fishing nearby.

 & all major credit cards accepted. Open all year exc. 24-26 December.

Directions Fm M1 take junc 23a/24 A50 direction Stoke, First rdbt left for Castle Don'ton; hotel in centre of village

Nearby attractions
Calke Abbey & Kedleston Hall (NT), Race Circuit & Museum, Nat'l Space Museum.

Distances
M1-4, Derby 12, Notti'ham 15, London 115

Derbyshire, Castle Donington

Blenheim House
56-58 Main Street, Etwall, Derbyshire DE65 6LP
T (0870) 860 8433 **F** (01283) 733860 **E** info@theblenheimhouse.com
T (International) +44 [0] (1283) 732254 **W** www.theblenheimhouse.com

Blenheim House Hotel is situated in the heart of the village of Etwall, seven miles from Derby. It's a country hotel, a village pub, a local restaurant and a conference venue all rolled into one, with an overriding commitment to quality and service. The restaurant offers a modern European menu, featuring such dishes as Blenheim Greek Salad or pan-fried scallops & black pudding to start with, followed by peppered beef mignons with Yorkshire pudding or red snapper, king prawn and risotto rice, rounded off by one of their famous desserts. Sunday lunch is an equally special occasion. Weekday lunches are popular with conference attendees. Each bedroom has its individual design and is named after a local dignitary: *Sir Thomas Gerrard, Sir Samuel Sleigh* and so on. One has a four-poster. All bathrooms have been refurbished this year to a luxurious standard. Goosedown pillows and duvets and best Egyptian cotton sheets will ensure a good night's sleep. There are three function rooms with every modern aid and the hotel can help with layout and the organisation of attendees. Whether on business or on holiday exploring Derbyshire, the Blenheim's bed and board will soon relax even the most jaded traveller.

Inspired dining and elegant accommodation 7 miles from Derby

🛏 10 (inc 2 suites) ⚡ 2x 🍽30 🅿 20

Directions
From M1/A50 take A516 at Hilton twds Derby. 1m rt to Etwall. Blenheim in ctre on rt

Nearby attractions
Alton Towers, Peak District, Sudbury Hall NT, Calke Hall NT, Mus of Brewing (Coors)

Distances
Derby 7, M1-12,Burton-u-T 8, London 132

Rates Single room with breakfast from £65; double from £85. [Ad]
Meals Blenheim Brasserie alc; lunch & spec. diets available; last orders 2130.
Leisure Breaks Weekend breaks (Fri&Sat), dinner, b & b from £240 per couple
Other activities Massage. Fishing, golf, shooting, squash, riding nearby.

 & major credit cards accepted. Open all year

Derbyshire, Etwall

The Wind in the Willows

Derbyshire Level, Glossop, Derbyshire SK13 7PT

T (0870) 418 8105 **F** (01457) 853354 **E** info@windinthewillows.co.uk
T (International) +44 [0] (1457) 868001 **W** www.windinthewillows.co.uk

137

The Wind in the Willows is a romantic early Victorian country house hotel which has retained its original charms including oak panelled rooms, traditional furnishings and open log fires. It is situated at the edge of the Peak District National Park, the approach from the East being dramatic, passing Ladybower Reservoir and crossing the Southern end of the Pennine Way. The romance continues inside as you relax in the *Erika Louise Room* or *Toad Hall* - bedrooms are named after characters from the book. You then choose from the exceptional menu - our seared chicken salad followed by King sea bass was some of the best food we had tasted all summer - with drinks available from a huge oak dresser - in one of the comfortable lounges. Helpful staff will point you in the direction of local walks and the many sights nearby. Golf can be played next door on the 9-hole Glossop course. The hotel's conference suite lends prestige to any meeting. Adjoining it is an airy conservatory, ideal for a snack or light buffet lunch. The *Wind in the Willows* provides an elegant escape from modern day life.

 12 🍴 �9 🛁 🎿🚶 16 **P** 16

Victorian country house hotel on the edge of th Peak District

Rates Single room with breakfast from £88; double from £125.
Meals 3-cse tdh dinner £29; spec. diets available; last orders 2030.
Leisure Breaks 2-day break, dinner, b & b from £165 per person.
Other activities Riding, sailing, shooting, fishing, watersports nearby.

[Ad]

Directions
From West M6/M63/M67 to Hollingworth, A57 Sheffield Rd thru Glossop to E of town.
Nearby attractions
Chatsworth House, Kinder Scout, Ladybower Res'r, Pennine Way, Lyme Park.
Distances
Manchester 14, Sheffield 24, London 174

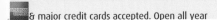 & major credit cards accepted. Open all year

Derbyshire, Glossop

Santo's Higham Farm Hotel

Main Road, Higham, Nr Alfreton, Derbyshire DE55 6EH

T (0870) 418 8095 **F** (01773) 520525 **E** reception@santoshighamfarm.demon.co.uk
T (International) +44 [0] (1773) 833812 **W** www.santoshighamfarm.co.uk

The core of Santo's is a 15th century farmhouse which has been extended to provide 28 bedrooms. Eight of these are 'Italian' themed with names like *Donatello, Botticelli* etc, two have 4-posters, three have waterbeds and two jacuzzi air baths. Most unusual are the themed bedrooms: *Mandela's*, with African furniture, *Bradman's* with cricketing memorabilia, *Camelot, Maharajah, Arabian Nights, Niagara, Hay-Making Time, The French Room* all with appropriate décor (but also modern comforts - the telephones may look antique but they do work!). *Guiseppe's* Restaurant serves excellent table d'hôte and à la carte menus, specialising in seafood, thanks to its state-of-the-art Seafood Holding Station. There is also an Italian restaurant and a Sports Bar for snacks. The Crystal Room is available for weddings, banquets and celebrations. The Rose Garden offers peace and seclusion for summer barbecues. Santos overlooks the spectacular Amber Valley, and is easily reached from Sheffield, Derby and the motorway network, as well as being convenient for East Midlands, Birmingham and Manchester Airports.

Popular hotel with exotic themed bedrooms & exceptional views

28 (inc 4) 100 80

Directions
From M1 northbound exit J28, take A38 W then A615 to Fourlane Ends, then N on B6013

Nearby attractions
Chatsworth, Alton Towers, American Adventure, Peak District NP, Chesterfield

Distances
Chesterfield 4, M1 5,Derby 15, London 136

Rates Single room with breakfast from £73; double from £103.
Meals Guiseppe's 3-cse tdh dinner £23(Mon-Fri)/£26 (Sat); alc, lunch & spec. diets available; last orders 2130; bfst from 0700.
Leisure Breaks Weekend Break Jan-Nov Fri ¹/₂ bottle wine, fresh flowers, 3-cse dinner, b & b; Sat bottle of wine, dinner b & b; Sunday full Eng bfst £69 pppn
Other activities Riding, tennis, shooting, squash, fishing, golf within 5 miles.

& major credit cards accepted. Open all year.

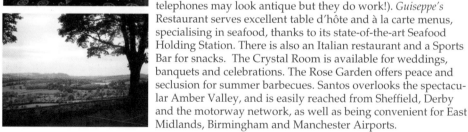

Derbyshire, Higham

The Red House Country Hotel

Old Road, Darley Dale, Matlock, Derbyshire DE4 2ER

T (0870) 418 8096 F (01629) 734885 E enquiries@theredhousecountryhotel.co.uk
T (International) +44 [0] (1629) 734854 W www.thredhousecountryhotel.co.uk

139

David and Kate Gardiner took over the Red House seven years ago and, in that time, have enhanced its reputation for personal service, hospitality and good food. It commands superb views over its own lawned garden to the Derwent Valley. Three of the ten bedrooms are on the ground floor of the adjacent 19th century coach house, one with a four-poster bed. One of the house bedrooms has a four poster and one an antique French bed. Menus in the recently refurbished candle-lit dining room are changed regularly with the emphasis being on fresh herbs and local ingredients. Chef Alan Perkins has built up an enthusiastic following both among local customers and hotel guests who return regularly. Breakfast includes superb smoked haddock and kippers from Achiltibuie, or guests can try a Derbyshire breakfast complete with local oatcake. The elegant setting and breathtaking views make the Red House ideal for meetings or small wedding receptions. Next to the hotel is the Red House Carriage Museum, whose carriages can be hired. The Derbyshire Dales, Chatsworth, Haddon Hall and Eyam Hall are all nearby.

 🛏 10 🍴 ✈ 👥 24 🅿 15

Family owned hotel with relaxing gardens and breathtaking views

Rates Single room with breakfast from £60; double from £100.
Meals 4-cse tdh dinner £25; spec. diets available; last orders 2000.
Leisure Breaks 2-night 'minibreak' - dinner, b & b two people sharing £275 per room.
Other activities Riding, walking nearby.

Visa, Mastercard & Switch cards accepted. Open all year exc Jan 1-14.

Directions
On south side of A6 between Matlock & Rowsley, opposite Audley Court
Nearby attractions
Chatsworth, Heights of Abraham, American Adventure, Peak District NP, Haddon Hall
Distances
Matlock 2, M1 13, Derby 24, London 155

Derbyshire, Matlock

East Lodge Country House Hotel & Restaurant
Rowsley, Matlock, Derbyshire DE4 2EF
T (0870) 418 8098 **F** (01629) 733949 **E** info@eastlodge.com
T (International) +44 [0] (1629) 734474 **W** www.eastlodge.com

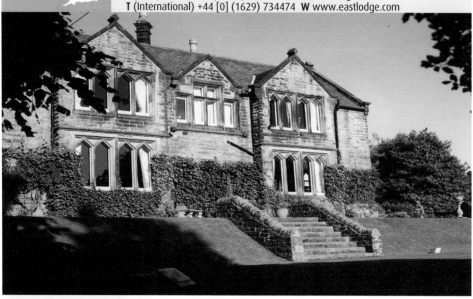

Over the past two years, there has been a major refurbishment at East Lodge: five bedrooms have been extended and upgraded to luxury levels with modems, broadband internet connection and de luxe bathrooms. Set in 10 acres of picturesque Derbyshire countryside, this was originally the East Lodge to Haddon Hall, seat of the Duke of Rutland. It is one of the nearest hotels to Chatsworth, recently voted Britain's finest stately home and has a high reputation for comfort, service and style in a warm and friendly ambience. Many guests come a long way to sample the AA ⊕ ⊕ restaurant. Sunday lunches, light weekday lunches and Derbyshire cream teas are also available. There is a separate dining room for meetings and private parties. Drinks and snacks can also be taken in the Garden Room conservatory, where chilled champagne is now available by the glass! We stayed in one of the expanded rooms without seeing the benign ghost who is reputed to appear occasionally! The hotel is well situated for weddings and business meetings. Unsurprisingly the AA has nominated it *'one of the most romantic hotels in Britain'*.

Former shooting lodge to Haddon Hall estate, set in 10 acre grounds

🛏 12 (inc 1 &) 🍴 ⊕ ⏰ ♨ 60 **P** 40

Directions
On east side of A6 at Rowsley on the corner of B6012 junc; up long drive.

Nearby attractions
Chatsworth, Heights of Abraham, American Adventure, Peak District NP, Haddon Hall

Distances
Matlock 3, M1 12, Sheffield 16, London 155

Rates Single room with breakfast from £110; double from £140.
Meals Tdh dinner £29 (3-cse)/£33(4-cse); lunch & spec. diets available; last orders 2100.
Leisure Breaks Two-day breaks available, including dinner, b & b.
Awards AA ★★★ ⊕ ⊕ 85%. ETC Gold Award.
Other activities Fishing, walking nearby.

Visa, Mastercard accepted. Open all year.

Derbyshire, Rowsley

Lower Brook House

Lower Street, Blockley, Gloucestershire GL56 9DS

T (0870) 860 8475 **F** (01386) 701400 **E** info@lowerbrookhouse.com
T (International) +44 [0] (1386) 700286 **W** www.lowerbrookhouse.com

141

Lower Brook House is a gem of a property, in the centre of the picture postcard village of Blockley, in the heart of the north Cotswolds. Each of its six bedrooms is different, ranging from four-poster to small, contemporary-style double. Most have views over the cottage garden and surrounding countryside. All are furnished in style and come with up-to-date facilities, fresh fruit, home made cookies and fluffy bathrobes. There is an imaginative seasonally changing dinner menu, offering four choices per course and taking advantage of local produce. Afterwards guests can relax in front of the cosy log fire. You can be sure of a warm welcome from hosts Julian and Anna, who have opened up their home to guests. Blockley is one of the Cotswolds' best kept secrets. The brook babbles through the hotel's grounds. It used to provide power for no less than 12 mills, including several silk mills, after which the House's rooms are named. The village church with its 12th century tower and Blockley's 17th & 18th century houses and gardens can be readily explored on foot. The villages of Chipping Campden and Broadway, Hidcote and Kiftsgate Gardens are nearby.

 6 ⚲ ❀ ⚤ **P** 6

Charming small hotel in picture postcard North Cotswold village

Rates Single/double room with breakfast from £95.
Meals 3-cse tdh dinner £25; spec. diets available; last orders 2100; bfst fm 0800.
Leisure Breaks Special midweek breaks available. Pse call for details.

Directions From Moreton take A44 westbnd. After Bourton-on-the-Hill turn rt for Blockley; hotel on right as you enter village
Nearby attractions
Snowshill Manor, Kiftsgate & Hidcote Gardens, Stratford-upon-Avon, Warwick Cas.
Distances
Stratford-u-A 10, Cheltenham 24, London 75

Visa, Mastercard accepted. Open all year.

Gloucestershire, Blockley

142

The Dial House Hotel
High Street, Bourton-on-the-Water, Gloucestershire GL54 2AN
T (0870) 418 8064 **F** (01451) 810126 **E** info@dialhousehotel.com
T (International) +44 [0] (1451) 822244 **W** www.dialhousehotel.com

Bourton-on-the-Water is one of the prettiest Cotswold villages, with the river Windrush running through it, a perfect Model Village made from local stone to walk around, exotic birds at Birdland Zoo Gardens, the Village Life exhibition in the Old Mill and the Cotswold Motor Museum. At its heart is the Dial House, a 17th century mellow stone country house hotel. Adrian and Jane Campbell-Howard bought the property in 2000 and have brought their youthful enthusiasm and good taste to the establishment. The cosy, beamed award winning restaurant enjoys an excellent local reputation. In winter log fires burn in the public rooms. In Summer guests can relax in the $1^1/_2$ acre garden. The Dial House is the perfect place for a restful break all year round. Two of the country style bedrooms have four posters and one a half-tester. Flowers, chocolates and champagne can be arranged for that special occasion. Bourton is well placed for touring the Cotswolds and is handy for Stow-on-the-Wold, Cheltenham, Stratford and Oxford.

Small & comfortable country house hotel in th heart of the Cotswolds.

🛏 13 ✂ 🅿 20

Directions
Turn off A429 Fosse Way for Bourton, hotel on left in centre of vill. back fm rd

Nearby attractions
Cotswold Motor Museum, Model Village, Birdland, Village Life Exhib,Kiftsgate Gdn

Distances
Stow-o-t-Wold 4, Burford 10, London 84

Rates Single/double/twin with bkfst fm £55 per person; 4-poster fm £75 pp
Meals Tdh dinner; alc, lunch & spec. diets available; last orders 2100. [Ad]
Leisure Breaks Winter breaks, Mon-Thurs Nov-Feb min. 2-nt stay, dinner, b & b fm £65 pppn. Rest of year, dinner, b & b from £76 pppn 2-night+ stay.
Other activities Fishing, riding & golf nearby.
Awards & accreditations Which? Hotel of the Year 2005 - *Most Ravishing Restaurant with Rooms.* Lonely Planet England 2005: *"probably one of the best places to stay in the Cotswolds."*
Diners, Visa, Mastercard, JCB, Switch cards accepted. Open all year.

Gloucestershire, Bourton-on-the-Water

Hotel on the Park

34 Evesham Road, Cheltenham, Gloucestershire GL52 2AH

T (0870) 860 8516 **F** (01242) 511526 **E** stay@hotelonthepark.com
T (International) +44 [0] (1242) 518898 **W** www.hotelonthepark.com

143

The Hotel on the Park is a breathtaking townhouse hotel on the outskirts of Regency Cheltenham. It has been carefully restored to provide 12 striking and individual bedrooms, stylish reception rooms and the smart Parker's Brasserie. Bathrooms are exceptional, some with aromatherapy/chromotherapy baths, bath pillows, state-of-the-art whirlpools and one with an infinity bath. Just the thing to revive the weary traveller after a hard day at work, at the races, or touring the Cotswolds. Bedroom colours are bold and materials luxuriant, with Bedouin stripes, Regency cornices and best Egyptian linen. Cuisine in the Parkers Brasserie is under the supervision of chef Wayne Sullivan. Dinner might start with pan fried scallops and continue with slow roasted shoulder of Cotswold lamb. The award winning restaurant is a mobile-free zone! The library has a rotating scrabble board and other games, books and magazines for guests to browse. Outside the small walled garden has a giant draughts set. There is a well stocked bar and wireless broadband is available throughout. Altogether a very different and unique place to stay in the 'Centre for the Cotswolds'

🛏 12 ✗ 🅿 12 WIFI

Striking Regency townhouse hotel in Centre for the Cotswolds

Rates Single room with bkfst fm £106 per person; double from £126. [Ad]
Meals Alc dinner, two courses ca £24; lunch & spec. diets available; last orders 2130; bfst fm 0730 Mon-Fri.
Leisure Breaks Luxury weekend breaks, dinner, b & b, champagne on arrival, teddy bear from £105 per person per night.
Other activities Horse racing & golf nearby.
Awards & accreditations *Cotswold Life* Restaurant of the Year 2006. AA Top 200 ★★★ ✿✿
Diners, Visa, Mastercard & JCB cards accepted. Open all year.

Directions Fm London A40, rt Hewlett Rd, branch left All Saints Rd to Pittville Circ, str't over to Evesham Rd; hotel in frt of you
Nearby attractions
Pittville Pump Room, Racecourse, Holst Museum, Sudeley Castle, Crickley Hill Prk
Distances
Gloucester 9, Oxford 43, London 99

Gloucestershire, Cheltenham

Burleigh Court Hotel
Burleigh, Minchinhampton, Gloucestershire GL5 2PF
T (0870) 418 8122 **F** (01453) 886870 **E** info@burleighcourthotel.co.uk
T (International) +44 [0] (1453) 883804 **W** www.burleighcourthotel.co.uk

The overused phrase *hidden gem* could not be more appropriate for Burleigh Court. It lies off the beaten track near the pretty village of Minchinhampton and is set in $3^1/_2$ acres of beautiful gardens with the most outstanding views over The Golden Valley. It is a privately owned hotel and proprietor Louise Noble believes that happy and friendly staff are the key to running a successful hotel. Burleigh Court is impressive and sophisticated and yet has the feeling and welcome of a family home. The AA ☺ restaurant is under the supervision of award-winning chef Stephen Woodcock, who reworks classical dishes into individual creations, using the freshest local produce, complemented by herbs and vegetables from the hotel's own gardens. An imaginative wine list accompanies this fine dining and prior booking is recommended. The bar is friendly and relaxing, strewn with magazines, with panelled walls and comfortable sofas and chairs. Bedrooms are individually decorated and the coach house has some wonderful family rooms leading into the garden and the Victorian plunge pool. With its log fires in winter and fresh flowers in summer, this is certainly an hotel for all seasons.

Gem in a hidden Cotswold valley with award winning restaurant

🛏 18 (inc 2 suites) ✗ ♿ ⚡ 🍴 ☰ 50 🅿 20 🐎

Directions
A419 from Cirencester, turn left at Brimscombe, up hill, turn left at church

Nearby attractions
Slimbridge Wildfowl Trust, Gloucester Cathedral, Westonburt Arboretum.

Distances
Stroud 4, Cirencester 10, London 75.

Rates Single room with breakfast from £90; double from £125.
Meals 3-cse tdh dinner £29.50; alc, bar snacks & diets avail; lunch £22.95; last orders 2100; bfst fm 0730.
Leisure Breaks 2 nights min, double room, dinner & breakfast £160 per night
Other activities Golf, riding, tennis nearby.

Visa, Mastercard, Diners cards accepted. Open all year.

Gloucestershire, Minchinhampton

Three Choirs Vineyard Restaurant with Rooms

Newent, Gloucestershire GL18 1LS

T (0870) 860 8434 **F** (01531) 890877 **E** ts@threechoirs.com
T (International) +44 [0] (1531) 890223 **W** www.threechoirs.com

Situated on the edge of the Forest of Dean, Three Choirs Vineyard is a delight to visit in any season. It produces over 250,000 bottles of wine per year from the 100-acre vineyard which straddles the Gloucestershire/Herefordshire border. Nestled in an area of remarkable beauty and tranquillity, the vineyard enjoys a low rainfall and warm climate, perfect for growing the grapes which have produced some of England's finest single estate wines since 1975. The eight very comfortable and well appointed bedrooms have stunning views, each with its own terrace on which a glass of wine from the vines below can be enjoyed. The atmosphere is relaxed and welcoming. The award winning restaurant serves an excellent menu with the emphasis on locally produced food to accompany the wines. In summer you can dine *al fresco* on the terrace and in winter an open fire burns. A tour around the vineyard and winery is a must. You can see the presses, fermentation tanks and bottling line. A video presentation tells the story of both wine and beer making. Before leaving, a visit to the well stocked shop will ensure that you can take with you a souvenir of a memorable stay.

'Vineyard with Rooms' on the edge of the Forest of Dean

Rates Single room with breakfast from £75; double from £95.
Meals Vineyard restaurant alc, lunch & diets avail; last orders 2100; bfst fm 0800.
Leisure Breaks Wine tasting break, dinner, b & b, sparkling wine in room, choice of Three Choirs wine with meal, guided tour of winery + wine tasting. Romantic breaks also available.

Mastercard & Visa cards accepted. Open all year exc. 24 Dec-5 Jan.

Directions From M50 junc 3, go to Newent, then B4216 signed Ledbury. Follow brown tourist signs.
Nearby attractions Gloucester Cathedral & Docks, Forest of Dean, Hereford, Hay-on-Wye, Cotswolds
Distances Newent 2, Ross-on-Wye 9, London 110

Gloucestershire, Newent

The Grapevine Hotel

Sheep Street, Stow-on-the-Wold, Gloucestershire GL54 1AU

T (0870) 860 8435 **F** (01451) 832278 **E** enquiries@vines.co.uk
T (International) +44 [0] (1451) 830344 **W** www.vines.co.uk

Set in the heart of this classic Cotswold town, the 17th-century Grapevine Hotel is renowned for the warm welcome extended to its guests, many of whom return again and again. The bedrooms are exceptionally well appointed, whether in the main house or in the Garden Rooms in the courtyard. Each has its own stylish decor, individual atmosphere and many luxuries. Some have period murals - verse or madrigals script. Whether you choose to eat in the AA ☺ Conservatory Restaurant with its trademark Grapevine canopy now approaching 100 years old, the cosy Gigot Bar or the newly opened contemporarily styled *La Vigna* Brasserie, you will be assured of an exceptional meal, prepared and presented with flair and imagination. The restaurants are also popular with local clientèle. The service is impeccable but not intrusive and requests are met with a smile and prompt action. Stow is a unique market town where antique shops and galleries vie with traditional local shops. It is a centre for exploring the Cotswolds and for visiting the stunning gardens of Kiftsgate and Hidcote.

17th-century town centre inn of immense character

🛏 22 (inc 2 ⌂) 🚭 🐾 ☷ 20 🅿 30 🐾

Directions
Take A436 Chipping Norton rd, Grapevine in ctre on rt opp Methodist Chapel

Nearby attractions
Sudeley Cas, Blenheim, Batsford Arboretum, Hidcote Manor, Kiftsgate House

Distances
Cheltenham 18, Oxford 23, London 84

Rates Single room with breakfast from £85; double £140. [Ad]

Meals Conservatory/La Vigna 3-cse tdh dinner £28; alc, lunch, bar meals & special diets available; last orders 2130; bfst fm 0730.

Other activities Golf, shooting nearby.

Leisure Breaks Midweek rates available Nov-May. See website or call Reservations for details. Also weekend breaks, min 2-night stays.

 & major credit cards accepted. Open all year.

Gloucestershire, Stow-on-the-Wold

The King's Head Inn & Restaurant

The Green, Bledington, Stow-on-the-Wold OX7 6XQ

T (0870) 418 8033 F (01608) 658902 E kingshead@Orr-Ewing.com
T (International) +44 [0] (1608) 658365 W www.kingsheadinn.net

The King's Head occupies a striking position on the village green of this pretty Cotswold village, frequent winner of the Bledisloe Cup *Best Kept Village* Award. Cosy bedrooms are either in the 15th century older part of the inn (access to some via an outside staircase) or in the newer block, approached across a leafy small courtyard. The owners have refurbished most bedrooms in restful pastel colours. Most have flat screen TVs. Bathrooms have been upgraded with tongue-and-groove woodwork, better lighting and power shower heads. The restaurant, with inglenook fireplace, pews and oak chairs, has earned a high local reputation for creative personal cuisine. Aberdeen Angus beef comes from the family's farm in the next village whilst fresh fish comes straight off the boat from Looe in Cornwall three times per week. Starter might be Thai fishcakes with soy & sesame dip, main might be a char-grilled beef fillet or homemade steak and kidney pie. Whether you go for a snack in the bar (popular with locals) or eat *à la carte* from the enterprising menu, you will be well satisfied.

12 (inc 1 🏠) ❈ 🕭 ✻ 🅿 20

Award-winning village inn with charming bedrooms and great food

Rates Single room with breakfast from £55; double £70-125; 4-poster £125.
Meals 3-cse alc dinner ca £20; lunch, bar meals & vegetarian dishes available; last orders 2100; bfst fm 0730. Good wine list. Real ale.
Other activities Golf, clay pigeon shooting, quad biking, fishing, riding nearby.
Leisure Breaks Sun-Thurs, get 3rd night half-price or stay 3 nts get 4th free. Exc. July.Aug,School hols, Cheltenham week and New Year.
Awards Runner-up *Sunday Times Pub of the Year 2000.* Daily Telegraph Central England Pub of the Year 2005. Les Routiers *Inn of the Year Central England 2004.*
Visa, Mastercard, Switch cards accepted. Open all year.

Directions
From Stow take A436 Chipping Norton Rd, br rt B4450 to Bledington. Inn on rt
Nearby attractions
Cotswold Wildlife Park Burford, Hidcote Manor, Kiftsgate House, Stow Antiques
Distances
Stow-o-t-Wold 3,Oxford 21, London 81

Gloucestershire, Nr. Stow-on-the-Wold

148

Corse Lawn House Hotel & Restaurant

Corse Lawn, Nr. Tewkesbury, Gloucestershire GL19 4LZ
T (0870) 418 8123 **F** (01452) 780840 **E** enquiries@corselawn.com
T (International) +44 [0] (1452) 780771 **W** www.corselawn.com

An elegant Grade II Listed Queen Anne building, Corse Lawn House is set back from a quiet village green and stands in 12 acres of its own grounds. The house has belonged to the Hine family (of Cognac fame) since 1978 and since then has been carefully extended and refurbished to create a stunning country house hotel. Each bedroom is different and guests are greeted with fresh fruit and home made biscuits. The restaurant is very much the heart of the hotel with an emphasis on local and seasonal produce. Management are very much in evidence, seeing to their customers' needs. Less formal dining is available in the Bistro and a private dining room/conference room can be used. There are two comfortable drawing rooms. As Corse Lawn is also a home, there are horses in the paddocks and two well behaved dogs. The atmosphere is happy and relaxed, the service attentive but unobtrusive. Corse Lawn lies in an unspoiled backwater of Gloucestershire, yet is well placed for visiting the Cotswolds, Malvern Hills and the Forest of Dean and easily accessible from major roads and motorways.

Elegant Queen Anne small hotel set back from the village green

🛏 19 ⌨ 🍴 🔟 ⚬ 🐾 ♨ 20 🅿 30

Directions
From junc 1 M50, take A38 twds Tewkesbury then A438 Ledbury Rd, then left on B4211.
Nearby attractions
Bredon Hill, Birtsmorton Court, Eastnor Cas Ledbury, Studeley Cas Winchcombe
Distances
Tewkesbury 6, Ledbury 10, London 107

Rates Single room with breakfast from £90; double from £140.
Meals 3-cse tdh dinner £29.50; alc & lunch avail; last orders 2130.
Leisure Breaks 2 nights+ dinner, b & b from £175 per couple per night.
Other facilities Satellite TV. Golf & riding nearby.
Accreditations AA Top 200 Hotel 77% ☺☺. Winner Good Hotel Guide César Award *Best Country Hotel 2005*

 & major credit cards accepted. Open all year.

Gloucestershire, Nr. Tewkesbury

Moccas Court
Moccas, Nr. Hereford, Herefordshire HR2 9LH

T (0870) 860 8483 F (01981) 500095 ('phone first) E bencmaster@btconnect.com
T (International) +44 [0] (1981) 500019 W www.moccas-court.com

149

Moccas Court is a Grade I listed Georgian House set in its own estate in a unique position on the river Wye. The grounds were laid out by Capability Brown and Humphrey Repton. A black labrador greets you as you crunch up the drive and ring the bell of this country house and you will then be shown to your sumptuous room by one of the family proprietors. All five bedrooms are decorated to a high standard with views over the surrounding countryside. You will be offered an *apéritif* in the drawing room, them move into the exquisite Round Room, with its Robert Adam designed ceiling for dinner at one communal table. Ben specialises in locally reared game, venison and beef, accompanied by organically grown vegetables. After dinner your charming host and hostess might join you for coffee or a liqueur. Walks along the Wye or across the parkland to the 12th century parish church will further enhance your stay in this area of outstanding natural beauty, on the threshold of the Brecon Beacons National Park. *"The loveliest view of England I could ever expect to find.....there is no area in the British Isles which is more beautiful."* - James Lees-Milne.

 5   [Ad]

Private house in exquisite parkland, now a small hotel

Rates Single inc. breakfast & dinner from £112; double/twin £140-195.

Directions A438 10m west of Hereford left at Staunon-Wye signed Hay. Left at T junc Red Lion Hotel, Moccas 2m on left

Other activities Golf, riding, sailing nearby.

Nearby attractions
Hay-on-Wye, Hereford Cathedral & Mappa Mundi, Hampton Court, Llanthony Priory

Distances
Hereford 16, Hay-on-Wye 9, London 146.

& all major credit cards accepted. Open all year.

Herefordshire, Moccas

150

Stapleford Park Country House Hotel

Stapleford, Nr. Melton Mowbray, Leicestershire LE14 2EE
T (0870) 418 8065 **F** (01572) 78001 **E** reservations@stapleford.co.uk
T (International) +44 [0] (1572) 787019 **W** www.staplefordpark.com

Casual luxury at its very best is how Stapleford has been described and, with its unique character and sumptuous comforts, it is one of the finest country house hotels in England. Across acres of Capability Brown created parkland, up a tree-lined avenue, under the arched wing, you reach the stunning façade of this great country mansion, designed by Inigo Jones and John Webb. The public rooms reflect the majesty of the house: high ceilings, mahogany panelling, open fires and unique features such as a *trompe d'oeil* ceiling and a 450-year old vaulted kitchen. Meals are taken here and in the ornately carved Grinling Gibbons dining room which serves an outstanding cuisine conveying traditional and modern British 'country' cooking at its best. The bedrooms have been individually created by famous designers such as Wedgwood, David Hicks, Zoffany and Crabtree & Evelyn and all are unashamedly luxurious, with splendid marble bathrooms. Every conceivable leisure activity is on offer here, including a state-of-the-art gym in the newly converted stable block. A stay at Stapleford is unforgettable, combining as it does the grand style of byegone centuries with present day luxury.

Impeccable 'Stately Home' hotel with every leisure activity available

Directions Fm M1 Junc 21a, take A46, then A607 Melton Mowbray, then B676 twds Colsterworth. Hotel on rt.
Nearby attractions
Belvoir Castle, Barnsdale Gardens, Rockingham Speedway, Burghley House.
Distances
Leicester 15, Grantham 16, London 104

Rates Double/twin inc. breakfast from £250.
Meals Grinling Gibbons Fine Dining AA ❀❀ RAC Gold Ribbon Restaurant £44; alc, lunch & spec. diets available; last orders 2130; bfst from 0730.
Leisure Breaks Midweek break 3 nts for price of 2 inc full Eng. bfst, VAT; includes a short falconry display and fruit & flowers on arrival. From £500 per rm
Other activities Falconry, golf academy, aromatherapy & reflexology.

 & all major credit cards accepted. Open all year.

Leicestershire & Rutland, Melton Mowbray

Barnsdale Lodge Hotel

151

The Avenue, Rutland Water, Nr. Oakham, Rutland LE15 8AH
T (0870) 418 8117 **F** (01572) 724961 **E** enquiries@barnsdalelodge.co.uk
T (International) +44 [0] (1572) 724678 **W** www.barnsdalelodge.co.uk

Overlooking Rutland Water and the undulating hills of England's smallest county, this former 17th century farmhouse adjacent to the estate of the Earl of Gainsborough, is an idyllic retreat for anyone wishing to escape. Lovingly rstored and at the head of a tree lined avenue, Barnsdale is located to the North of Oakham, with its well preserved Market Square *(market days Wednesdays & Saturdays)*. En suite bedrooms offer complete relaxation. Two are specially designed for disabled guests, some are inter-connecting or four-poster and many offer panoramic views South over Rutland Water. Dining is available in one of the three dining rooms, the conservatory or, weather permitting, in the courtyard garden. Conferences, wedding receptions, product launches and private parties take place in the separate Banqueting Suite. *Vicienté at Barnsdale*, the hotel's new beauty therapy room, can offer the ultimate in relaxation and pampering. On and around Rutland Water, there is sailing, windsurfing or cycling around its perimeter. Geoff Hamilton's gardens are close by and Belton House (NT), Grimsthorpe and Belvoir Castles are easily accessible.

🛏 44 ⊙ ⌾ ⍛ 🐾 (£10 flat fee) 🏊 🎿 🍸 ⚲ ◎ ⚓ 🖊 ⛳ 200 🅿 200 🐎

Former farmhouse, now charming hotel overlooking Rutland Water

Rates Single room inc. breakfast from £70; double from £80.

Meals AA ⊛ dinner ca £30; alc, lunch & spec. diets available; last orders 2130; bfst from 0700.

Leisure Breaks Stay three nights and receive free entrance into Geoff Hamilton's famous Barnsdale Gardens. Rates from £255. Pse ask for details.

Other activities In house beauty treatments, relaxation massage. Riding, sailing, watersports, cycling, Rock Bloc climbing, fishing, birdwatching nearby & all major credit cards accepted. Open all year.

Directions
Frm A1, onto A606 at Stamford. 5 m on rt side just b4 Xrds, 2m E of Oakham

Nearby attractions
Belvoir Castle, Barnsdale Gardens, Rockingham Speedway & Cas, Burghley House

Distances
Oakham 2, Stamford 5, London 98.

Leicestershire & Rutland, Nr. Oakham

Branston Hall Hotel
Branston, Nr. Lincoln, Lincolnshire LN4 1PD
T (0870) 418 8107 **F** (01522) 790549 **E** info@branstonhall.com
T (International) +44 [0] (1522) 793305 **W** www.branstonhall.com

We are pleased to have been able to include Branston Hall in Signpost, in an area where country house hotels are few and far between. The Old Hall was built in 1735 although the present building dates from 1885. It sits in 88 acres of its own parkland, woodland and lakes and has been the subject of considerable refurbishment in recent years to make it a leading light in the area. The hotel retains the high ceilings and spacious feel of the Victorian era. Dining is either in the AA award winning Lakeside Restaurant or in the less formal Melville Bar area. Most bedrooms overlook the lake and grounds and reflect the architecture of the original building. Rooms in the separate Courtyard Annexe have large corner baths and provide a bit of extra privacy. The leisure centre has an indoor pool with impressive murals and a sauna and fitness suite. The hotel is a popular and romantic venue for a wedding reception and an ideal location for large or small conferences. Special events - balls, concerts, special weekends &c are run throughout the year as well as an annual Wedding Fayre. Branston Hall is ideal for those visiting Lincoln on business or pleasure.

Victorian country mansion set in 88 acres of parkland, woodland & lakes

🛏 50 ⊙🍴 🌂 🛋 ♨ 🍽 ⛳ ⚽ 200 🅿 100

Directions
B1188 Canwick Rd south fm Lincoln twds Hetherington. Branston 3m. Hotel on rt.
Nearby attractions
Lincoln College. Lincoln Cathedral & Bishops Palace, Hartsholme Cntry Park.
Distances
Lincoln 3, Sleaford 15, London 140.

Rates Single room inc. breakfast from £70; double from £99.

Meals 3-cse tdh AA ☺ dinner £24; alc, lunch & spec. diets available; last orders 2100; bfst from 0700.

Leisure Breaks 2 nights dinner, b & b £114.50 per room per night.

Other activities Fishing, golf, watersports, riding, tennis nearby.

 & all major credit cards accepted. Open all year.

Lincolnshire, Nr. Lincoln

Washingborough Hall Hotel

Church Hill, Washingborough, Lincolnshire LN4 1BE

T (0870) 860 8436 **F** (01522) 792936 **E** enquiries@washingboroughhall.com
T (International) +44 [0] (1522) 790340 **W** www.washingboroughhall.com

153

Washingborough Hall is a beautiful Georgian country house situated in four acres of landscaped gardens and woodland offering a relaxing venue away from the bustle of the city. It is situated at the heart of the village, next door to the church, having formerly been the rectory. Just three miles from the city centre, it provides an oasis of calm for those visiting Lincoln and the surrounding countryside. The 12 individual bedrooms include two four-posters and are fitted out to a high standard and with the usual amenities. The Wedgwood Restaurant offers fine cuisine in tranquil surroundings overlooking the front lawns. New owners Richard and Sue Warren are very much hands-on, Richard helping in the dining room. Our dinner of scallops - fresh from Grimsby that day - and steak was excellent and was accompanied by a sensibly priced half bottle of *Côte de Rhône*. There are five or six choices per course. The hotel also caters for private functions, weddings, meetings and conferences in a separate room. There is an outdoor swimming pool and wireless internet connection is now available throught the hotel.

🛏 12 ☺ ✗ ❄ ⚓ 🚴 ⛲ 50 🅿 40 🏊 WIFI

Tranquil Georgian country house, three miles from the centre of Lincoln

Rates Single room inc. breakfast from £65; double from £90; dinner b & b from £85 single; £130 double/twin.
Meals 3-cse dinner ca £25; alc, lunch & spec. diets available; last orders 2130; bfst from 0730.
Leisure Breaks Details on application.
Other activities Leisure centre, squash, golf, tennis, riding & fishing nearby

Directions Take B1188 out of Lincoln twds Branston, left at cemetery onto B1190. In village Church Hill is 1st rt at mini-rdbt.
Nearby attractions
Doddington Hall, Lincoln Cathedral & Bishops Palace, Hartsholme Country Pk
Distances
Lincoln 3, Sleaford 14, London 141

Lincolnshire, Nr. Lincoln

Fawsley Hall

Fawsley, Nr. Daventry, Northamptonshire NN11 3BA

T (0870) 418 8110 F (01327) 892001 E info@fawsleyhall.com
T (International) +44 [0] (1327) 892000 W www.fawsleyhall.com

Fawsley Hall has rapidly established itself as one of the finest hotels in the Midlands. It stands in 2000 acres of quiet parkland where sheep graze beside the 14th century ironstone church, beyond which stretch lakes landscaped by Capability Brown. The Hall has three distictive styles of architecture: the original Tudor rooms form the core of the house and include the wonderful panelled Great Hall and eight authentically furnished bedrooms. This part of the house includes the Queen Elizabeth Chamber, where the Tudor monarch is reputed to have stayed. There are then 14 Georgian rooms with large windows and high ceilings and eight Victorian rooms and 13 modern classic rooms. All have dataports, digital TV and power showers. Spring 2007 will see the opening of Knightley Court - a further eight Georgian rooms plus a cinema, syndicate and function rooms with capacity for 130 for a private dinner, product launch or conference. The AA☺☺☺ Knightley Restaurant is under the supervision of chef Philip Dixon. Fawsley is well placed for visits to Althorp and Sulgrave Manor and for Northampton and Stratford-upon-Avon. The perfect place to be pampered for that promised short break.

Stately mansion with Tudor origins, set in 2000 acres of parkland

🛏 44 ☺ ⅍ ⌷ ⌂ ☌ 🐕 ⬇ 🍸 📷 ☎ ✏ ⠿ 150 🅿 150 🐎 WIFI

Directions
From M1 J16 take A45 for Daventry, then A361 for Banbury. Fawsley 4th turn to left

Nearby attractions
Althorp, Sulgrave Manor, Farnborough Hall, Broughton Castle, Canons Ashby.

Distances
Northampton 10, Banbury 13, London 86

Rates Single room inc. breakfast from £149; double from £189. [Ad]
Meals 3-cse tdh dinner £37.50; alc, lunch & spec. diets available; last orders 2130; bfst from 0800.
Leisure Breaks Fawsley Weekender 2 nights dinner, b & b £510 per person (club room) to £950 (suite).
Other activities Golf & swimming pools within 5 miles.

Northamptonshire, Nr. Daventry

Rushton Hall

Rushton, Nr. Kettering, Northamptonshire NN14 1RR

T (0870) 860 8517 **F** (01536) 713010 **E** reservations@rushtonhall.com
T (International) +44 [0] (1536) 713001 **W** www.rushtonhall.com

155

Rushton Hall is the epitome of the new generation of elegant country house hotel. Decorated with imagination, Rushton exudes an ambience of comfortable, informal splendour. Exquisite state rooms are furnished with antiques. The 45 luxurious bedrooms, each with its own style, some with French sleigh beds, some four-posters, come with all 'mod cons' - plasma TV screens, dvds and broadband in every room. Some have enormous bathrooms (converted from bedrooms) with free standing central baths and all have Moulton Brown toiletries. Rushton Hall stands in its own parkland, surrounded by tranquil countryside with many country pursuits on the doorstep. The famous Triangular Lodge - signifying The Trinity and built in 1593 - is nearby. Rushton is the perfect setting for conferences, private events and weddings. As well as the Great Hall, the Dairy and the Cricket Pavilion, in the grounds can be used. The team of award winning chefs are dedicated to creating inspirational food of a consistently high calibre, whatever your reason for visiting the Hall. A Spa is due to open in the Spring of 2007.

45 ⚓ 200 P150 **Stately Gothic mansion with generous sized bedrooms and public rooms**

Directions Fm A14 J7 take A6003 Corby rd. After 2m sign left Rushton. In vill rt & rt again past church. Left at T, hotel on rt.

Rates Single/double room inc. breakfast from £140.

Meals 3-cse tdh dinner £35; alc, lunch & spec. diets available; last orders 2130; bfst from 0700.

Leisure Breaks 20% off second night if two or more nights are booked.

Other Activities Golf within 5 miles.

Nearby attractions
Triangular Lodge, Boughton House, Althorp. Wickstead Park, Rockingham Cas.

Distances
Kettering 5, Corby 5, No'ton 18, London 80

& all major credit cards accepted. Open all year.

Northamptonshire, Nr. Kettering

156

The Falcon Hotel

Castle Ashby, Northampton, Northamptonshire NN7 1LF

T (0870) 418 8109 F (01604) 696673 E falcon.castleashby@oldenglishinns.co.uk
T (International) +44 [0] (1604) 696200 W www.falconhotel-castleashby.co.uk

This traditional 16th century country cottage is made for relaxation. The Falcon is cosy, warm and comfortable. The pretty AA ❀ restaurant , serves modern English cuisine using produce from the hotel's own vegetable garden, where possible. In May each year there is a special 'asparagus menu'. The oak-beamed cellar bar offers a cosy atmosphere and excellent value bar meals. Five of the individually decorated bedrooms are in the main old house, with 11 more modern rooms in a converted stable block across the car park, including some ground floor rooms. They have pretty fabrics, scrubbed or painted pine wardrobes and restful lighting. You access those in the main house along crooked stairs and corridors but they have all modern facilities, the bathrooms with power showers, complimentary toiletries and bathrobes. The hotel can also cater for business meetings and wedding receptions, the garden being very popular for these. The Falcon is minutes from Castle Ashby House and well placed for Stratford, Woburn Abbey and Althorp.

Traditional country inn with extensive gardens and access to parkland

🛏 16 ╳ ❀ ♨ 60 🅿 50 🐎

Directions
From M1 J15 take A508 then No'ton ring road to A428 signed Bedford. C Ashby 6m

Nearby attractions
Castle Ashby, Billing Aquadrome, Bromham Mill, Woburn Abbey, Althorp

Distances
Northampton 8, Bedford 16, London 76

Rates Single room inc. breakfast from £95; double from £125; premier rooms £139.50.

[Ad]

Meals 3-cse tdh dinner £27.50/lunch £16.95; alc, lunch & spec. diets available; last orders 2200; bfst from 0730.

Leisure Breaks Min. 2 nights dinner, b & b £79.50 per person per night.

Other activities Golf, riding, clay pigeon shooting, fishing nearby.

& all major credit cards accepted. Open all year.

Northamptonshire, Nr. Northampton

The New French Partridge

Newport Pagnell Road, Horton, Northampton NN7 2AP

157

T (0870) 860 8518 **F** (01604) 870032 **E** info@newfrenchpartridge.co.uk
T (International) +44 [0] (1604) 870033 **W** www.newfrenchpartridge.co.uk

The New French Partridge reopened in 2002, completely refurbished under the expert direction of Ian Oakenfull, who presides in the AA⊛⊛ kitchen, and Tanya Banerjee, whose style is evident in the décor throughout the hotel. The ten individually designed bedrooms have painted French furniture, brass bedsteads and cheerful fabrics. Bedrooms either face the quiet courtyard or the rear garden. Each is equipped with flat screen TV and high speed internet connection. Gourmet dinner might start with quail escabèche, be followed by tortellini of crab & shellfish velouté, and move on to corn fed duck roulade with Iberian black pudding, figs and morrel juice. A simpler yet equally delicious menu is available at lunchtime. Choices change regularly. Less formal dining is available in the Cellar Bar which serves *tapas* dishes. The hotel has a pretty garden at the rear for small weddings and is conveniently situated 10-15 minutes from both Northampton and Milton Keynes in a quiet village. It is ideal for those on business in the area or for weekenders seeking a break just 75 minutes from Central London.

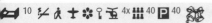 10 🍴 🏇 ✝ ❀ ♀ 🐟 4x ⚌ 40 🅿 40 🐎

Rates Single/double room inc. breakfast from £140.   Ad

Meals 5-cse tdh dinner £41. 50; alc, lunch & spec. diets available; last orders 2200; bfst from 0630.

Other activities Golf, riding, clay pigeon shooting, fishing nearby.

 & all major credit cards accepted. Open all year.

Stylish Restaurant with Rooms btwn Northampton & Milton Keynes

Directions
From M1 J15 take A508 twds No'ton,then B526 right at 1st roundabout to Horton

Nearby attractions
Castle Ashby, Billing Aquadrome, Delapre Abbey, Woburn Abbey, Althorp.

Distances
Northampton 7, M Keynes 10, London 68

Northamptonshire, Nr. Northampton

158

Whittlebury Hall Hotel & Spa
Whittlebury, Nr. Towcester, Northamptonshire NN12 8QH
T (0870) 860 8519 **F** (01327) 857867 **E** sales@whittleburyhall.co.uk
T (International) +44 [0] (1327) 857857 **W** www.whittleburyhall.co.uk

Whittlebury Hall is a modern Georgian-style building surrounded by parkland and golf courses. Inside rich furnishings and fabrics combine to create an impressive hotel. All bedrooms are spacious doubles with many modern touches and thoughtful extras. Executive suites come with whirlpool spa bath and double shower. An apéritif can be taken in the Silverstone Bar where you can view motor racing memorabilia before heading to either the informal Astons Restaurant or the fine dining AA ©© Murrays. Bentleys, a third outlet, provides a pizza and pasta option. The award winning spa has the very latest in health, fitness and beauty facilities. For the energetic there is an extensive Gymnasium. Or there is the whirlpool spa set amongst Roman ruins, together with a steam room and sauna. A range of beauty treatments is on offer, from facials to massage, hydrotherapy baths and body wraps. Pamper Day Packages and Pamper Me Breaks are available to both residents and outside members. Adjacent to the hall is the independent Whittlebury Golf Course with a choice of four 9-hole courses to challenge every level of handicap. Silverstone Circuit is within walking distance and the hotel can arrange special 'stay and drive' packages.

Purpose built hotel, spa, golf course & conference centre, set in parkland

211 🛏 & 🏛 🍴 🐕 ☉ 🚻 🏇 ♪ ⛳₁₈ ☂ ✈ ♨ 🛎 ⊕ ✎ 🐟 🦌
🛥 ⚓ ♨ 🎣 🍸 🎿 🏄 ♥♥ ✎ 52x 👥 500 🅿 200

Directions From London M1 junc 14 Milton Keynes, then A5 north 13m brown sign left just before Towcester racecourse.
Nearby attractions Silverstone Circuit, Althorp, Castle Ashby, Stowe School, Sulgrave Manor
Distances Towcester 4, Milton Keynes 15, London 70

Rates Single/double room inc. breakfast from £100. `[Ad]`
Meals Astons, Bentleys, Murrays Restaurants; meals from £17.50; Sunday lunch, spec. diets available; last orders 2130; bfst from 0700.
Leisure Breaks Pamper Breaks, Silverstone Circuit breaks.
Other activities Sailing 15 miles; squash 5 miles.

Mastercard, Visa & Diners cards accepted. Open all year.

Langar Hall

Langar, Nr. Nottingham, Nottinghamshire NG13 9HG

T (0870) 418 8111 **F** (01949) 861045 **E** imogen@langarhall.co.uk
T (International) +44 [0] (1949) 860559 **W** www.langarhall.com

I always love my visits to Langar Hall. Although close to Nottingham, it is beautifully situated overlooking the Vale of Belvoir - a lovely country house, built in 1837, standing beside an early English church, with glorious views over the gardens and parkland. The Hall is the family home of Imogen Skirving, whose father used to entertain famous cricketers of the 1930's. Nowadays the Test Match Special team stay here during Trent Bridge test matches! The public rooms are delightful. The charming proprietor and her excellent team make every effort for their guests' happiness. Together with her chef Gary Booth, Imogen works to produce excellent, reasonably priced menus of French and English food, using local produce, garden vegetables and herbs, Langar lamb, stilton & pork, game from the Belvoir estate and fish from Brixham. The restaurant has two AA ☺☺. Recently the library has been extended and a bar area with high 'billiard stools' has been created, where Imogen's celebrated fruit juice mixes are served. All the bedrooms are charming and uniquely furnished; one is themed in silver trees and called the *Barbara Cartland Room*. This is a truly lovely spot, with a peaceful and relaxing atmosphere.

🛏 10 🛎 🐾 ♨ 🎣 🐕 (by arr't - £10 fee) 🎪 20 🅿 20

Beautifully situated small hotel within 1/2 hour of central Nottingham

Rates Single room inc. breakfast from £75; double from £150; suite fm £210
Meals 3-cse tdh dinner weekdays £25; alc menus from £35; lunch from £12.50; spec. diets available; last orders 2130; bfst from 0800. [Ad]
Leisure Breaks Weekend breaks, 2 night stay b & b for 2 people from £175. Sunday & monday nights, double rooms sold at single rates.
Other activities Golf 4 miles; hunting & shooting can be arranged.

Directions
From Nottinghm take A52 Grantham Rd as far as Bingham, turn rt, follow signs.
Nearby attractions
Belvoir Castle, Angel Row Gallery, Castle ,Lace Mkt & Playhouse, Nottingham
Distances
Nottingham 12, Grantham 15, London 120

Mastercard & Visa cards accepted. Open all year.

Nottinghamshire, Langar

Colwick Hall Hotel
Colwick Park, Racecourse Rd, Nottingham NG2 4BH
T (0870) 860 8520 **F** (0115) 924 3797 **E** reservations@colwickhallhotel.com
T (International) +44 [0] (115) 950 0566 **W** www.colwickhallhotel.com

Colwick Hall is a magnificent Palladian style Georgian country house mansion nestling in over 60 acres of parkland. A historic building dating back to Saxon times, it was once the ancestral home of Lord Byron. Located just two miles from Nottingham City Centre, Colwick Hall is a Grade II* Listed manor overlooking Nottingham racecourse and offering exquisite facilities, from the award winning Georgetown Restaurant, the 1776 Grand Ballroom - popular for grand weddings and conferences - to the Lakeside Pavilion, a marquee within the grounds overlooking the lake. Superior bedrooms, some accessed via the grand staircase, are palatial, with large harp-shaped mirrors, sofas and chairs and sumptuous bathrooms: double basins, bidets, telephone extensions and separate shower cubicles with wide shower heads. Executive bedrooms are mainly located on the second floor and are more contemporary in style, with plasma TV screens and wireless internet access. The Georgetown Restaurant specialises in Malaysian cuisine, but also offers a range of Chinese, Thai and Indian dishes.

Converted stately home on the outskirts of Nottingham

🛏 17 🍴 ☉ 🏨 ♿ 🖥 ♻ ✝ 🧍🚶🏂 6x ♨ 500 🅿 120 🎣

Directions
Fm Nottingham pick up signs to West Bridgford & the Racecourse, 2m SE of the city.

Nearby attractions
Nott'm Racecourse, Nott'm Arena/Ice Stadium, Castle ,Lace Mkt & Playhouse

Distances
Nottingham 2, Grantham 26, London 132.

Rates Single room inc. breakfast from £85; double from £95.
Meals 3-cse alc dinner from £25; alc. lunch & spec. diets avail; last orders 2230; bfst from 0730.
Other facilities Fishing, health club, golf, riding, sailing, river bathing, watersports nearby.

 Mastercard, Visa & Diners cards accepted. Open all year.

Nottinghamshire, Nottingham

The Country Cottage Hotel

161

Easthorpe Street, Ruddington, Nr. Nottingham NG11 6LA
T (0870) 418 8124 **F** (0115) 921 4721 **E** cottagehotel@ntlworld.com
T (International) +44 [0] (115) 984 6882 **W** www.thecountrycottagehotel.com

Experienced hoteliers Andrew and Julie Sturt took over The Country Cottage in 2003 and their enthusiasm has ensured that this charming hotel is now realising its full potential. The Cottage has won many awards including the Conservation Award for the best restoration of an old building in a village setting. Bedrooms are spread between four cottages of 17th century origin, grouped around a courtyard and patio which even has its own wishing well! Each bedroom is individually designed with lots of little extras. When our inspector stayed, he was able to sit in the garden undisturbed writing reports, with one of the honeysuckle and rose covered cottages as a backdrop. He had an excellent dinner in the enlarged dining room followed by a nightcap in the snug ingle-nook sitting room. Recently the dining room has been extended and five smart new rooms have been added.There are two meeting rooms in the newly renovated lodge. There is ample parking and Ruddington is just three miles from Nottingham, off a quiet side road, and provides a welcome and relaxing change from the bustle of the City.

🛏 23 ⊙ ⦀ 50 🅿 30 🐾 100

Rates Single room inc. breakfast from £75; double from £90; junior suite from £85 (single)/£110 (double).
Meals 3-cse alc dinner from £25; last orders 2100; bfst from 0700 (Mon-Fri)/ 0800 Sat/Sun. Til 0930.
Other facilities Golf, fishing, riding, tennis nearby.

 & major credit cards accepted. Open all year.

Award-winning cottage conversion just 3 miles from Nottingham city ctre

Directions
From Nottingham take A60 Loughborough Rd then rt into Ruddington Ctre, hotel on lft
Nearby attractions
Nottingham Castle ,Lace Market & Playhouse
Distances
Nottingham 3, M1 Junc 26-4, London 120.

Nottinghamshire, Nottingham

162

The Old Vicarage
Worfield, Nr. Bridgnorth, Shropshire WV15 5JZ
T (0870) 418 8113 **F** (01746) 716552 **E** admin@the-old-vicarage.demon.co.uk
T (International) +44 [0] (1746) 716497 **W** www.oldvicarageworfield.com

Situated in the pretty conservation village of Worfield, the Old Vicarage Hotel is a peaceful retreat for travellers, whether on business or pleasure. The original style has been preserved with subtle refurbishment in keeping with modern comfort, and pretty watercolours add an intimate and homely touch. The AA ✪✪✪ restaurant is renowned for its first class modern British cuisine, award-winning wine list and efficient service. People travel from far afield just to enjoy a superb dinner. My bedroom was in the main house. It had great Victorian charm with a huge antique bed and wardrobe, and a marvellous view over the tranquil Shropshire countryside. Further large bedrooms have been converted from former stables and all are exquisitely decorated. There is a ground floor suite for disabled guests. The hotel is close to Ironbridge Gorge Museum and Severn Valley Railway. David & Sarah Blakstad, the resident proprietors, are attentive and welcoming hosts who will do their best to make your stay memorable.

Gem of a hotel, off the beaten track, with exceptional cuisine and views

🛏 14 (inc 2 suites) ✗ 🍴 🕭 📺 🐎 ∷∷ 30 🅿 40

Directions From Bridgnorth A454 twds Wolverhamp-ton. Left 3m in Wyken, hotel just after village of Worfield on right.
Nearby attractions Ironbridge Gorge Museum, Wenlock Priory, Severn Valley Rlwy, Weston Park
Distances Bridgnorth 4, Wolverhampton 10, London 182

Rates Single with breakfast from £80; double from £115.
Meals Tdh dinner £19.50; alc, lunch & spec. diets available; last orders 2100.
Leisure Breaks Any two days (or longer) from £135 per room per night, dinner, b & b. Sunday saver ££99 per room b & b.
Other facilities Tennis, fitness centre, golf, squash, swimming pools nearby.

Major credit cards accepted. Open all year.

Pen-y-Dyffryn Country Hotel

163

Rhydycroesau, Oswestry, Shropshire SY10 7JD
T (0870) 860 8437 F (01691) 650066 E stay@peny.co.uk
T (International) +44 [0] (1691) 653700 W www.peny.co.uk

Built in 1845 for an eccentric Celtic scholar, Pen-y-Dyffryn stands in five acres of its own south-facing grounds overlooking stunning hillside scenery on the Shropshire/Wales border. The ambience is very much 'country house' with stylish decor and fine antique furniture, set in idyllic surroundings. Some bedrooms in the main hotel have spa baths and are priced according to size and view. Those in the coach-house have a Mediterranean style, each with private patio; these are particularly suited to those bringing dogs. There is no better way to round off exploring Offa's Dyke or walking in the surrounding countryside (the hotel can supply free walking leaflets) than to dine in the AA ☺☺ restaurant, where the emphasis is on local and organic produce wherever possible. Non-residents come from far and wide for this dining experience. You can come here simply for total peace and quiet or spend an active few days exploring the area. Oswestry, which hosts the largest street market in Shropshire on a Wednesday, is three miles away; the NT properties of Powis Castle, Chirk Castle, Attingham and Erddig are all nearby, as is Wales' highest waterfall.

🛏 12 ⚒ 🏃 ⛩ 🐕 🅿 18

Idyllic off-the-beaten track country retreat on English/Welsh border

Rates Single with breakfast from £84; double from £106.
Leisure Breaks Weekend breaks from £80 per person per night, min 2-night stay, dinner, b & b. Weekday Breaks from £76 pppn.

Other facilities Golf, fishing, gym, riding, tennis, shooting, squash, indoor pool all nearby.

 & major credit cards accepted. Open all year.

Directions
Leave Oswestry on the B4580 Llansilin road. Hotel 3 miles from town centre.

Nearby attractions
Erdigg House, Powis Castle, Chirk Castle, Attingham, Chester, Offa's Dyke Path.

Distances
Oswestry 3, Shrewsbury 18, London 185.

Shropshire, Oswestry

Prince Rupert Hotel

Butcher Row, Shrewsbury, Shropshire SY1 1UQ

T (0870) 418 8126 **F** (01743) 357306 **E** post@prince-rupert-hotel.co.uk
T (International) +44 [0] (1743) 499955 **W** www.prince-rupert-hotel.co.uk

Once the home of Prince Rupert, King James I's grandson, the hotel is tucked away in the 16th century heart of England's finest Tudor town. On entering the building, there is a feeling of understated luxury. The reception area is well organised and operated by smart and helpful staff. The Royalist dining-room is quiet and has a cosy intimate ambience. It features an inglenook fireplace and authentic suits of armour. Menus change according to the seasons. More relaxed dining is available in the *Chambers* brasserie or *La Trattoria* authentic Italian restaurant. Bedrooms are individually designed, many with original exposed beams. The hotel's 12th century *Mansion House* suites, recently refurbished under the auspices of English Heritage, have been patronised by the infamous Monica Lewinsky, among others! Corridors change levels, following the contours of the original building, and are connected by fine oak staircases. My only regret when staying was that I did not have time to be pampered in the health and beauty salon. Next time.....

Historic town centre hotel of understated luxury, with spa

🛏 70 (inc 12 suites) 🍴 🛗 🎿 🍷 ⛳ 🏊 120 🅿 valet up to 65 cars -£4 per day

Directions From A5/A458 East, follow signs to town centre, beginn'g of one-way system Fish St on rt, go to end & turn rt.

Nearby attractions
Shrewsbury Castle, Ironbridge Museum, Hodnet Hall Gardens, Weston Park.

Distances
Telford 11, Bridgnorth 21, London 154.

Rates Single with breakfast from £85; double from £105.

Meals Tdh dinner from £25; alc, lunch & spec. diets available; last orders 2215; bfst from 0730.

Leisure Breaks Special reduced weekend rates throughout year from £67 per person per night, dinner, b & b.

 & major credit cards accepted. Open all year.

Shropshire, Shrewsbury

Soulton Hall
Wem, Nr. Shrewsbury, Shropshire SY4 5RS
165

T (0870) 418 8116 **F** (01939) 234097 **E** enquiries@soultonhall.co.uk
T (International) +44 [0] (1939) 232786 **W** www.soultonhall.co.uk

John and Ann Ashton turned their Elizabethan manor house into a small hotel in 1988 and the result is one of the best kept secrets of Shropshire! The Manor of Soulton featured in the Domesday Book and the site of the original moated manor house may be seen nearby. Rowland Hill, first protestant Lord Mayor of London, bought the present house in 1556 and a descendant, Thomas Hill, has his coat of arms above the front door to this day. Guests here are treated like members of the family. Drinks are taken in the cosy drawing room, whilst making a choice from the four course menu, which might start with smoked bacon and vegetable soup or carrot and coriander fritters with mint yoghurt and whose main course might be roast Shropshire pheasant or sirloin of beef, followed by desserts made from home grown fruit. Four of the bedrooms are in the main house, while the Coach House outside has two further ground floor bedrooms. The courtyard outside is becoming a popular wedding venue. Alternatively Cedar Lodge has a suite and garden rooms. Soulton is a working farm, and a peaceful spot in which to just relax or from which to explore the beauties of North Shropshire, the Welsh hills and border country.

🛏 10 ⅙ ⅗ ⅔ 🅿 50

Rates Single with breakfast from £49.50; double from £78.
Meals 4-cse tdh dinner £28.50-35; spec. diets available; last orders 2030.
Leisure Breaks Winter breaks available 2-3 nights, dinner, b & b two sharing from £69.50 per person per night; 7 nights for £55 pppn.

 & all major credit cards accepted. Open all year.

Elizabethan manor house, now a small hotel, with some bedrooms in annexes

Directions From A49 Shrewsbury-Whitchurch Rd, take B5065 at Prees Green twds Wem, hotel 2m on left.
Nearby attractions Hawkstone Park, Ironbridge Museum, Powis Castle & Gradens, Weston Park.
Distances Whitchurch 7, Shr'wsby 10, London 154

Shropshire, Nr. Shrewsbury

The Peacock Hotel

149 Warwick Road, Kenilworth, Warwickshire CV8 1HY

T (0870) 860 8521 **F** (01926) 864644 **E** reservations@peacockhotel.com
T (International) +44 [0] (1926) 851156 **W** www.peacockhotel.com

Established in 1998, the Peacock is a centrally located comfortable hotel within 15 minutes of the NEC, Royal Showground, Warwick University and Birmingham International Airport. It is popular with both corporate and leisure customers alike. Its décor is vibrant and colourful. Club bedrooms are particularly spacious, decorated in 1920s colonial style with chandeliers, Persian rugs and Javanese furniture, luxury bathrooms, DVD players and minibars. The award winning Coconut Lagoon Restaurant serves the cuisine of four South Indian States: Kerala, Goa, Karnataka and Andhra Pradesh. Alternatively the Malabar Room serves European dishes such as Fricassee of Beef with Drambuie sauce or Grilled Swordfish in grapefruit and tequila salsa. The nearby Raffles Restaurant, under the same ownership, provides an alternative Malaysian fine dining experience. Behind the main hotel, a separate building provides ground floor bedrooms and four state-of-the-art conference rooms. Owners Pearl Hotels & Restaurants Group have recently taken over the luxury Colwick Hall Hotel. (*See Nottinghamshire section of this guide.*)

Well located family-run hotel in Central Midlands market town.

🛏 29 (inc 3🛏 & 1🛏) ✗✓ ☺ 3x ♦♦♦180 🅿 20 🐾

Directions
From M40 junc 15 take A452 thru' Warwick to Kenilworth; hotel on rt in town ctr

Nearby attractions
Warwick Castle, Royal Showground, NEC, RSC Stratford-u-Avon, Birmingham ✈

Distances
Warwick 5, NEC 16, Bir'm 19, London 102

Rates Single with breakfast from £45; double from £55; club rooms fm £80.
Meals Alc dinner 2-cse ca £19; lunch & spec. diets available; last orders 2245; bfst fm 0700.   [Ad]

Other Facilities Golf, gym nearby.

& all major credit cards accepted. Open all year.

Buckland Manor

167

Buckland, Nr. Broadway, Worcestershire WR12 7LY
T (0870) 860 8522 **F** (01386) 853557 **E** enquire@bucklandmanor.com
T (International) +44 [0] (1386) 852626 **W** www.bucklandmanor.com

Buckland Manor is quite simply one of the finest small hotels in the Cotswolds, itself one of the most visited parts of England. It nestles beneath the Cotswold escarpment, with views over the Vale of Evesham and is mentioned in the records of Gloucester Cathedral and 600 years earlier in the Domesday Book. Next to the 13th-century church and in ten acres of mature gardens, the Manor has three ample sitting rooms, with a roaring log fire and antiques giving a home from home feel. Bedrooms are country house style; their ample bathrooms have separate shower cubicles with fluffy towels and bathrobes. The extensive gardens with their sweeping lawns, ancient statuary and shady trees create an oasis of peace and tranquillity. Guests can play croquet or tennis, take a stroll or just settle down with a good book in the summer house at the end of the rose garden. The AA ⊕⊕⊕ cuisine is predominantly English with European influences. It features fresh produce from the neighbouring Vale of Evesham, herbs from the Manor's own garden and wines from the extensive cellar. The Cotswold Way passes close to this gem of a hotel.

🛏 13 (inc 3 🛏) ✿ 🔟 ♪•/ 🏃 ♀ **P** 30

Hotel of 13th century origins in area of outstanding natural beauty

Rates Single with breakfast from £225; double from £235.
Meals Alc dinner; lunch & spec. diets available; last orders 2100; bfst fm 0800.
Other Facilities Massage. Golf, riding, shooting nearby.

& all major credit cards accepted. Open all year

Directions
From A44 Broadway take B4632 signed Cheltenham. Hotel 2m outside vill on left
Nearby attractions
Sudeley Castle, Hidcote Manor, Stratford Warwick Cas, Snowshill Manor, Blenheim
Distances
Evesham 6, Stow 12, Chelt'm 15, London 95

Worcestershire, Broadway

Holdfast Cottage Hotel
Marlbank Road, Little Malvern, Worcestershire WR13 6NA
T (0870) 418 8120 **F** (01684) 311117 **E** enquiries@holdfast-cottage.co.uk
T (International) +44 [0] (1684) 310288 **W** www.holdfastcottage.co.uk

This friendly and intimate hotel was bought by Guy and Annie Dixon early in 2005. Holdfast Cottage dates from the 17th century and was enlarged in Victorian times. The public rooms are comfortable and welcoming, with pretty fabrics and antique furniture. You enter through a plant-filled conservatory into the old oak beamed hall with its original cast iron range. The emphasis is on friendly and unobtrusive service. There are just eight bedrooms. All are individually decorated and each is named after one of the surrounding hills. The Dining Room serves an award-winning AA ® menu, constantly changing and making use of the finest seasonal produce. Special touches include home baked rolls, home made ice cream & chocolates and herbs from the hotel's own garden. Set in its own high wooded grounds surrounded by orchards and open farmland, it is secluded and quiet - an ideal place to relax after a day at the Malvern Showground or walking in the Malvern Hills. The Wye Valley, Forest of Dean, the Cotswolds, Worcester, Hereford and Gloucester are all within easy driving distance.

Intimate small cottage hotel on the edge of the Malvern Hills

🛏 8 ⚲ 🔟 👤 🐕 (by arr't - £5 per night) ♨ 25 🅿 20

Directions Turn off A449 Ledbury-Gt Malvern Rd at Little Malvern onto A4104 twds Upton. Hotel after 2¹/₂m on left.

Nearby attractions Elgar's Birthplace Museum Worcester, Eastnor Castle, Commandery - Worcester

Distances Gt Malvern 3, Worcester 12, London 119

Rates Single with breakfast from £55; double from £94.

Meals 4-cse tdh dinner £27.50; lunch & spec. diets available; last orders 2100.

Away Breaks Two+nights, dinner, b & b £70 per person per night, sharing. 3rd & subs. nts £66 pppn. 7 nights for price of 6 - accommodation only.

Mastercard, Visa, Solo, Switch accepted. Open all year

Worcestershire, Little Malvern

Colwall Park

Colwall, Nr. Malvern, Worcestershire WR13 6QG

T (0870) 418 8125 **F** (01684) 540847 **E** hotel@colwall.com
T (International) +44 [0] (1684) 540000 **W** www.colwall.com

169

Colwall Park is a country house style hotel situated on the sunny Western side of the breathtaking Malvern Hills, where the famous water is bottled, in the centre of peaceful Colwall village. Surrounded by beautiful gardens, there are footpaths from the hotel leading directly onto the Malvern Hills, where views over the surrounding countryside are spectacular. Efficient, knowledgeable and very friendly staff, winners of the prestigious *AA Courtesy & Care Award for England*, will show you to one of twenty-two guest bedrooms and suites. All are individually furnished and decorated to a very high standard, all en suite and featuring satellite TV, telephone with data port, coffee & tea-making with home made biscuits and other amenities. The highly acclaimed Seasons Restaurant (Birmingham Area Restaurant of the Year, AA ☺☺, Michelin, Egon Ronay) is a contemporarily furnished oak panelled room serving gourmet food at sensible prices. Alternatively the popular Lantern Bar, a meeting place for locals and residents alike, serves an exciting menu of freshly made meals and snacks using local produce.

🛏 22 ☺ ⚡ 💷 🖈 🐕 4 🏨 100 🅿 40

Gourmet food hotel in the heart of the Malvern Hills

Rates Single with breakfast from £79; double/twin from £120.
Meals 3-cse alc dinner ca £32; lunch & diets avail; last orders 2100; bfst from 0730.
Gourmet Breaks Two night+ breaks, alc dinner, b & b £79 per person per nt.
Other activities Fishing, golf, riding, shooting nearby.

Mastercard & Visa accepted. Open all year.

Directions
Turn off A449 Ledbury-Malvern Rd 3m fm Ledbury onto B4218 for Colwall. Hotel on rt
Nearby attractions
Elgar's Birthplace Museum Worcester, Eastnor Castle, Commandery - Worcester
Distances
Gt Malvern 4, Worcester 12, London 122.

Worcestershire, Nr. Malvern

Signpost Guide 2007
North West

Fact File
Illustrated Guide to
Historic Houses and Gardens,
Attractions and Walks.

The Lake District

North West

The North West, with the Lake District, is one of the most visited areas of Britain, yet it was only opened up by the railway some 150 years ago. Wordsworth and Tennyson's poetry helped to spread the word then about this remarkable, natural corner of Britain and it has remained popular ever since.

CUMBRIA

LANCASHIRE

MERSEYSIDE GREATER MANCHESTER

CHESHIRE

Hotels guide

Cheshire	page 175
Cumbria	page 176
Lancashire	page 193

Further information:
Cumbria Tourist Board
Ashleigh, Holly Head, Windermere,
Cumbria LA23 2AQ
Tel: 015394 44444

www.golakes.co.uk

North West Tourist Board
Swan House, Swan Meadow Road,
Wigan, Lancashire WN3 5BB
Tel: 01942 821222

www.visitnorthwest.com

The Lake District

Chester Cathedral

Liverpool

Cheshire and Lancashire

Chester

Forest of Bowland

The stark industrial towns of **Runcorn** and **Warrington** contrast sharply with the charms of the old walled city of **Chester** and the picturesque villages that dot **Cheshire**'s countryside. Iron age forts, Roman ruins, medieval churches, Tudor cottages and elegant Georgian and Victorian stately homes are among the many attractive sights of the county. **South Cheshire**, like Cumbria to the North, has long been where the magnates of the cities of Liverpool and Manchester have made their abode. It has good communications, pretty countryside with the wilder terrain of the Peak District and North Wales within easy reach.

Lancashire's **Forest of Bowland** is an area of outstanding natural beauty with wild crags, superb walks, streams, valleys and fells. **Blackpool** on the coast has been the playground of the North West for many years and still draws millions of holiday makers every year, attracted to its seven miles of beach, illuminations, Pleasure Beach Amusement Park and golf. **Morecambe**, **Southport**, **Lytham St Annes** and **Fleetwood** also offer wide beaches, golf and bracing walks. **Lancaster**, a city since Roman times, has fine museums, castle and university and an imitation of the Taj Mahal, the Ashton Memorial.

Canal near Chester

Blackpool

 TOP 10 Historic Houses Gardens and Parks

Arley Hall & Gardens, Nr Northwich, Cheshire
Beeston Castle, Tarporley, Cheshire
Capesthorne Hall, Macclesfield, Cheshire
Lancaster Castle, Lancaster
Leighton Hall, Carnforth, Lancs
Lyme Park, Disley, Stockport, Ches.
Roman Walls & Amphitheatre, Chester
Stapeley Water Gardens, Knutsford, Cheshire
Stonyhurst Abbey & College, Lancs
Tatton Park, Knutsford, Cheshire

 TOP 10 Attractions

Blackpool Tower & Pleasure Beach,
The Boat Museum, Ellesmere Port, Ches
Butterfly World, Bolton, Lancs
Camelot Theme Park, Chorley, Lancs
Chester Cathedral, Chester
Chester Zoo, Upton-by-Chester
Gullivers World, Warrington, Ches
Noel Edmonds World of Crinkly Bottom, Morecambe, Lancs
Peckforton Castle, Tarporley, Ches
Port Sunlight Visitor Centre, Wirral

 TOP 10 Walks and Nature Trails

Abbey Village > Roddlesworth Reservoir > Tockholes Plantations, Lancs
Alyn Waters Country Park > Gwersyllt-Bryn Alyn, Nr Chester
Carnforth Canal Circuit. From Carnforth Railway > Bolton-le -Sands, Lancs
The Gritstone Trail. Leek (Staffs) to Macclesfield, Ches
Jodrell Bank Science Centre & Arboretum, Nr Holmes Chapel, Cheshire
Pendle Way Walk. Pendle Heritage Centre, Pendle, Lancs
The Sandstone Trail. Malpas > Mouldsworth, Ches
Silverdale Sta > Jenny Brown's Point > Silverdale. Carnforth, Lancashire
Walk the Walls, Chester
The Whitegate Way. Cuddington > Wharton, Ches

Cumbria

Rydalwater

In this lovely corner of England, **The Lake District**, there is beauty in breathtaking variety. It is loved by many who come back time and again to its inspirational magic, brilliant blue lakes and craggy mountain tops.

The central Lake District with its mountains, lakes and woods is so well known and loved that there is a tendency to forget that the rest of Cumbria contains some of the most varied and attractive landscape in Britain. In the East of the county, the lovely peaceful **Eden Valley** is sheltered by the towering hills of the Pennines, and everywhere are dotted charming little red sandstone villages. **Alston**, with its cobbled streets is the highest town in England, and has been used for numerous TV location sets.

Cumbria's long coastline is itself full of variety. There are rocky cliffs with myriad sea birds, sandy estuaries, miles of sun-trapping sand dunes and friendly harbours, and everywhere something interesting to see, from reminders of the Roman occupation to the **Flookburgh** shrimp fishermen who go fishing not in boats, but on tractors!

Wherever you choose to stay in Cumbria, you will not be far away from beautiful scenery and there is a wide choice of accommodation from gracious country house hotels to country inns and bed & breakfasts.

Don't think that Summer is the only time when Cumbria is beautiful. In Autumn the deciduous woodlands and bracken coloured hillsides glow with colour. In Winter, the snow covered mountain tops stand out in dazzling magnificence against blue skies. In Spring, you can discover the delights of the magical, constantly changing light and the joy of finding carpets of wild flowers. This is really the best time of the year to go walking or climbing - spending each day in the fresh air, to return in the evening with a healthy appetite to enjoy a delicious Cumbrian meal by the fireside in a cosy pub or friendly hotel.

Cartmel

Elterwater

There are many holidays in **Lakeland** which offer both activity and instruction in a range of sports - walking, climbing, orienteering, potholing, cycling, riding, golf, sailing, sailboarding, canoeing, fishing and water-skiing. Although beware - **Lake Windermere** has just banned any boat faster than 30 knots.

A good way to take in the beauty of this unique area is to plan your own personal route on foot or cycle. The **Cumbria Cycle Way**, designed to avoid all the cyclist's problems like main roads and precipitate inclines, takes a circular route 250 miles long around this beautiful county. There are also good cheap public transport services, and where the big coaches cannot go, Mountain Goat minibuses run, even over the steepest mountain passes.

For a change from the great outdoors, there is a wealth of historic houses to visit, including a uniquely constructed thatched farmhouse, stately homes that have seen centuries of gracious living and the small cottages

where famous writers have lived without having their style cramped. Other houses are important because of their architecture, like the round house in **Belle Isle** or majestic **Hutton-in-the-Forest**, which has a central tower dating from the 14th century, surrounded by later additions.

The Cumbrian climate is ideal for gardens and the area is famous for the rhododendrons and azaleas which grow in abundance.

You will find out more about the secrets of this ancient kingdom by watching, or even joining in, some of its old customs, some of which are unique to Cumbria. There are many traditional agricultural shows displaying the essence of the English countryside - spiced in Cumbria with local specialities like hound trailing, which is like hunting but without the fox – which has now become the law in the whole of the UK - and fell races: crazy lung-bursting ascents of the nearest hill, followed by a bone bruising descent.

Ad	Advantage Card accepted
◎	archery
⇥	baby listening service
⊘	badminton court
⚓	beach
⫻	beauty salon
⚔	billiards/snooker
⚑	birdwatching
⚓	boating
⦿	boules, pétanque
⚘	civil wedding licence
⚠	childrens play area
⚶	children welcome
⚲	climbing
⚏	conferences/meeting rms (no)
⚐	croquet
♿	disabled rooms available
⚄	family room
⊙	fax/modem points
⚲	fishing
⏂	fitness centre/gym
⌂	four poster
✿	gardens
⛳/⛳	golf course
⛑	helicopter landing pad
⚴	indoor games room
⚲	indoor swimming pool
⚳	jacuzzi
⊞	lift
⛉	minibar
⚞	non-smoker rooms avail.
⚮	outdoor swimming pool
P	parking (no)
♀	parkland setting
⚲	pets welcome (+ fee)
⚲	pets not allowed
⚲	private cinema
⚲	putting green/pitch n putt
∪	riding
⚲	running track
⚲	safety deposit box
△	sailing
⚲	sauna
⚲	shooting
⚲	shower only
⚲	solarium
⚲	squash
⚲	stalking
⚲	stately home/hotel
⚲	tennis
⚲	24-hr room service
⚲	walks
⚲	waterski-ing
⚲	watersports

174

 Historic Houses Gardens and Parks

Liverpool and Manchester

Bluecoats Arts Centre, Liverpool
Bramall Hall, Bramhall,
  Greater Manchester
Croxteth Hall & Country Park,
  Nr Liverpool
Dunham Massey,
  Altrincham, Gter Manchester
Fletcher Moss Botanical Gardens,
  Manchester
Heaton Hall, Middleton,
  Greater Manchester
Knowsley Safari Park,
  Prescot, Liverpool
Platt Hall, Manchester
Speke Hall, Liverpool
Werneth Lowe Country Park,
  Hyde, Greater Manchester

 Attractions

Alexandra Craft Centre,
  Saddleworth
Barton (Victorian) Arcade,
  Manchester
The Beatles Story,
  Albert Dock, Liverpool
Castlefield Urban Heritage Park,
  Manchester
Granada Studio Tours, Manchester
Imperial War Museum North,
  Trafford Park, Greater Manchester
Liverpool Cathedral
Liverpool Metropolitan Cathedral
  of Christ the King (RC)
Liverpool Museum
  & Walker Art Gallery
The Lowry Gallery, Manchester
Manchester Cathedral
Manchester City Art Gallery
Manchester Museum
Manchester Museum of Science
  & Industry
Manchester United Football
  Museum
Merseyside Maritime Museum
Museum of Liverpool Life,
  Albert Dock
Pilkington Glass Museum,
  St Helens
Roman Fort,
  Liverpool Rd, Manchester
The Tate Gallery at Albert Dock,
  Liverpool

Albert Dock, Liverpool

Lowry Gallery, Manchester

Manchester Science & Technology Museum

Liverpool was an important city long before The Beatles emerged from their Cavern in the Swinging Sixties. It grew from a village into a prosperous port, an entrepot where emigrants sailed for the New World and immigrants arrived from Ireland.

Today the ocean going liners are fewer, but the new dock complex ensures that the city is as vibrant as ever. Liverpool's waterfront regeneration is led by the **Albert Dock Village**, which includes the **Maritime Museum** and **Tate Gallery Liverpool**. The city has two modern cathedrals, a symphony orchestra, eight museums and Britain's oldest repertory theatre The Playhouse. It has two commercial radio stations and the popular TV programmes *The Liver Birds, On the Waterfront* and *Brookside* were made here. Liverpool has seen the opening of several contemporary hotels and it has over 100 cafes and restaurants with many *gastronomes* making the short trip to **Chinatown** to sample the culinary delights of that area.

Manchester's prosperity can be traced back to the 14th century when Flemish weavers arrived to transform a market town into a thriving boom city at the forefront of the Industrial Revolution. It is now known as *The Capital of the North* and is a great centre of learning and culture as well as of economic success. The city that spawned 20 Nobel Prize Winners and where Rutherford worked on splitting the atom has not been resting on its laurels. It is rich in galleries, museums, libraries and theatres. The **City Art Gallery** displays its famous pre-Raphaelite collection while the **Halle Orchestra** regularly fills the **Bridgewater Hall**. At **Granada Studios** Coronation Street's *Rovers Return Pub* can be seen. The city boasts a booming 24 x 7 economy, has high quality shopping and sporting (particularly football) traditions and is within an hour's drive of the Peak District and Lake District National Parks. It too has spawned a family of boutique hotels.

Broxton Hall Hotel & Restaurant
Whitchurch Road, Broxton, Chester, Cheshire CH3 9JS
T (0870) 418 8130 F (01829) 782330 E reservations@broxtonhall.co.uk
T (International) +44 [0] (1829) 782321 W www.broxtonhall.co.uk

175

Whilst you are receiving a warm welcome from owners Angela and John Ireland, you will appreciate the atmosphere of this elegant family run hotel. You will immediately feel relaxed and at home in this fine example of a Cheshire half-timbered house with its fascinating antiques and artefacts, superb fireplaces and staircase, oak-panelled walls and elegant furniture. The award-winning restaurant serves international cuisine, including game in season and freshly caught fish, with a lightness of touch and delicacy of flavour. Breakfast is served in the sunny Garden Room. Broxton Hall is an ideal centre for exploring Cheshire and the surrounding countryside. Chester and Bangor races are within easy reach, as is the motor racing circuit at Oulton Park. The gardens of Cholmondeley Castle and Erdigg House are nearby and, for enthusiastic walkers, both the North Wales border and the Sandstone Trail are close at hand. There are also numerous local golf courses. The hotel is licensed for civil weddings and the house and pretty 5-acre garden are an ideal backdrop for these special occasions. There is even a helicopter pad!

10 (inc 1 suite) 🌸 ☺ (+WIFI) 🐟 ♨ 40 🅿 36 🐾

Elegant half-timbered house in the heart of Cheshire countryside

Rates Single room with breakfast from £75; double from £85.
Meals 3-cse tdh dinner (2 RAC Blue Ribbon Dining Awards) £32; lunch & spec. diets available; last orders 2130.
Leisure Breaks 3 nights b & b for price of 2 - from £171 per room.

Directions
A41 Chester-Whitchurch Rd, pass over A534 X-rds and hotel 200 yds on left.
Nearby attractions
Tatton Park, Beeston Castle, Erdigg House, Cholmondeley Castle, Stretton Mill
Distances
M6 (J16) 20, Chester 12, London 197

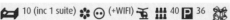
& all major cards accepted. Open all year.

Cheshire, Nr Chester

176

Lovelady Shield Country House Hotel
Nenthead Road, Nr. Alston, Cumbria CA9 3LF
T (0870) 418 8132 F (01434) 381515 E enquiries@lovelady.co.uk
T (International) +44 [0] (1434) 381203 W www.lovelady.co.uk

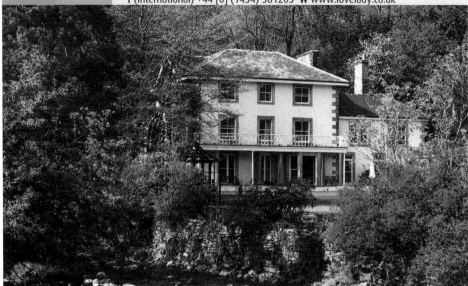

Lovelady Shield. The name conjures up an image of the peace and tranquillity that you will certainly find in this gracious country house hotel. Set beside a river in a wooded valley high in the Pennines, just $2^1/_4$ miles from Alston (England's highest market town), this quiet retreat is an ideal situation for exploring the border country, the Lake District, Hadrian's Wall and the Yorkshire Dales. Only 35 minutes from the Penrith exit of the M6, via the dramatic A686 - one of the world's top drives - it is a very pleasant stopover. The owners, Mr & Mrs Haynes, together with their friendly staff, are maintaining the hotel's tradition of warm hospitality and service. The new rooms in the extension have every comfort and amenity: DVD/CD players, power showers in the bathrooms and squishy duvets. Chef Barrie Garton produces imaginative and beautifully presented meals and has been awarded an AA rosette for his cooking. Service in the pretty dining room is discreet and attentive. The hotel is well furnished and welcoming, with log fires. A very peaceful spot.

Romantic Cumbrian hideaway where the loudest noise is the running stream

Directions From Alston take A689 Crook Rd; just before Nenthead take B6294 signed Hexham. Hotel on right.
Nearby attractions Hadrians Wall, Killhope Mining Centre, Weardale Museum, Whitley Castle.
Distances Penrith 20, Carlisle 31, London 300

Rates Single room with breakfast from £85; double from £170.
Meals Tdh ☺ dinner £37.50; bar lunches & spec. diets available; last orders 2030.
Leisure Breaks November-March, midweek, dinner, b & b from £140 per night for two people; weekend from £160 per person.
Other Activities Shooting, golf, riding nearby

 & all major cards accepted. Open all year.

Cumbria, Alston

Ees Wyke Country House

Near Sawrey, Hawkshead, Ambleside, Cumbria LA22 0JZ

T (0870) 418 8140 E mail@eeswyke.co.uk
T (International) +44 [0] (15394) 36393 W www.eeswyke.co.uk

177

Ees Wyke lies above the still waters of Esthwaite, overlooking the beautiful scenic forest and fells of one of the least spoiled parts of the Lake District. Wordsworth described it as *"That sweet valley; when its paths, its shores and its brooks were like a dream of novelty"* It was once the holiday house of Beatrix Potter, who made the village her home. You are assured of a good welcome in the comfort of this house, which is surrounded by mature gardens ablaze with rich colour throughout the year. Dinner is served in the dining room (*pictured*) and will be an experience to remember. It might start with *roasted pepper tartlet with red onion, aubergine, garlic, thyme, rosemary and goat's cheese*, move on to *noisettes of local lamb pan fried and served with a wine jus* and finish with one of their celebrated desserts like *strawberry and plum crumble with orange and pine nuts*. Most bedrooms have sweeping views of the surrounding hills as well as every modern convenience. There is fishing, sailing, riding and walking nearby or you can visit Hill Top - the nearby home of Beatrix Potter. Either way you will not forget your stay at Ees Wyke.

🛏 8 ⌗ 🕭 🐾 (by arr't- no charge)

Manor house overlooking Esthwaite, once the holiday home of Beatrix Potter

Rates Dinner, bed & breakfast from £79 (single)/£158-178 double.
Leisure Breaks Winter Breaks - 3 or more days £79 per person per night.

Other Activities Fishing, sailing, walking, riding nearby

Mastercard, Visa & Maestro cards accepted. Open all year.

Directions From M6/Windermere, take Bowness-Hawkshead ferry B5285 Hotel past Sawrey on right side of road
Nearby attractions
Hill Top, Brantwood, Ruskin Museum Coniston, World of Beatrix Potter, Wind
Distances
Windermere 5, Ambleside 8, London 280

Cumbria, Ambleside

178

Rothay Manor Hotel
Rothay Bridge, Ambleside, Cumbria LA22 0EH
T (0870) 418 8133 **F** (015394) 33607 **E** hotel@rothaymanor.co.uk
T (International) +44 [0] (15394) 33605 **W** www.rothaymanor.co.uk

Rothay Manor is a fine venue in which to enjoy good food, wine and tranquillity.The hotel has been voted top of the list by a publication on hotel breakfasts, and the excellence of the lunches and dinners complements the sumptuous surroundings. Antiques and fresh flowers are abundant, and the feeling of warmth and well-being are everywhere. The whole ambience is orchestrated by Nigel and Stephen Nixon and their wives, and the reputation that they have gained for all round excellence is more than justifiably deserved. Children are welcome with family rooms and suites available and high chairs, cots and childrens' high tea provided. One ground floor bedroom and one suite have been adapted to be accessible for wheelchair users. It seems unnecessary to add that the surrounding mountains, lakes and the air of the Lake District, make a superb backdrop in which to enjoy your stay here. In Winter the hotel organises holidays on such themes as music, antiques, Lake District heritage and bridge. Rothay Manor won the Small Hotel of the Year Award 2006 in the *Cumbria for Excellence* awards.

Listed Regency manor ¹/₄ mile from Lake Windermere and Ambleside town

19 (inc 2) 22 [Ad]

Directions
On north side of A593 Ambleside-Coniston road at Rothay Bridge.

Nearby attractions
Rydal Mount, Dove Cottage, Ruskin Mus Coniston, World of Beatrix Potter.

Distances
Windermere 5, Kendal 13, London 280

Rates Double/twin room with breakfast from £160 for two people; dinner, b & b from £210. **Meals** Last orders 2100; spec. diets available.
Leisure Breaks Two-night weekend breaks from £310 b & b or £440 dinner, b & b for two people sharing for two nights. 3-night midweek break £405 b&b/£585 dinner, b&b 2 people sharing, 2 nts. Extra discounted rates Nov-Dec. Christmas & New Year House Parties. Special Interest Holidays Oct-May.
Other Activities Free use of nearby leisure centre, tennis and fishing (free permits), sailing, boating nearby.
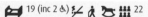 & all major credit cards accepted. Open all year exc. 3-26 January.

Cumbria, Ambleside

Appleby Manor Country House Hotel & Leisure Club

Roman Road, Appleby-in-Westmoreland, Cumbria CA16 6JB

T (0870) 418 8134 **F** (017683) 52888 **E** reception@applebymanor.co.uk
T (International) +44 [0] (17683) 51571 **W** www.applebymanor.co.uk

179

Appleby Manor stands high in the Pennines, commanding views of the historic little town, its romantic castle and the sweeping countryside and fells beyond. Within you will find relaxing and friendly courtesy, and most attractive and spacious public rooms. Facing south, the house gives shelter to its sunny gardens onto which some of the delightful rooms in the new wing have direct access. The spotlessly clean bedrooms are comfortable and furnished in keeping with the period of the house. The popular AA ◎◎ restaurant offers an international and imaginative selection of tasty dishes. The wine list offers a selection of wines from 20 countries and the bar stocks over seventy single-malt whiskies. There is a gym and pool to work off those extra calories and plenty to see and do locally, with walks to suit all abilities. Appleby is ideally situated for touring the scenic Lake District, and the Borders, Hadrian's Wall, the Roman Camps, the High Pennines and the Yorkshire Dales are all within easy motoring distance.

🛏 30 (inc 10 grd fl & 5 ⌗) 🕐 🛎 🎿 🐴 🚲 ♨♨♨ 30

Rates Per person start at £60 for bed & breakfast; £75 for dinner, bed & breakfast; weekly rates from £432, dinner, b & b.
Meals See above. Last orders 2100; spec. diets available.
Leisure Breaks Min two nights from £68 per person pppn. Also the "Cloud Nine Experience" from £175 pppn and "Hangover Breaks" from £168 inc,dbb
Other Activities Jacuzzi, sauna, solarium, leisure centre, squash, golf nearby; riding 13 miles.

▨ & major credit cards accepted. Open all year exc. 3 days at Xmas.

Comfortable hotel and leisure club in historic town in the High Pennines.

Directions
Leave A66 Scotch Cnr-Penrith rd town bypass at southern end. Hotel on rt.
Nearby attractions
Appleby Castle & Conservation Centre, Dalemain-Penrith, Crosby Ravensworth.
Distances
Penrith 13, Kendal 25, London 272.

Cumbria, Appleby-in-Westmoreland

180

Armathwaite Hall Hotel

Bassenthwaite Lake, Keswick, Cumbria CA12 4RE

T (0870) 418 8135 F (017687) 76220 E reservations@armathwaite-hall.com
T (International) +44 [0] (17687) 76551 W www.armathwaite-hall.com

Few hotels are as beautifully situated as Armathwaite Hall - one of the original stately homes of England, set magnificently in 400 acres of deerpark and woodland, bordered by the beauty of Bassenthwaite Lake and framed by the dramatic vista of Skiddaw Mountain and the surrounding fells. The Graves family, who have owned and run Armathwaite Hall for thirty years, know exactly how to pamper their guests. Cuisine is under the supervision of Masterchef Kevin Dowling. Style is traditional English, with Cumbrian specialities and using local produce, but with a light touch. This is just a prelude to all the activities available. Discreetly hidden is the 'Spa' Leisure Club with indoor pool, gymnasium, holistic beauty salon and in the grounds is Trotters World of Animals with exotic and rare animals and a Birds of Prey Centre. Armathwaite Hall is also the perfect base from which to enjoy and discover the beauties of the Lake District.

Stately home hotel in 400 acres of parkland with most leisure activities available

Directions
Leave A591 Keswick-Carlisle Rd at Kilnhill B5291 twds Cockermth. Hotel on rt
Nearby attractions
Trotters World of Animals, Wordsworth House & Printing House Mus Cockermouth
Distances
Cockermouth 7, Keswick 7, London 295.

Rates Single room with breakfast from £100; double from £210.
Meals 6-cse tdh dinner £41.95; lunch & spec. diets avail; last orders 2115.
Leisure Breaks Easter, Christmas/New Year, Bank Holiday and other packages available. Details on request.
Other Activities Falconry, wildlife park. Golf nearby.

 Mastercard, Visa & Diners cards accepted. Open all year.

Cumbria, Bassenthwaite Lake

Rothay Garden Hotel

Broadgate, Grasmere, Ambleside, Cumbria LA22 9RJ

T (0870) 418 8154 F (015394) 35723 E stay@rothay-garden.com
T (International) +44 [0] (15394) 35334 W www.rothay-garden.com

Situated on the outskirts of picturesque Grasmere village, and nestling in two acres of riverside gardens surrounded by majestic fells, this elegant proprietor operated hotel is surely the perfect choice for a relaxing Lakeland break. The elegant AA ☺☺ contemporarily designed Conservatory Restaurant, overlooking the gardens, is a superb setting in which to enjoy the renowned five-course candlelit dinner, complemented by the 140-bin wine list. There are three grades of bedroom to suit every taste, with all the modern facilities expected by today's discerning guest. Ground floor rooms and four-poster bedrooms with whirlpool baths are also available. Higher grade bedrooms enjoy complimentary mineral water and chocolates. New for 2007 is the Loft Suite. Situated on the second floor, this is a particularly elegant room with king size bed, air conditioning, two TVs, designer bathroom and luxury toiletries. There are two very comfortable lounges in which to relax. All this, together with the hotel's friendly and professional service, ensures a memorable Lakeland holiday.

🛏 20 (inc 1 🛏 & 1 suite) 🚶 🗶 🐾 (£15 fee per stay)

Rates Single room with breakfast from £55; double from £110.
Meals Tdh lunch £14.95/dinner £31; spec. diets avail; last orders 2100.
Leisure Breaks Summer Savers - 4+ nights = £10 off per person; 7 days+£15 off pers. Winter Midweek Breaks - 4 nights from £219 per person, dinner, b & b, two sharing. Weekend Breaks - stay Fri & Sat nts d, b & b and enjoy complimentary Sunday lunch.
Other Activities Complimentary leisure centre, indoor pool, gym, sauna 5m. Golf, riding, tennis, watersports, sailing nearby.
Major credit cards accepted. Open all year.

Charming hotel on the river Rothay with some striking ground floor rooms

Directions
From North - Penrith/M6 take A591 and fst rt into Grasmere Centre; hotel on left.
Nearby attractions
Dove Cottage & Wordsworth Museum, Rydal Mount & Gardens, Hill Top.
Distances
Keswick 13, Kendal 17, London 271.

Cumbria, Grasmere

182

The Borrowdale Gates Country House Hotel
Grange-in-Borrowdale, Keswick, Cumbria CA12 5UQ
T (0870) 860 8441 F (01768) 777254 E hotel@borrowdalegates.com
T (International) +44 [0] (1768) 777204 W www.borrowdalegates.com

Originally a private residence situated on the edge of the historic hamlet of Grange, Borrowdale Gates maintains the lovely homely atmosphere of a genuine country house, where the cares of the world just ebb away. Location is sublime. Set in two acres of wooded gardens, with a backdrop of high, rising fells, close to the shores of Derwentwater, the hotel offers seclusion without remoteness. The hotel aspect is perfect, providing panoramic views of the dramatic Lakeland scenery. AA rosetted cuisine, an outstanding wine list and personal service result in a very memorable guest experience. The lounges are an ideal place to read, chat or take tea, maybe sampling the hotel's home made cakes. Bedrooms, ten of which are on the ground floor, have every amenity and are wonderful to retire to after a day's invigorating walking or sightseeing. Most have views of either the Borrowdale Valley or of the Fells. Guests can also relax in the gardens with views of the impressive Castle Crag, Jaws of Borrowdale and with majestic Lake District scenery all around.

Secluded hotel set in breathtaking location under Derwent Fells

🛏 27 ✿ ♿ ✂ 🐴 ⋮⋮ 30 🅿 60

Directions
Fm Keswick take B5289 signed Borrowdale After 4m trn rt for Grange, hotel ¹/₄m on rt
Nearby attractions
Derwentwater Cruises, Lodore Falls, Bowder Stone, Newlands Valley.
Distances
Keswick 4, Penrith 22, London 289.

Rates Single room with breakfast from £65; double from £114.   Ad
Meals 5-cse tdh dinner £34.50; alc, lunch & spec. diets avail; last orders 2045; bfst fm 0800.
Leisure Breaks Winter Bargain Breaks available - 'Excuses to Escape' - 4-day Christmas Break, 3-day 'In-Between Break', 3-day New Year Break. Pleaseask fo full details.
Other Activities Fishing, golf, river bathing, riding, sailing nearby. & major credit cards accepted. Open all year.

Cumbria, Nr. Keswick

Derwentwater Hotel

183

Portinscale, Nr. Keswick, Cumbria CA12 5RE

T (0870) 418 8119 **F** (017687) 71002 **E** info@derwentwater-hotel.co.uk
T (International) +44 [0] (17687) 72538 **W** www.derwentwater-hotel.co.uk

The epitome of a Lakeland Country House Hotel, the Derwentwater has undergone, since the mid-1980s, a substantial programme of upgrading and refurbishment. Still privately owned, it now offers guests a comfortable though unpretentious standard of accommodation. Guestrooms have every modern convenience, some having separate sitting areas. Many enjoy stunning views of the lake. The Deers Leap Restaurant serves a good selection of dishes, locally sourced where possible, home baked pastries and breads, locally matured cheeses, freshly made soups and sauces being featured. The hotel sits in 16 acres of grounds, much of which is dedicated to the preservation of local wildlife. The owners have worked alongside English Nature to enhance a protracted area of wetland, a natural habitat for birds, mammals and deer. In the same grounds is Derwent Manor, a selection of one and two-bedroomed self-catering apartments; also Glaramara Cottage. Both hotel and manor guests can take advantage of the Oxley's Heath Spa at Underscar, some two miles away.

🛏 46 ♿ 🔍 🐕 🔟 🍴 🍽 ⚲ ⛏ 12 🅿 50

Tranquil haven on the lakeshore in 16 acres of conservation grounds

Rates Single room with breakfast from £90; double room from £150.
Meals 4-cse tdh dinner £27.50; bar meals & spec. diets available; last orders 2100
Leisure Breaks Stays of two nights+ from £52.50 per person per night dinner, b & b inc cream tea on arrival & liqueur with coffee after dinner ea nt
Other Activities Golf, fitness studio, indoor pool,massage, sauna, jacuzzi 2m.

& all major credit cards accepted. Open all year.

Directions A66 Keswick by-pass twds Cockermouth, left to Portinscale, then left again after Farmers Arms PH to hotel
Nearby attractions Lodore Falls, Keswick Museum, Castlerigg Stone Circle, Sourmilk Waterfall
Distances Keswick 1, Cockermouth 13, London 291

Cumbria, Nr. Keswick

184

The Lodore Falls Hotel
Borrowdale, Nr. Keswick, Cumbria CA12 5UX
T (0870) 418 8150 F (017687) 77343 E lodorefalls@lakedistricthotels.net
T (International) +44 [0] (17687) 77285 W www.lakedistricthotels.net/lodorefalls

Recently refurbished, this imposing 200-year old hotel holds a commanding presence in the Borrowdale valley. Standing in 40 acre grounds with lake frontage and the dramatic backdrop of the spectacular Lodore Falls and surrounding mountains, this hotel has one of the finest settings in the Lake District with access to some of the most impressive walks in the area directly from the front door. Bedrooms overlook either lake or fell and offer all modern facilities including Sky TV, playstation and Internet access. Family room and suites are also available. 2006 saw the opening of a brand new health spa where guests can enjoy a wide range of treatments from the practical and functional to the ultimate in pampering. Treatments include a choice of massages, facials, tanning, waxing, manicures, pedicures, anti-ageing, sunbed, bridal and eye treatments. Excellent leisure facilities include tennis, squash, indoor and outdoor swimming pools, beauty treatments, childrens play area and free midweek golf at nearby Keswick Golf Club.

Imposing hotel overlooking Derwent-water -'The Queen of English Lakes'

70 (inc 3 suites) 🛏️ ⚃ ☂ ⚘ 🅰 🖨️ 🍴 ♿ 🏠 ⚓ ☎ 🐕 (£10 fee) 👥 200 🅿 80 🚲

Directions
M6 Junc 40, then A66 to Keswick; then B5289 twds Grange; hotel on left.

Nearby attractions
Lodore Falls, Keswick Mus, Castlerigg Stone Circle, Trotters World of Animals.

Distances
Keswick 3, Penrith 23, London 285.

Rates Single room with breakfast from £81; double room from £138. [Ad]
Meals 4-cse tdh dinner £32.95; lunch & diets avail; last orders 2100; bfst fm 0700.
Leisure Breaks 2,3,4,5,& 7 night special offers available all year. Separate brochure available on request.
Other Activities Fishing, watersports from hotel land; free midweek golf at Keswick; clay shooting, riding nearby.
& all major credit cards accepted. Open all year.

Cumbria, Nr. Keswick

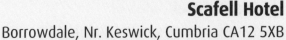

Scafell Hotel
Borrowdale, Nr. Keswick, Cumbria CA12 5XB

T (0870) 418 8141   F (017687) 77280   E info@scafell.co.uk
T (International) +44 [0] (17687) 77208   W www.scafell.co.uk

It is not surprising that the Scafell has become one of Lakeland's leading hotels following its recent improvements and the consistent efforts of its management. Situated almost at the head of the beautiful Borrowdale Valley, its position is as outstanding as the service and comfort which it provides for all its guests. There is an excellent table d'hôte menu and, for those wishing to dine later, a comprehensive à la carte grill menu. Both menus are accompanied by a well balanced wine list. Year after year guests return to walk and climb in this area of the Lake District for they know that they are going to be comfortable and well looked after. For the less energetic, there are cosy and homely lounges. The en suite bedrooms are comfortable and attractively furnished. Pleasant views are to be had of the sheltered garden ringed by mighty mountains on which internationally famous climbers have learned their craft. Yes, this is a home from home for the visitor seeking peace or exercise and wishing to 'get away from it all'.

24 (inc 8 grd fl)

Pleasant family hotel just south of Derwent Water, near Lodore Falls

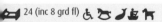

Rates Room with breakfast from £48.50; dinner, room & breakfast from £72.50.
Meals See above; bar meals also available.
Leisure Breaks Available Spring, Summer & Winter. Please apply for details.
Other Activities Tennis 6m, Golf 10m.

Visa & Mastercard accepted. Open all year.

Directions
From Keswick take B5289 to southern end of lake, through Grange, hotel on left
Nearby attractions
Lodore Falls, Keswick Museum, Castlerigg Stone Circle, Sourmilk Waterfall
Distances
Keswick 6, Penrith 24, London 291.

Cumbria, Nr. Keswick

Skiddaw Hotel
Main Street, Nr. Keswick, Cumbria CA12 5BN
T (0870) 860 8439 F (017687) 74850 E skiddawhotel@lakedistricthotels.net
T (International) +44 [0] (17687) 72071 W www.lakedistricthotels.net

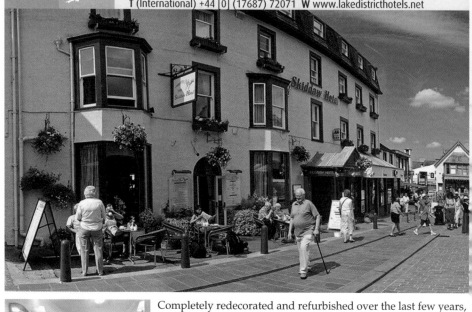

Completely redecorated and refurbished over the last few years, the Skiddaw Hotel must be the most centrally placed hotel of note in the Lake District. It is the hub of the town. Locals gather here, holiday makers meet here and walkers, climbers, naturalists, artists and poets have always, and still do, use it as a base. The hotel's restaurant *31 The Square* offers delicious table d'hôte and à la carte menus, using local fresh meats, game, fish and vegetables prepared by the Head Chef and his team. To round off, a wide selection of cheeses is on offer, including the hotel's own *Skiddaw Damson Cheese*, custom made for the hotel. All the hotel's 40 bedrooms offer a high standard of comfort. The Summit rooms, a little bit more, with towelling robes, mineral water, and deluxe toiletries. Guests are welcome to use the leisure facilities at the Skiddaw's sister hotel. Discounted golf can be played weekdays at the nearby Keswick Golf Club. Conference facilities are available, making the Skiddaw an equally good base for the business traveller.

Town centre hotel in the middle of the Lake District

🛏 40 🍴 ☺ ♟ 👥 90 🐾

Directions
From North A66 Keswick, A5271 tn ctre, flw signs Derwentwater/pay & display🅿

Nearby attractions
Derwentwater Lake, Theatre by the Lake, Pencil Museum, Thirlmere Stone

Distances
M6 j40 - 17, Carlisle 31, London 294

Rates Single room with breakfast from £62; double room from £116. 📧
Meals 4-cse tdh dinner 31 The Square £20.95; lunch & spec. diets available; last orders 2130; bfst fm 0800.
Leisure Breaks Full range of seasonal offers always available. Call now or see website for details.
Other Activities Golf, fishing, watersports, sailing, shooting, tennis, riding nearby

 & all major credit cards accepted. Open all year.

George Hotel

Devonshire Street, Penrith, Cumbria CA11 7SU
T (0870) 860 8440 **F** (01768) 868223 **E** georgehotel@lakedsitricthotels.net
T (International) +44 [0] (1768) 862696 **W** www.lakedistricthotels.net/georgehotel

187

Situated in the centre of the town, the George is the epitome of an old Coaching Inn. Here the townsfolk have met for years to gather the *crack* over a drink, to enjoy a simple meal or to dine more formally in the splendid dining room. Chef makes extensive use of local produce, including Ullswater Trout, Herdwick Lamb, Angus Beef and Cumbrian cheeses and cream, plus many seasonal items. There is a choice of brasserie or à la carte menus. The public rooms are sympathetically and most comfortably furnished and a magnificent staircase leads up to the fine bedrooms. Over the past few years the hotel has been refurbished and it should be first choice for anyone looking for accommodation in this area, whether on business in the town or as a complete holiday base. For that special occasion you might treat yourself to one of the Executive Rooms or suites, or even the four-poster. These come with towelling robes and other little extras. There are several golf courses nearby and recommended local walking routes include the Coast to Coast Path, Lady Anne's Way, Gowbarrow Fell and Pooley Bridge.

 32 (inc 2 🛏) ⚫⊙↩♀ **P** 53 👥 120 🐕

Town centre hotel in historic building

Rates Single room with breakfast from £65; double from £102.

Meals 3-cse alc £23; lunch, bar meals & diets available. Last orders 2130; bfst from 0700.

Leisure Breaks Wide range of seasonal breaks available. Call for colour brochure or see website for details.

Other Activities Fishing, golf, watersports, clay shooting, indoor pool, tennis, riding nearby.

 & major credit cards accepted. Open all year.

Directions M6 exit 40, take A592 to Penrith. Go 1^1/₂ m thru one-way system, left into Burrowgate, hotel 🅿 100 yds on rt

Nearby attractions
Lowther Country Park, Rheged, Ullswater Steamers, Brougham Castle

Distances
Carlisle 24, Kendal 31, London 290

The Inn on the Lake Hotel

188

Glenridding, Lake Ullswater, Penrith, Cumbria CA11 0PE
T (0870) 418 8152 **F** (01768) 482303 **E** innonthelake@lakedistricthotels.net
T (International) +44 [0] (1768) 482444 **W** www.lakedistricthotels.net/innonthelake

This imposing building, one of the few purpose built hotels in the Lake District, stands in 15 acres of gardens sweeping down to the shore of Ullswater. Family owned and run, the hotel offers a wide range of excellent facilities as well as stunning views of the surrounding scenery. Comfortable lounges provide a calm environment in which to relax with a drink, whilst dinner can be enjoyed in the Lake View Restaurant, or a snack and real ale in the hotel's own pub. Most of the 46 en suite bedrooms look across to the lake or the fells and five lake view four poster rooms add an extra touch of luxury. The hotel welcomes wedding ceremonies and receptions and can provide conference facilities for up to 120 delegates. Watersports can be enjoyed from the hotel's jetties and croquet, putting, bowls and 9-hole pitch & putt in the grounds. The hotel's lesiure suite offers gym, jacuzzi and sauna. Trips round the lake can be taken aboard the Ullswater steamers and many of the most stunning Lake District walks begin from the hotel.

Imposing hotel in 15 acres of grounds on the shores of Ullswater

46 💤 ⚒ ♿ ☺ 🐕 (£5 fee) 🍴 🍷 ⚗ 🚭 🏊 ♨ 🧖 ⛰ 🎾 120 🅿 170 💻 🛶

Directions
Fm Junc 40 M6 take A592 twds Windermere. Hotel near bottom end of lake.

Nearby attractions
Dalemain House & Ashkam, Rydal Mt & Dove Cottage, Trotters World of Animals

Distances
Penrith 12, Windermere 14, London 298

Rates Single room with breakfast from £75; double from £134. [Ad]
Meals 4-cse tdh dinner £32.95; lunch, alc & diets available; last orders 2100; bfst fm 0800.
Leisure Breaks 2,3,4,5 & 7 night special offers available throughout the year.
Other Activities Golf 10m.

& major credit cards accepted. Open all year.

Cumbria, Ullswater

Sharrow Bay Country House Hotel

189

Howtown, Ullswater, Penrith, Cumbria CA10 2LZ

T (0870) 418 8142 **F** (01768) 486349 **E** info@sharrowbay.co.uk
T (International) +44 [0] (1768) 486301 **W** www.sharrowbay.co.uk

Sharrow Bay was the first Country House Hotel in England and the first British *Relais et Châteaux* member. It was founded in 1948 by the late Francis Coulson and Brian Sack. Since then it has set standards for other hotels to follow. Improvements and enhancements are constantly being made. Recently Garden Rooms were opened. These consist of three luxury suites and two king size doubles, 100 metres from the hotel and all over-looking the gardens and lake. There is no reception desk when you arrive at Sharrow, but you are expected and escorted to your comfortable room. Staff are attentive but not over-intrusive when taking your dinner order. Both the lounge and intimate dining room enjoy the fabulous view. Recently a new conservatory area was added, well stocked with magazines and games, enhancing the after dinner experience. Or you can enjoy the hotel's mature gardens or walk further afield along the shores of Ullswater. For the third year running, Sharrow will be open for Christmas and New Year, with a tempting package available. Whatever time of year you visit, you will not forget your Sharrow Bay experience.

24 (inc 6 suites) 20 40

Legendary hotel in a beautiful setting on the shores of Ullswater

Rates Double/twin room from £350 inc dinner.
Leisure Breaks Christmas & New Year packages available. Pse enquire for details.
Other Activities Golf nearby.

Directions
Fm Junc 40 M6 take A592 twds Winder-mere. Left at Pooley Bridge, Hotel 3m.
Nearby attractions
Dalemain House & Askham, Nr Penrith
Rydal Mount & Dove Cott, Ambleside.
Distances
Penrith 7, Kendal 33, London 289.

Visa & Mastercard accepted. Open all year.

Cumbria, Ullswater

190

Gilpin Lodge Country House Hotel

Crook Road, Nr. Windermere, Cumbria LA23 3NE
RELAIS & CHATEAUX

T (0870) 418 8143 F (015394) 88058 E hotel@gilpinlodge.co.uk
T (International) +44 [0] (15394) 88818 W www.gilpinlodge.co.uk

Six new suites have individual gardens and outdoor hot tubs at this friendly, unpretentious luxury hotel near Lake Windermere. *Crinkle Cragg, Dollywagon Pike* and *Sergeant Man* are some of the names of the luxurious new Garden Suites. Other rooms have names such as *Kentmere, Buttermere* and *Troutbeck*. All bedrooms have crisp, white linen, exquisite fabrics, wonderful upholstery and delicious art on the walls. Meticulously run by the Cunliffe family and a team of dedicated and long serving staff whose experience shows in every corner, Gilpin Lodge is set in 20 tranquil acres of woodland, moor and country garden. Just 12 miles from the M6 and almost opposite Windermere Golf Course (*"the miniature Gleneagles"*), this Relais & Châteaux hotel is at the heart of the Lake District's wealth of sightseeing, history and activities. There are no conferences, business meetings, weddings or young children at the hotel, simply the promise of extreme luxury and, at the end of each day's exploration, exquisite food and wine in the Michelin starred restaurant. This is the art of relaxation - perfected.

Family run small hotel in the matchless surroundings of the Lake District

🛏 20 ⚔ ↻ ♞₁₈ 🅿 40

Directions
M6 J 36, then A590/591 twds Windermere, then B5284 through Crook. Hotel on right

Nearby attractions
Sizergh Castle; Levens Hall, Abbot Hall Art Gallery/Arts & Crafts Hse, Kendal.

Distances
Kendal 8, Windermere 4, London 246.

Rates Single room with breakfast and 5-cse dinner from £175; double from £250. **Meals** Tdh dinner £45; alc & tdh lunch Mon-Sat; tdh Sunday luncheon £32; spec. diets available; last orders 2115.

Leisure Breaks Special 3-night *'Great Little Escapes'* from £300 per person, dinner, b & b. 3 night Golf Breaks inc. half board + two games of golf at Windermere from £375 per person. Special Christmas/New Year arrangements.

Other Activities Fitness centre, gym, fishing, jacuzzi, watersports, sauna, sailing, indoor pool, tennis, riding all nearby.
& major credit cards accepted. Open all year.

Cumbria, Windermere

Lindeth Howe Country House Hotel

Lindeth Drive, Longtail Hill, Bowness, Cumbria LA23 3JF

T (0870) 418 8155 **F** (015394) 46368 **E** hotel@lindeth-howe.co.uk
T (International) +44 [0] (15394) 45759 **W** www.lindeth-howe.co.uk

191

Lindeth Howe is a quiet gem of a property formerly owned by Beatrix Potter, who illustrated *Timmy Tiptoes* and *Pigling Bland* whilst staying there. Set in its own private grounds with views to the lake and the fells beyond, the hotel boasts comfortable bedrooms, cosy lounges, log fires, an attractive restaurant and bar, and an in-house leisure facility (for resident use only), consisting of feature pool, sauna, sunbed and fitness room. Dinner is a highlight of the day, starting with canapes and drinks in the lounge while guests choose from a seasonal menu with plenty of choice to suit all tastes. Our chef sources local ingredients wherever possible and the food is complimented by a value for money wine list. You can do as much or as little as you please here. Tee times at the local golf course can be arranged, the hotel holds a number of fishing permits and a range of self-guided walks booklets, watersports and activities can be arranged and sightseeing tours via the Mountain Goat MiniCoach tours. On the other hand, guests may prefer to just sit and relax inside or in the gardens outside.

🛏 36 (inc 2 grd fl) 🚫 ♿ ☺ 🐕 🎣 🏊 🛁 🍸 ⚙ 30 🅿 50

Once the home of Beatrix Potter, comfortable hotel in 6-acre gardens

Rates Single room with breakfast from £60; double from £120.
Meals Last orders for dinner 2030-2100; lunch available; bfst from 0815.
Leisure Breaks Midweek 2,3,4 & 5 night breaks available year round exc Xmas/New year/Bank Hols. Please enquire for details.
Other Activities Golf, riding, fishing, sailing, boating, watersports nearby

Directions
M6 J36, then A590/591 to Kendal. Left onto B5284, strt on twds ferry, hotel on lft
Nearby attractions
Levens Hall, Holker Hall, Blackwell Arts & Crafts Hse, Hill Top, World of Beatrix Potter
Distances
Kendal 10, Lancaster 28, London 280

Visa, Mastercard, Switch & JCB cards accepted. Open all year.

Linthwaite House Hotel & Restaurant

192

Crook Road, Windermere, Cumbria LA23 3JA

T (0870) 418 8144 **F** (015394) 88601 **E** stay@linthwaite.com
T (International) +44 [0] (15394) 88600 **W** www.linthwaite.com

Linthwaite House is set in 14 acres of superbly kept grounds with magnificent views of Lake Windermere and of every major peak in the Lake District. There is a well stocked tarn (in which 5 lb trout have been caught) and where one can while away the day with a picnic. The golf practice area is surrounded by lovely woodland walks. Inside, the hotel is immaculate, tastefully interior designed. A feature is the use of old trunks and suitcases. The food is superb and many of the guests return to Linthwaite again and again. There is a daily changing table d'hôte menu which might start with a goat's cheese soufflé with onion purée and sun-dried tomatoes, continue after an 'intermediate' soup, with scotch beef fillet with rösti or Cornish sea bass, followed by dessert and petit fours. The AA has awarded the cuisine ◎◎ and Linthwaite is an AA Top 200 hotel. The hotel is ideally situated for walking, cycling or touring the Lake District and is close to the major heritage attractions including Beatrix Potter's Hilltop house and Wordsworth's former homes.

Peaceful hotel overlooking Lake Windermere in its own 14-acre grounds

🛏 27 (inc 7 grd fl) ⌖ ✦ ♪ 🚲 ♨ 52

Directions
M6 J36, then A590/591 past Kendal. Left onto B5284, hotel on left b4 Bowness

Nearby attractions
Hill Top, Rydal Mount & Gardens, Blackwell Arts & Crafts hse, Dove Cottage.

Distances
Kendal 7, Windermere 3, London 280

Rates Room with breakfast £145-300.
Meals 4-cse tdh dinner £46; last orders 2100; light lunches & spec. diets available; no under 7s in restaurant; childrens menu available 1800-1900.
Leisure Breaks Romantic Breaks (min two nts) including champagne on arrival, box of chocs, canopied lake view king size bed, bfst & dinner. Pse apply for details.
Other Activities Sauna, gym, massage, spa pool, golf, riding, fishing, sailing, boating, watersports 1m & all major credit cards accepted. Open all year.

Cumbria, Windermere

The Gibbon Bridge Hotel

Chipping, Forest of Bowland, Lancashire PR3 2TQ

T (0870) 860 8442 **F** (01995) 61277 **E** reception@gibbon-bridge.co.uk
T (International) +44 [0] (1995) 61456 **W** www.gibbon-bridge.co.uk

193

The Simpson family converted Gibbon Bridge from a farm into a country hotel some 25 years ago and it has now established itself as one of the finest hotels in the NorthWest of England, although it is actually situated bang at the geographical centre of Britain. The 29 guest rooms and split level suites offer a high level of comfort. Many suites have whirlpool baths, four-posters, half-testers or Gothic beds. Small wonder Gibbon Bridge has become such a popular place to tie the knot! The restaurant and conservatory, with a covered terrace for summer *al fresco* dining, uses local produce wherever possible, complemented by vegetables and fruit from the hotel's own award-winning gardens, frequently winners of *Britain in Bloom* competitions. There are meeting rooms and a small gym. Something for everybody! The hotel lies on the edge of the Forest of Bowland, an area of outstanding natural beauty, with rolling pastures and dense forestry, said to be a favourite of HM The Queen. For business or pleasure, short break or longer holiday, meeting or wedding, the Gibbon Bridge offers a superb location and comes highly recommended. A ⊘ hotel.

The jewel in the heart of the Ribble Valley

🛏 29 🍴 ♿ ☉ ✿ 🗡 🛍 🏨 🏃 ♞ 🔍 🍸 🍽 ⁝⁝⁝ 35 P 40 🎱

Rates Single with breakfast from £80; double from £120.
Meals 4-cse alc dinner fm £30; lunch & spec. diets avail; last orders 2100.
Leisure Breaks Special tariff midweek (Sun-Thurs) £75 per pers per night, dinner, b & b, based on two sharing standard accommodation.
Other Activities Golf, shooting, riding nearby.

Directions
From south exit M1 junc 31a, take B6243 thru' Longridge. Hotel on rt before Chipping
Nearby attractions
Forest of Bowland, Pendle Witches Trail, Stonyhurst Coll + Tolkien connection
Distances
Preston 10, Blackburn 12, London 240.

& all major credit cards accepted. Open all year.

The Chadwick Hotel

South Promenade, Lytham St Annes, Lancashire FY8 1NP
T (0870) 418 8151 **F** (01253) 714455 **E** sales@thechadwickhotel.com
T (International) +44 [0] (1253) 720061 **W** www.thechadwickhotel.com

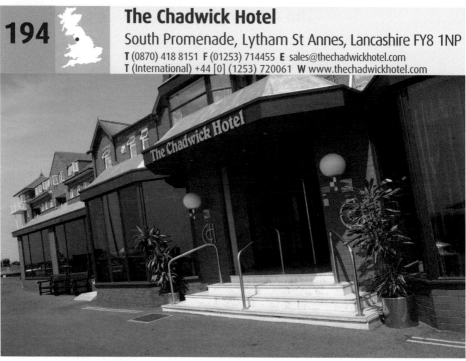

The Chadwick Hotel has been owned and run by the Corbett family since 1947 and is now with the third generation. In a wonderful sea front position overlooking the Ribble Estuary, the hotel offers ideal facilities for those looking for a leisure break, family holiday or business stopover. The lounges are bright, comfortable and have panoramic sea views; the cosy Bugatti Bar features over 100 malt whiskies and serves mouth-watering bar meals every lunchtime. The Four Seasons Restaurant serves an extensive table d'hôte menu, includung local seafood speciali- ties, traditional English cooking and international specialities. The 75 en suite bedrooms have excellent amenities including individual temperature control. Some have spa baths and others four poster beds. The Atlantis Health Centre has a state-of-the- art gym, sauna, Turkish room and indoor pool. Children are catered for with a high tea menu, a soft play adventure area, games room, baby listening service and launderette. Add to this excellent service throughout from friendly and helpful staff, and you have a very well-run operation - a hotel for all seasons.

Family owned hotel on sea front with indoor pool and spa

75 (2 &)

Directions M6 J32, then M55 to Black-pool. Take A5230 to seafront, (+ on yr lft) trn lft at sea, then rt onto South Prom

Nearby attractions
Blackpool Zoo, Illuminations, sea life c'tre, tower, amusement park, beach

Distances
Blackpool 5, Preston 14, London 224

Rates Double/twin room with breakfast from £35 per person per night.
Leisure Breaks Midwinter break, two persons sharing, £43 pp, dinner, b & b. Weekend Breaks inc. dance & banquet 2 nts £103.50 per person.
Accreditations AA★★★RAC/ETC. Tourism Awards *1999 Best Small Hotel of the Year.*
Other Facilities Internet booth. Championship golf courses, riding, sailing / boating, tennis & squash nearby. Lake district, Forst of Bowland nearby. & all major credit cards accepted. Open all year.

Lancashire, Lytham St Annes

Fact File
Illustrated Guide to
Historic Houses and Gardens,
Attractions and Walks.

Hadrian's Wall

Yorkshire & the North East

Yorkshire, Durham and Northumberland – fiercely independent counties which make up the North East. Yorkshire includes two national parks, the Dales and the North Yorks Moors, James Herriot and Last of the Summer Wine country. Northumberland's border lands have high moors, ragged cliffs, sandy beaches and offshore islands. The dynamic city of Newcastle divides it from County Durham, with its fine cathedral and castle.

Hotels guide

Northumberland	page 200
North Yorkshire	page 201

Further information:
Yorkshire Tourist Board
312 Tadcaster Road, York,
North Yorkshire YO2 2HY
Tel: 01904 707961

www.yorkshiretouristboard.net

One NorthEast
Stella House, Goldcrest Way,
Newburn Riverside,
Newcastle-upon-Tyne NE15 8NY
Tel: 01271 336 182

www.tourismnortheast.co.uk

Harrogate

Beverley Minster

Scarborough Harbour

Northumberland

Bamburgh Castle

Northumbria is an undiscovered holiday paradise, where the scenery is wild and beautiful, the beaches golden and unspoiled and the natives friendly. The region is edged by the **North Sea**, four national parks and the vast **Border Forest Park**.

Its **Eastern** sea boundary makes a stunning coastline, stretching 100 miles from **Staithes** on the Cleveland boundary, to **Berwick-on-Tweed**, England's most northerly town, frequently fought over and with the finest preserved example of Elizabethan town walls in the country. In between you'll find as many holiday opportunities as changes of scenery.

Inland there's **Hadrian's Wall**, the **National Park**, hills, forests, waterfalls, castles, splendid churches and quaint towns. Visitors can trace man's occupation of the region from prehistoric times: rock carvings, ancient hill forts, Saxon churches, Norman priories, medieval castles, through a wealth of industrial archaeology.

The region has a rich maritime heritage too. Ruins like **Dunstanburgh** or fairy-tale **Lindisfarne** are relics of a turbulent era. You can take a trip from **Seahouses** to the **Farne Islands** - a marvellous bird sanctuary and breeding ground of the Atlantic Grey Seal.

Agriculture is one of the region's most important industries. **Heatherslaw Mill** near Ford, (a delightful model village) has a restored water-driven corn mill and agricultural museum. Fans of *One Man and His Dog* can see the skills of shepherd and dog at numerous sheepdog trails and county shows in the summer.

Alnwick Castle

Newcastle and Durham

Millennium Bridge, Newcastle

Newcastle-upon-Tyne, once a shipbuilding centre, is a rejuvenated city of proud civic tradition, fine restaurants and theatres, with one of the liveliest arts scenes outside London. The **Theatre Royal** is the third home of the Royal Shakespeare Company and a venue for major touring companies. The **Metro Centre** in neighbouring **Gateshead** attracts shoppers form all over the North-East with more than 300 outlets and 11 cinema screens.

Newcastle-upon-Tyne

Durham's Norman cathedral, once a prison, soars above the plain and was the Bishops Palace from 1072 to 1837. Fine small **University and Oriental Museum**, housing a unique collection of Chinese, Indian & Egyptian Art.

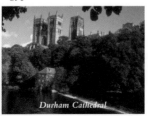
Durham Cathedral

York

The Shambles, York

No visit to the North-East would be complete without savouring the delights of **York**. Wherever you turn within the city's medieval walls, you will find fascinating glimpses of the past. These can be seen in the splendours of the 600-year old **Minster**, the grim stronghold of **Clifford's Tower**, the **National Railway Museum**, the medieval timbers of the **Merchant Adventurers' Hall** and the **Jorvik Viking Centre** which illustrates life in a 10th century Viking village. Throughout the city, statues and monuments remind the visitor that this was where Constantine was proclaimed Holy Roman Emperor, Guy Fawkes was born and Dick Turpin met his end.

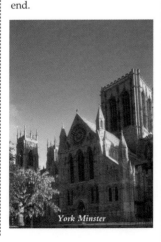
York Minster

TOP 10 Historic Houses Gardens and Parks

Assembly Rooms
Beningborough Hall
Cliffords Tower
Fairfax House
The Guildhall
Multangular Tower
Newburgh Priory
Nunnington Hall
Treasurer's House
York Minster

Micklegate, York

TOP 10 Attractions

Castle Museum
Friargate Wax Museum
Jorvik Viking Centre
Kings Manor
Museum of Automata
Museum Gardens
National Railway Museum
York City Art Gallery
York Dungeon
The York Story

TOP 10 Walks and Nature Trails

Cleveland Way.
 Helmsley to Clay Bank
Cleveland Way.
 Saltburn to Filey
Ebor Way.
 Wetherby > York > Helmsley
Forest Drive.
 Pickering to Deepdale Forest
Keld > Muker > River Swale, Yorks Dales
Lyke Wake Walk.
 Claybank to Ravenscar
Minster Way.
 York > Market Weighton >Hull
Sutton Bank Nature Trail.
 Between Helmsley & Thirsk
The Walls, York
Wolds Way. Pocklington to Filey

North Yorkshire

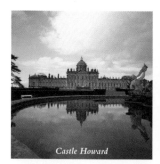

Castle Howard

So rich in history, **North Yorkshire** boasts some of the country's most splendid scenery. The **North Yorks Moors National Park** has 500 square miles of hills, dales, forests and open moorland, neatly edged by a spectacular coastline. Walking, cycling and pony trekking are ideal ways to savour the scenery; alternatively take the steam train from Pickering to Grosmont on the famous **North Yorkshire Moors Railway**.

Numerous greystone towns and villages dotted throughout the **Moors** are ideal bases from which to explore the countryside. From **Helmsley**, visit the ruins of **Reivaulx Abbey**, founded by Cistercian monks in the 12th century. In **Hutton-le-Hole**, moorland life is depicted in the **Ryedale Folk Museum**. Likewise the **Beck Isle Museum** in **Pickering** provides an insight into the life of a country market town. A few miles down the road, you'll find **Malton**, once a Roman fortress, and nearby **Castle Howard**, the setting for *Brideshead Revisited*.

From the Moors, cross the A1 for a total change of scene. Wherever you go in **The Dales**, you'll come across visible reminders of the rich and changing past. In medieval days, solid fortresses like **Richmond** and **Middleham** were built to protect the area from marauding Scots. **Knaresborough**, the home of the prophetess Mother Shipton, **Ripley** and **Skipton** all had their massive strongholds while **Bolton Castle** in **Wensleydale** once imprisoned Mary, Queen of Scots. The pattern of history is also enshrined in the great abbeys, like **Jervaulx Abbey**, near **Masham**, where the monks first made **Wensleydale** cheese, **Eastby Abbey** on the banks of the river **Swale**, and the majestic ruins of **Fountains Abbey** in the grounds of **Studley Royal**.

West, East & South Yorkshire

Mill on the River Aire

For centuries cloth has been spun from the wool of the sheep grazing in the **Pennine** uplands. The fascinating story of England's industrial heritage can now be seen in the numerous craft centres and folk museums throughout **West Yorkshire**. To enjoy the countryside, take a trip on the steam hauled **Keighley and Worth Valley Railway**.

Bronte Parsonage, Haworth

Stop off at **Haworth**, home of the Bronte sisters, and experience the rugged atmosphere of Wuthering Heights. Not far from Haworth is **Bingley**, where the Leeds & Liverpool canal makes its famous uphill journey. In the past, coal barges came this way; nowadays holiday makers in gaily painted boats have taken their place. **Leeds** itself is now a vibrant city with its Victorian shopping arcades, Royal Armouries Museum, Corn Exchange and lively arts scene.

Moving into the **East Riding**, the scenery changes again. From the dramatic 400ft high cliffs at **Flamborough Head**, there sweeps south a 40-mile stretch of perfect sandy beach. Along this coastline you will find the boisterous entertainment centres of **Cleethorpes** and **Bridlington** or the quieter attractions of **Hornsea** and **Withernsea**. The **Wolds** are near all these seaside resorts and **Beverley**, with its magnificent 13th century minster and lattice of medieval streets, is a jewel of architectural heritage. **Hull** is a modern city rebuilt since the war, linked to **Lincolnshire** via the 1452yd **Humber Bridge** - the world's longest single span.

Abbeydale Industrial Hamlet, Sheffield

The area around **Sheffield** - the steel city - in **South Yorkshire** is dominated by the iron and steel industries. Cooling towers and power stations still nudge the M1 motorway as it cuts through this industrial heartland. The first city in England to pioneer free public transport, it now produces a steely brand of politician. The Industrial Museum and City Museum display a wide range of Sheffield cutlery and oplate. Meadowhall shopping centre, with 270 stores under one roof, has proved a great magnet for visitors.

Bramham Park, Wetherby, W. Yorks
Brodsworth Hall & Gardens,
  Nr Doncaster, S Yorks
Burton Agnes Hall, Driffield, E. Yorks
Harewood House, Leeds, W Yorks
Lotherton Hall, Leeds, W Yorks
Nostell Priory, Wakefield, W. Yorks
Sledmere House, Driffield, E Yorks
Wentworth Woodhouse,
  Nr Rotherham, S. Yorks
Worsborough Mill & Country Park,
  Barnsley, S. Yorks
York Gate Garden, Adel, Leeds

Abbeydale Industrial Hamlet,
  Sheffield, S Yorks
Beverley Minster, Beverley, E Yorks
Bishops House, Sheffield, S Yorks
Eureka! The Museum for Children,
  Halifax, W Yorks
Fulneck Moravian Settlement
  & Museum, Pudsey, W Yorks
Industrial & City Museums,
  Sheffield, S Yorks
Kirstall Abbey, Leeds, W Yorks
National Museum of Photography,
  Film & TV, Bradford, W Yorks
North Holderness Museum of
  Village Life, Hornsea, E Yorks
Sheffield Ski Village, Sheffield, S Yorks

Binns Green > Pots'n Pans >
  Pobgreen. Nr Greenfield, W Yorks
Bretton Country Park, Wakefield,
  W Yorks
Calderdale Way. Halifax >
  Todmorden > Hebden Bridge
Elsham Park Country & Wildlife
  Park, Brigg, E Yorks
Hebden Bridge > Widdop, Upper &
  Lower Gorple Reservoirs, W Yorks
Humber Bridge Country Park,
  Hull, S Yorks
Marston Moor, Huddersfield,
  W Yorks
Pennine Way. Keighley > Marsden >
  Glossop (Derbs)
Rother Valley Country Park,
  Sheffield, S Yorks
Wolds Way. Welton (Hull) >
  Market Weighton > Filey

200

Waren House Hotel

Waren Mill, Belford, Northumberland NE70 7EE

T (0870) 418 8163 **F** (01688) 214484 **E** enquiries@warenhousehotel.co.uk
T (International) +44 [0] (1688) 214581 **W** www.warenhousehotel.co.uk

Set in six acres of gardens and woodland, Waren House is a peaceful and tranquil centre from which to visit one of this country's most naturally beautiful and historic areas, largely unspoiled by tourism and commercialism. The castles of Bamburgh, Dunstanburgh, Alnwick and Warkworth are all easily accessible; there is a wealth of birdlife along miles of magnificent coastline, particularly at Budle Bay and Farne Islands and there is the Holy Island of Lindisfarne, the Cheviots and Scottish Borders near at hand. After a day out sightseeing, you can return to the quiet luxury of Waren House where owners Peter and Anita Laverack and their staff will pamper you. Bedrooms are decorated in various styles including Victorian, Oriental and French. The public areas are full of beautiful antiques and collectibles - in particular antique dolls. In the evening, enjoy a gastronomic treat in the dining room and reflect on your good fortune. How many people speed by on the A1 without knowing the splendours that lie just off it both in this historic region in general and at Waren House in particular?

Picturesque small hotel near the A1 overlooking Budle Bay

🛏 13 (inc 3 suites & 2 🏠) 🍴 ✕ ♿ 🐕 ♨ 🔍 ♨ 20 🅿 15

Directions
Leave A1 opp. Belford on B1342, down to Budle Bay, hotel on right.
Nearby attractions
Alnwick Castle & Garden, Bamburgh Castle, Chillingham Cas, Holy Island.
Distances
Berwick 14, Alnwick 14, London 350.

Rates Single room with breakfast from £110; double room from £145. [Ad]
Meals Tdh dinner £29.50 ; spec. diets avail; last orders 2030.
Leisure Breaks Two nights 4-cse dinner, b & b from £199 per person standard room. For stay of 7+ nights, free upgrade, standard to superior, superior to suite
Other Activities Tennis & golf 2m; riding 5m.

 & major credit cards accepted. Open all year.

Northumberland, Bamburgh

Rudding Park

Follifoot, Harrogate, North Yorkshire HG3 1JH

201

T (0870) 860 8400 **F** (01423) 872286 **E** sales@ruddingpark.com
T (International) +44 [0] (1423) 871350 **W** www.ruddingpark.com

Rudding Park's location is unrivalled - just $2^1/_2$ miles south of Harrogate, yet minutes from the motorway network and A1. Often referred to as *Yorkshire's Premier Hotel & Golf Resort*, the hotel's restful bedrooms have a contemporary design whilst retaining traditional touches to create a peaceful setting in harmony with the picturesque parkland. The award winning Clocktower Restaurant serves seasonal menus making best use of local ingredients. The hotel is a superb venue for that special occasion, be it a birthday, anniversary or wedding. The 19th century chapel in the grounds is a popular venue for blessings, concerts and carol services. There are 15 function rooms and the hotel can organise team building activities, from 4x4 driving to falconry. Society and Corporate Days can be arranged on the par 72 18-hole parkland golf course. Golfing groups travel from far and wide to sample this award winning hotel and its stunning golf course. There is also a driving range and professional PGA instruction if required. Other activities are available in nearby Harrogate.

 50 (inc 3 suites)  15x 300 250

'Yorkshire's Premier Hotel & Golf Resort', near Harrogate

Rates Single room with breakfast from £150; double room from £180.
Meals Alc dinner; lunch & spec. diets avail; last orders 2130; bfst fm 0700.

Leisure Breaks Seasonal breaks available fm £75 per person to inc. dinner, b & b + one round of golf. Pse call for details.
Other Facilities Gym, massage, sauna/solarium, indoor pool all close by.

 & all major credit cards accepted. Open all year.

Directions
Fm Harroagte A661 Wetherby rd, 2m at rdbt turn right; hotel on rt after $^1/_2$ mile.
Nearby attractions
Fountains Abbey, Harewood House, Castle Howard, Yorvik Museum York
Distances
Leeds 13, York 20, Skipton 20, London 209

North Yorkshire, Nr. Harrogate

The Sportsman's Arms Hotel & Restaurant

Wath in Nidderdale, Pateley Bridge, Harrogate HG3 5PP

T (0870) 418 8165 **F** (01423) 712524 **E** info@sportsmansarms.fsnet.co.uk
T (International) +44 [0] (1423) 711306 **W** www.signpost.co.uk/sportsmansarms

The Sportsman's Arms Hotel and Restaurant nestles close to the river Nidd (on which it has fishing rights) at Wath in Nidderdale - a conservation village, and one of the most picturesque and unspoiled villages in a beautiful part of the Yorkshire Dales. Reached by a pack horse bridge and set in its own gardens, this attractive 17th century mellow sandstone building attracts you like a magnet. Once inside, the cosy lounges, log fires, bar and charming, softly lit restaurant exude warmth and this and the welcome and hospitality of owners Jane and Ray Carter will remain with you throughout your stay. The local reputation for the Sportsman's Arms is that it is a first class restaurant with bedrooms. However this is not fair to the bedrooms which are comfortable and tastefully decorated, retaining many original features. At the heart of the Sportsmans Arms, however, is the restaurant and the first class food and wine on offer. Working with the best fresh local game, fish and vegetables, the Sportsman's Arms provides a feast for its guests.

Well known sporting hotel deep in the Yorkshire Dales

🛏 12 ⊁ ⅙ 🐕 ✓ 🎵 🅿 30

Directions
Fm Harroagte A61, then B6165 to Pateley Bridge. Turn off signed Wath-in-Nidd.

Nearby attractions
Fountains Hall & Abbey, Ripon. Ripley Castle. Nidderdale Museum. Newby Hall

Distances
Harrogate 14, Skipton 20, London 217

Rates Single room with breakfast from £70; double room from £110.
Meals Alc dinner; lunch & spec. diets avail; last orders 2100.
Leisure Breaks End October-mid March Nidderdale Midweekers - 2 pers sharing, min stay two nights, dinner, b & b from £130 per person Sun-Thurs inc

Visa, Mastercard & Switch cards accepted. Open all year (exc. Christmas Day)

North Yorkshire, Nr. Harrogate

The Feversham Arms Hotel

Helmsley, York, North Yorkshire YO62 5AG

T (0870) 418 8168   F (01439) 770346   E info@fevershamarmshotel.com
T (International) +44 [0] (1439) 770766   W www.fevershamarmshotel.com

Deeply embedded in rural life, you will find Helmsley just on the edge of the beautiful North York Moors National Park and with it the Feversham Arms. Recently bought by Simon Rhatigan (fresh from launching Seaham Hall in Co. Durham), this hotel has had care and attention to detail put back into it. Here you will find country warmth with a designer twist - Mousey Thompson classic furniture blending perfectly with Julia Burns contemporary paintings. What comfy bedrooms too, with everything you need for total relaxation and oh, for that relaxing bath after a hard day's walk out on the Moors. You can easily fall asleep, but before that perhaps an aperitif by the beautifully landscaped outdoor pool to soak up the last of the day's sun or next to a roaring fire in the winter months. The light and airy conservatory serves scrumptious food from local produce - fresh fish from Whitby and locally reared lamb and beef. Taking the best from the country and giving it a Feversham nod towards the slightly modern. What a delightful hotel this is with so much to offer. You'll need a return visit or a very long stay to make the most of the myriad interesting places to see in the area - that is, if you can get out of the super-comfy bed.

24 (inc 12 suites)

Country warmth with a designer twist on the edge of North Yorks Moors

Rates Single room with breakfast from £140; double room from £150.
Meals The Conservatory alc dinner; lunch & spec. diets avail; last orders 2130.

Other Facilities Riding and golf nearby.

& major credit cards accepted. Open all year.

Directions
From A1 thru' Thirsk to A170, hotel on left on entering Helmsley, nr Market Pla.
Nearby attractions
Rievaulx Abbey, Newburgh Priory, Castle Howard, Duncombe Park.
Distances
Thirsk 14, York 20, London 222.

North Yorkshire, Helmsley

Lastingham Grange

Lastingham, Nr. Kirkbymoorside, York YO62 6TH
T (0870) 418 8169 **F** (01751) 417358 **E** reservations@lastinghamgrange.com
T (International) +44 [0] (1751) 417345 **W** www.lastinghamgrange.com

Unique and incomparable was how one guest described this super hotel to me whilst on one of her numerous return stays. And it is easy to see why guests return time and again to this charming hotel situated on the edge of the Moors in the historic village of Lastingham, a peaceful backwater in the heart of the North Yorkshire Moors National Park. The old, stone-walled country house, built around a courtyard and set within 10 acres of attractive gardens, is owned and personally run by the Wood family. Their charming friendliness and hospitality sets the mood for all guests to feel at ease in this elegant and tasteful country home. The atmosphere is unhurried and peaceful, the south facing terrace providing a tranquil setting in which to relax and enjoy the beautiful rose garden. The welcoming hall, the spacious lounge with its open fire, the comfortable bedrooms with their impressive views, the excellent food, the attention to detail and the location make the Grange a perfect spot for a restful break. Totally non-smoking from March 2007.

Old stone country house set in 10 acres of attractive mature gardens

Directions From A1 70 Helmsley-Pickering Rd, turn N to Appleton & Lastingham. Rt opp church then lft into High St. Hotel on rt
Nearby attractions
Rievaulx Abbey, Ryedale Folk Museum, Castle Howard, Nunnington Hall.
Distances
Helmsley 12, York 35, London 220.

Rates Single room with breakfast from £102; double room from £195.
Meals Tdh dinner £37.50; lunch from £18.75; sunday lunch fm £26.50; spec. diets avail; last orders 2030.
Leisure Breaks 2 nights+, dinner, b & b, two sharing, £245 per room per night. See also website.
Other Facilities Riding (4m) and golf (5m) nearby.

Major credit cards accepted. Open March-beginning of December.

North Yorkshire, Lastingham

Monk Fryston Hall Hotel

Monk Fryston, North Yorkshire LS25 5DU

T (0870) 418 8170 F (01977) 683544 E reception@monkfrystonhallhotel.co.uk
T (International) +44 [0] (1977) 682369 W www.monkfrystonhallhotel.co.uk

205

Monk Fryston Hall is a stately and picturesque Grade II Listed mansion, which celebrated 50 years as a hotel in 2004. It is set in its own beautiful grounds between Leeds and York. Indeed the grounds, with their 30-acre ornate garden, sunken paved patio, lake and early 20th century Lucerne Bridge and woodland park are thought to have been the inspiration for Frances Hodgson Burnett's *Secret Garden*. The Hall dates back to 1500 and has a rich and colourful history. The main staircase, fireplaces and panelling are original features. Bedrooms in the older part of the house are furnished with antiques, while those in the new extension are more contemporary. Meals can be taken either in the cosy oak-panelled bar or in the elegant restaurant which offers modern British cooking with Mediterranean and Eastern influences. The Hall has recently introduced special Murder Mystery Dinners, Theatre Dinners and Theatre Lunches. It is well placed for Leeds and York and provides a quiet, comfortable venue for a business meeting, wedding or weekend break.

29 (inc 2 🏠) ✗ ☉ ⌕ ⌂ ⌖ ⌐ 3x ⚌ 60 🅿 100 🐾

Stately hotel of 16th-century origins, set in 30 acre grounds

Rates Single room with breakfast from £85; double room from £120.
Meals 3-cse tdh dinner £27.50; lunch & spec diets avail; last orders 2115.
Leisure Breaks Min 2 nights, dinner, b & b, two sharing, £75 per person per night. Sunday bonus - dinner, b & b fm £67.50 pppn.
Other Facilities Riding, golf, tennis, swimming pool nearby.

Directions
From A1 (M) junct 42, take A63 Selby Rd. Monk Fryston 3m, hotel on left in centre
Nearby attractions
Leeds City Museum & Art Gallery, Lotherton Hall, Selby Abbey, York Minster.
Distances
Selby 8, Leeds 13, York 20, London 190

North Yorkshire, Monk Fryston

Solberge Hall Hotel

206

Newby Wiske, Northallerton, North Yorkshire DL7 9ER
T (0870) 860 8461 F (01609) 780472 E reservations@solbergehall.co.uk
T (International) +44 [0] (1609) 779191 W www.solbergehall.co.uk

The Solberge Hall Hotel, recently purchased by Thoroughbred Hotels is a magnificent Grade II listed building, set in nine acres of gardens and woodland. It has been tastefully modernised and developed into the luxury country house it is today. All the en suite bedrooms, ranging from singles to four-poster rooms with views of the surrounding countryside, are individually designed and decorated to the highest standard. Dining is either in the Garden Room Restaurant which offers fine cuisine in an elegant ambience or in the newly opened *Silks*, which offers a more relaxed dining experience. Located near the A1 (M), the A19 and the main line railway from London to Edin-burgh, the hall is easily accessible and offers genuine Yorkshire hospitality to both business and leisure guests. Solberge lies in the heart of the North Yorkshire countryside and is ideally placed for exploring the Yorkshire Dales, the North East coast and the city of York. For the horse racing enthusiast, the hotel is within easy reach of Thirsk, Ripon, York and Catterick racecourses.

Georgian country house hotel in the heart of James Herriot country

🛏 25 (inc 1 suite) 🚭 ☺ ⚕ 🐓 🐕 (£10 fee) ⤴ ▮⌂ 4x ⚏ 120 **P** 120 🐎

Directions
A1/A684 junction, take rd to North-allerton. Hotel 4m on right, brown sign.
Nearby attractions
Fountains Abbey, James Herriot Centre, Newby Hall, York Minster, Kiplin Hall
Distances
Northall'on 5, Thirsk 9, York 32, London 227

Rates Single room with breakfast from £80; double from £120.
Meals 3-cse tdh AA ❀ Garden Restaurant dinner £24.50; alc, lunch & spec diets avail; last orders 2115; bfst fm 0700. (Sat/Sun fm 0800).
Leisure Breaks Dinner, b & b , min 2 nights stay fm £50 per person per night.
Other Facilities Golf, fishing, riding nearby.

 & major credit cards accepted. Open all year.

North Yorkshire, Northallerton

The White Swan Inn

Market Place, Pickering, Ryedale North Yorkshire YO18 7AA

T (0870) 418 8171 **F** (01751) 475554 **E** welcome@white-swan.co.uk
T (International) +44 [0] (1751) 472288 **W** www.white-swan.co.uk

207

The White Swan Inn Hotel has been open for business as an inn since the 16th-century. The service is attentive but not intrusive and the atmosphere as warm and cheering as a log fire. It maintains a high standard in the kitchen and head chef Darren Clemmit and his talented team use fresh ingredients sourced locally including an exclusive meat supply from *The Ginger Pig*, National Food Producer of the Year 2005. Bedrooms within the inn are elegant and well equipped with plump beds and expensive fabrics, Two suites include a four-poster with a difference. Full local information is provided in each room, together with a copy of the extensive dinner menu. Sparkling white bathrooms have proper wide head showers and baths, Penhaligon toiletries and other little luxuries. An old stable block was transformed in 2005 to create eight new contemporary rooms and a further suite. Each room is tastefully furnished to achieve the ultimate in style and relaxation. Adjacent to the new rooms a beamed club room has recently opened exclusively for residents, where tea & coffee, a well stocked honesty bar, pool table and much more can be enjoyed....

 21 (inc 3 suites)   (£12.50) ☺ 2x ▦ 20 **P** 30

Rates Single room with breakfast from £89; double room from £129; suites from £169.

Meals 3-cse alc AA ☺ dinner ca £25; lunch, bar snacks & spec diets avail; last orders 2100; bfst 0745-1000.

Leisure Breaks Dinner, b&b, min two nights from £179 for two people sharing. Seasonal offers - see website.

Other Facilities DVD players in rms; bathrobes; golf, fishing, shooting, riding nearby

 Visa & Mastercard accepted. Open all year.

Award-winning town centre inn of exceptional comfort and cuisine

Directions
A64 from York to Malton, then A169 (Whitby Rd) to Pickering. Hotel in centre.

Nearby attractions
Castle Howard, Historic York, Pickering Castle, N York Moors Railway.

Distances
York 27, Scarborough 16, London 213.

North Yorkshire, Pickering

208

Red Lion Hotel
By the Bridge, Burnsall, Nr. Skipton, North Yorks BD23 6BU
T (0870) 860 8523 **F** (01756) 720292 **E** redlion@daelnet.co.uk
T (International) +44 [0] (1756) 720204 **W** www.redlion.co.uk

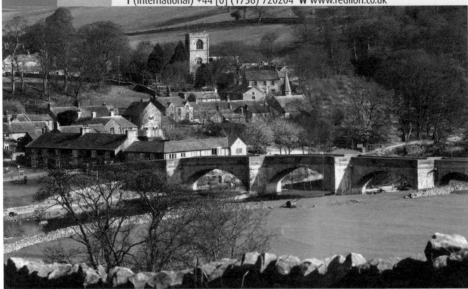

The Red Lion has been dispensing hospitality for centuries. The cellars (inhabited by a mischievous ghost who turns off the beer taps and icemaker from time to time) date from the 12th century. Over the years the inn has been gradually extended to form the lovely old building it is today, with beamed ceilings, creaky sloping floors and a wealth of character. AA ❀ cuisine features game in season from nearby estates, with fresh fish delivered daily and local cheeses on offer. Breakfasts are huge and very English with home made bread and preserves and free range eggs. The wine list has over 100 bins, drawn from the best of the old and new worlds. The Red Lion was named *Wine Pub of the Year* in 2003. Each bedroom is individually designed and furnished with brass bedsteads and antique furniture. Most rooms have views to the river Wharfe and the fells beyond. Wharfedale is part of the Yorkshire Dales National Park with the Dales Way running past the hotel. Burnsall is one of the few completely unspoiled villages in the country, with a population of just 90 souls. It makes the perfect base for exploring this area of Outstanding Natural Beauty.

Family run inn of great character on the banks of the river Wharfe

🛏 20 (inc 3 ⏠) ⅊ ↯ ❀ ♪ ⚐ 3x ⛁ 80 🅿 60 🐾

Directions
From A1, take A59 thru Harrogate to Bolton Abbey, rt on B6160, 7m to Burnsall

Nearby attractions
Bolton Abbey, Strid Wood, Stump Cross Caverns, Skipton Castle, Hesketh Fm Pk

Distances
Skipton 9, Ilkley 12, PateleyBr 12, London 219

Rates single rom with breakfast from £65; double room from £125.
Meals 3-cse tdh dinner £30.95. ALC, lunch & spec diets avail; last orders 2130; bfst fm 0730.
Leisure Breaks Autumn/winter £100 double room b&b midweek.
Other Facilities Golf, riding, shooting nearby.

& all major credit cards accepted. Open all year

North Yorkshire, Nr. Skipton

Crab Manor Hotel
Asenby, Thirsk, North Yorkshire YO7 3QL
T (0870) 418 8175 **F** (01845) 577109 **E** reservations@crabandlobster.co.uk
T (International) +44 [0] (1845) 577286 **W** www.crabandlobster.co.uk

209

Crab Manor was recommended to us as "sumptuously different - a unique experience" and I can think of no better way of describing this very popular and successful establishment. Each of the 14 individually decorated bedrooms allows you to sample the luxury of some of the world's most famous hotels. The list is impressive - *Waldorf Astoria, Raffles, Cipriani Palace, Turnberry, Sharrow Bay and Sandy Lane* are just some of the luxurious styles in this superb 18th century Georgian Manor. Three bedrooms are located in the authentic tropical beach house annexe and more recently two new Scandinavian log cabins have been added. Each room boasts its own, or shared, hot tub and sauna facilities. Good food remains, however, at the heart of Crab Manor's reputation. The highly acclaimed Crab & Lobster Restaurant, located in the hotel grounds, offers a wide variety of gourmet dishes, from fresh local seafood to traditional English fayre. Ideally located for visiting the Yorkshire Dales and Moors, Harrogate and York, Crab Manor offers an experience not to be missed.

14 ✔ 🍴 📺 2x ♨ 36 🅿 35 🎿

Georgian Manor House with 14 themed en suite bedrooms

Rates Double room with breakfast from £150.

Meals Alc dinner. Lunch menu £14.50 (2-cse)/£17.50 (3-cse); last orders 2100

Other Facilities Each room has its own or shared hot tub and sauna facilities.

& all major credit cards accepted. Open all year.

Directions
From A1 (junc 49), take A168 Thirsk Rd, 1st left to Asenby, hotel at top of slip road

Nearby attractions
Sion Hill Hall & Falconry, Newburgh Priory, Rievaulx Abbey, Norton Conyers

Distances
Thirsk 5, Ripon 5, York 24, London 222.

North Yorkshire, Thirsk

Fact File
Illustrated Guide to
Historic Houses and Gardens,
Attractions and Walks.

The Brecon Beacons from Landefalle

Wales

Wales is a land of untouched green countryside, beautiful coastline, lakes and forests, hidden valleys and high mountains. It has three National Parks, five official Areas of Outstanding Natural Beauty and long stretches of protected Heritage Coast, not to mention its own language, traditions and culture. It is also very accessible from London and the Midlands, making it an ideal short break or holiday destination.

Conwy Castle

Bodnant Gardens

Snowdonia

Hotels guide

Anglesey	page 216
Ceredigion	page 217
Conwy	page 218
Denbighshire	page 223
Gwynedd	page 225
Monmouthshire	page 232
Pembrokeshire	page 236
Powys	page 238

Further information:
Wales Tourist Board
Brunel House, 2 Fitzalan Road, Cardiff
CF24 0UY Tel: 0129 2049 9909
www.visitwales.com

North Wales

Ffestiniog railway

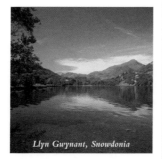

Llyn Gwynant, Snowdonia

North Wales has been attracting holiday visitors for over two hundred years - Wordsworth, Samuel Johnson, Turner, Nelson, George Burrows, Bismarck and Wellington to name a few. Nowadays the area still attracts artists, poets, politicians and sailors but the range of accommodation and attractions make North Wales a perfect venue, whatever choice of holiday.

Hotels, restaurants and inns are continually improving their standards and now compare with the best in Britain. Added to this North Wales has the unfair advantage of some of the best scenery in the world, the road from **Dolgellau** to **Tal-y-Lynn** having heart-stopping views. **Snowdonia** is justly famous for its magnificent mountains, lakes and forests but the **Hiraethog Mountains** in the North-East, **The Berwyns** south of **Llangollen** and the beautiful river valleys of the **Conwy**, **Clwyd**, **Dee** and **Glaslyn** have a magic all of their own. The variety of the scenery is what impresses first

time visitors. Within six miles of the resort of **Llandudno** you can find the peace of the **Carneddau**, one hundred square miles of beautiful mountain moorland, dotted with Neolithic tracks, standing stones, Bronze Age sites and beautiful lakes, without a single main road crossing it.

The past surrounds the visitor to North Wales. The history of man can be traced from the Neolithic tombs of 6000 years ago to the Iron Age hill forts that were inhabited when the Roman legions arrived, then through the cells and abbeys of the early Celtic church to the Nonconformist chapels of the 19th century so admired by Sir John Betjeman.

The 12th century Welsh castles and 13th century castles of Edward 1st reflect a more turbulent time, but what masterpieces of military architecture they left us - **Conwy**, **Caernarfon**, **Rhuddlan** and **Beaumaris** are breathtaking in their size and splendour, while the Welsh keeps of **Dolwyddelan**, **Dinas**

TOP 10 Historic Houses Gardens and Parks

Beaumaris Castle, Anglesey
Bodelwyddan Castle, Denbighshire
Bodnant Garden,
  Tal-y-Cafn, Conwy
Caernarfon Castle, Gwynedd
Conwy Castle
Erddig House & Garden, nr Wrexham
Harlech Castle, Gwynedd
Parc Glynllifon, Nr. Caernarfon
Rhuddlan Castle,
  Rhuddlan, Denbighshire
Plas Newydd,
  Llanfairpwll, Anglesey

TOP 10 Attractions

Alice in Wonderland Visitor
  Centre, Llandudno, Conwy
Anglesey Bird World / Dwyran Sea
  Zoo, Brynsiencyn
Dolbadarn Castle,
  Llanberis, Gwynedd
Ffestiniog Railway,
  Porthmadog, Gwynedd
Holyhead Maritime Museum,
  Anglesey
Llandudno Museum, Conwy
Llanfair Slate Caverns, Nr. Harlech
Lloyd George Museum,
  Criccieth, Gwynedd
Portmeirion Village,
  Nr. Porthmadog
Snowdon Mountain Railway,
  Llanberis, Gwynedd

TOP 10 Walks and Nature Trails

Bala Lake Walk.
  Llanuwychllyn > Bala
Bedgellert Forest, Gwynedd
Glyndwr's Way.
  Welshpool > Llanwyddyn >
  Machynlleth > Knighton
Llanrhaedr > Craig y Miwn &
  The Berwyns, Powys
Mawdach Estuary from
  Penmaenpool, Gwynedd
Offa's Dyke Path. Prestatyn >
  Llangollen > Welshpool
Port Swtan >Ynys y Fdlyn >
  Mynydd y Garn, Anglesey
Pengynchant > Tal y Fan, Conwy
The Precipice Walk.
  Llyn Cynwycg, Nr Dolgellau
Pyg Track/Watkin Path, Snowdon

212

 TOP 10 Historic Houses Gardens and Parks

Abbey Cwmhir, Nr. Rhayader, Pwys.
Castell y Bere, Nr Tywyn, Gwynedd
Cymer Abbey, Dolgellau, Gwynedd
Hay-on-Wye Castle & Clyro Gallery,
  Powys
Hergest Croft, Kington (Herefords)
Judges Lodging Museum,
  Presteigne, Powys
Museum of Modern Art,
  Machynlleth, Gwynedd
Offas Dyke Heritage Centre,
  Knighton, Powys
Pontrhydfendigaid Abbey,
  Tregaron, Ceredigion
Powis Castle, Welshpool, Powys

TOP 10 Attractions

Centre for Alternative Technology,
  Machynlleth, Gwynedd
Dyfi & Ynys-hir Bird Reserves,
  Aberdovey, Gwynedd
Elan Village, Rhayader, Powys
Gregynog House & Walks,
  Nr Newtown, Powys
Montgomery Castle, Powys
National Library of Wales,
  Aberystwth, Ceredigion
Royal Welsh Showground,
  Builth Wells, Powys
Sea Aquarium & Honey Bee
  Exhib. Aberaeron, Ceredigion
Talyllyn Railway & Museum,
  Tywyn, Gwynedd
Vale of Rheidol Railway.
  Aberystwth-Devil's Bridge

 TOP 10 Walks and Nature Trails

Cadair Idris Climb. From Minfford,
Coed y Brenin Forest Park &Visitor
  Centre, Ganllwyd, Dolgeallau
Gigrin Farm & Nature Trail Rhayader
Glyndwr's Way. Machynlleth >
  Llanidloes > Knighton
Lake Vyrnwy RSPB Reserve, Powys
Llyn Brianne Reservoir, Nr Rhayader
Offa's Dyke Path.
  Welshpool > Hay-on-Wye
Witches Cauldron > Moylgrove,
  Ceredigion
Wye Valley Walk.
  Rhayader > Hay-on-Wye
Ynis-hir Reserve & Visitor Centre,
  Machynlleth

Portmeirion

Bran and **Dolbadarn** will appeal to more romantic souls. Medieval towns such as **Conwy** and **Ruthin**, the splendid Elizabethan and Jacobean farmhouses and the tiny cottages show the ordinary side of life in the 16th-18th centuries.

The Industrial Revolution brought changes to North Wales. Slate was the major industry and the slate caverns of **Blaenau Ffestiniog** or **Glyn Ceiriog** and the **Quarry Museum** at **Llanberis** can be explored today. Most of the great **Little Trains of Wales** were first used to carry slate from the mines to the harbours, the one notable exception being the **Snowdon Mountain Railway**.

As soon as you cross the border into Wales, the scenery changes, the road signs seem unpronounceable and warm hospitable people greet you. The language, music and heritage of Wales add a special dimension. *Croeso* means Welcome and you will hear it often.

Mid Wales

Mid-Wales is a land of dramatic contrasts in which the pleasures of coast and countryside can be equally enjoyed. It is an area of immense natural beauty. Much of the **Snowdonia National Park** lies in this area.

A relaxing way to see these natural wonders is on horseback. Both the novice and the experienced rider will find fabulous pony trekking country. Alternatively, a ride on one of the **Great Little Trains of Wales** is a must for all steam enthusiasts. The **Cambrian Mountains** are Wales' backbone, an upland region where hamlets and farms nestle in the folds of seemingly endless hills. In this area farming life is centred around a series of strategic small towns, linked by splendid mountain roads or old drovers' ways, such as **Llanidoes**, with its 16th century market hall, standing almost at the centre of Wales at the confluence of the **Severn** and **Clywedog** rivers.

Powis Castle

Aberystwyth

National Botanic Gardens

Fishing in the Brecon Beacons

In **Mid Wales** life revolves around the historic market towns and former spa centres, while the coastline is dotted with small fishing villages and popular seaside resorts.

The **Western** districts are strongholds of Welsh culture, where the language is in everyday use. Expansive sandy beaches, spectacular estuaries and rugged cliffs lead down to secluded coves. Mid Wales has always had a seafaring tradition. Schooners used to set out from the little ports of **Aberaeron**, **Aberdovey**, **Aberystwyth**, **Barmouth** and **New Quay**. Today the harbours are still bustling but with a different type of craft. Some of the most spectacular roads in the British Isles are in this area. Try **Dolgellau** to **Tal-y-Llyn** or **Trawsfynydd** via **Llyn Celyn Lake** to **Bala**. But beware! New car launches and motorcycle rallies have also discovered their beauty!

To the **East** of Mid Wales are the **Welsh Marches** with their traditional half-timbered black and white buildings. Many centuries ago this area was governed by the Marcher Lords on behalf of the King.

Further back in time, Offa, an 8th century Saxon king, built a massive dyke to keep marauding Welsh forces out of his kingdom. Significant traces of these earthworks remain along the border, forming the basis of **Offa's Dyke Trail**, a long distance walkway of 168 miles North to South. At Knighton a special **Heritage Centre** illustrates the significance of the Dyke.

Llanwrtyd Wells

The whole of mid-Wales has a colourful and exciting history. Apart from the many castles, other popular attractions are the museums reflecting Welsh rural life: woollen weaving, pottery and craft work and these are to be found in displays at Llandrindod Wells, Llanidoes, Machynlleth, Aberystwth, Tre'r Ddol, Newtown and Welshpool. At Llandrindod Wells, a display of the Spas of Wales has been opened. There is also the opportunity to take the water here in the original pump room. The annual Welsh Show is held nearby.

Starting in the south-east, Wales' boundary with England is marked by the **Black Mountains**, north of **Abergavenny**, rising to 2660 feet at **Waun Fach**. **Hay Bluff**, near **Llanthony Priory** affords amazing views westwards. Great castles are the legacy of Llywelyn the Great's resistance to the English, whereas ancient monastic settlements embody the solitude sought by the Augustinian and Cistercian orders. The **Brecon Beacons National Park** includes breathtaking reservoirs, waterfalls and caves.

Further **South**, near Newport, is **Caerleon**, which was the site of the Roman fortress of Isca, built AD75. **Tintern Abbey**, in the **Wye** valley, is one of the finest relics of Britain's monastic age. It was founded in the 12th century by Cistercian monks, rebuilt in the 13th and sacked by Henry VIII during the Dissolution of the Monasteries. **Offa's Dyke**, part of an 168-mile rampart built by King Offa of Mercia to keep the Welsh out, and now a noted walk, runs past Tintern's ghostly empty portals.

214

South Wales continued

Laugharne Cemetery

Northwest of **Cardiff** is the late 19th century **Castell Coch** (Red Castle), a mixture of Victorian Gothic and fairytale styles. Well preserved is 13th century **Caerphilly Castle**, with its famous leaning tower. Further **West**, outside Port Talbot, the visitor comes to **Margam Country Park**, 850 acres including an Iron Age hill fort, a restored abbey church with windows by William Morris, **Margam Stones Museum** with stones and crosses dating form the 5th-11th centuries and the main house with its 327ft orangery.

The **Gower Peninsula**, West of **Swansea**, is a secluded world of its own, with limestone cliffs, remote bays and miles of golden sands. It is the Riviera of South Wales. Sites not to miss include 13th century **Weobley Castle**, the ruins of **Threecliff Bay** and **Gower Farm Museum** with its 100-yr old farm memorabilia. Near **Carmarthen** is Dylan Thomas' village of Laugharne, in whose churchyard he is buried. Up country are the **Dolaucothi** gold mines, started by the Romans and re-opened from 1870 to 1938, now a museum.

The rugged Pembroke coast is guarded on its Western rim by Britain's smallest city - **St David's**, whose cathedral was founded by the eponymous saint in the 8th century and is still used today. Around St David's and indeed all around the county runs the spectacular and excellently maintained **Pembrokeshire Coastal Path**. The **Pembrokeshire Coast National Park** has moorlands rising gently to the Preseli Hills. Here again Stone Age forts and Norman castles reflect the area's ancient history.

Aberglasney

Penmaen, Gower

Cardiff

Cardiff, Wales' capital, is essentially a young city, even though its history dates back many centuries. The development of its docks during the Industrial Revolution for the export of Welsh iron and coal was the basis of its prosperity. **Cardiff Castle** is part Roman fort, part medieval castle and part 19th century mansion. Its Chaucer Room has stained glass windows depicting the *Canterbury Tales*. Its Summer Smoking Room has a copper, brass and silver inlaid floor. The castle is the present home of the Welsh Assembly. The **National Museum of Wales** houses a wealth of exhibits, from impressionist paintings to examples of Swansea porcelain.

Techniquest

The Cardiff Bay development area is very impressive, with dual carriageway access from the M4 (West). The St Davids Hotel has recently opened there and two further 5-star hotels have opened in the city centre: The Hilton and Holland House. The **Cardiff Millennium Stadium**, one of the finest in Europe, plays host regularly to capacity audiences of 70,000. Cardiff is now firmly established as the decision making capital of Wales, following the opening of the National Assembly in July 1999.

Cardiff Bay

National Museum of Wales

The city has facilities one would normally associate with a city of three times the population. On the cultural side the Welsh National Opera and the BBC Welsh Symphony Orchestras have their homes there with major conference and concert venues in the **St Davids Hall** and **International Arena**. It is an important shopping and entertainment centre, the facilities combining the elegance of the old Edwardian arcades with St Davids Shopping Centre and the pedestrianisation of much of the central shopping and commercial area. The city's links with the rest of the UK are enhanced by the M4 and the now double Severn bridge. The A470 goes North via **Merthyr Tydfil** and the beautiful **Taf Fawr Valley** to **Brecon** and beyond and there is an international airport just West of the city.

TOP 10 Historic Houses Gardens and Parks

Castell Coch, Tongwynlais, Cardiff
Cardiff Bay Visitor Centre
Cardiff Castle
Cathays Park
City Hall
Dyffryn House & Gardens, St Nicholas, Cardiff
Fonmon Castle, Rhoose, Barry
Gorsedd Gardens, Cardiff
Llandaff Cathedral, Cardiff
St Fagans Castle, Cardiff

Civic Buildings, Cardiff

TOP 10 Attractions

Bute Docks & Park, Cardiff Bay
Chapter Arts Centre, Canton
Cosmeston Medieval Village, Penarth
Lovespoon Gallery Museum
Museum of Welsh Life, St Fagans
National Museum of Wales
1st The Queens Dragoon Guards Museum
Techniquest, Cardiff Bay
Wales Aircraft Museum, Cardiff Airport
Welsh Industrial & Maritime Museum

Cardiff view

216

Tre-Ysgawen Hall Country House Hotel & Spa
Capel Coch, Llangefni, Anglesey LL77 7UR
T (0870) 418 8184 **F** (01248) 750035 **E** enquiries@treysgawen-hall.co.uk
T (International) +44 [0] (1248) 750750 **W** www.treysgawen-hall.co.uk

Reached along a private wooded drive, Tre-Ysgawen is set in acres of landscaped gardens and woodland a short drive inland from the breathtaking east coast of Anglesey. The house has been sympathetically and luxuriously refurbished and extended to become one of the leading country house hotels in North Wales. Bedrooms in the main house are large and high-ceilinged, individually designed and decorated in traditional period style while the rooms in the Courtyard Wing are more modern in design. Tre-Ysgawen Spa, built and equipped to the highest standards, was converted from the Victorian stable block and retains many of the original features including the Clock Tower. Facilities include a 16m level deck pool, steam room, sauna, whirlpool, beauty/therapy suite and air-conditioned gymnasium. For the less energetic, the Clock Tower Café Wine Bar is located adjacent to the spa. Tre-Ysgawen is in the middle of the bewitching Isle of Anglesey with its safe, clean beaches, spectacular scenery and challenging golf courses. Tre-Ysgawen Hall provides the perfect environment for a luxury break for both mind and body.

Victorian country mansion in 11acre grounds with state-of-the-art spa

29 (inc 2 suites) ... 200 ☐ 100

Directions A55/A5114 to Llangefni, then B5111 signed Amlwch, after 2m right to Capel Coch. Hotel sign on left.
Nearby attractions
Plas Newydd, Beaumaris Castle, Caernarfon Castle, Glantraeth Animal Park
Distances
Bangor 14, Holyhead 14, London 251.

Rates Single room with breakfast fm £107; dble /twin £169; 4-poster suite £250.
Meals 3-cse tdh dinner £29; alc, lunch & spec. diets available; last orders 210C
Leisure Breaks Spa Breaks, min 2 nights 2 sharing in twin or double.
Spa Experience - 2 days fm £93.50 pppn - one Spa treatment per stay.
Spa Indulgence - 2 days fm £178 pppn, dinner, b&b + lunch & 2x 1 hour Spa Treatments per day. Champagne and gift on arrival. *Extra Nights* - 3rd nt disc (d,b&b) when staying 3+ nights inc Sunday. (4-poster suites not included)
Other activities Golf, watersports, sailing, Anglesey Coastal Path nearby & all major credit cards accepted. Open all year.

Ty'n Rhos Country House

Seion, Llanddeiniolen, Caernarfon LL55 3AE

T (0870) 860 8524 **F** (01248) 671772 **E** enquiries@tynrhos.co.uk
T (International) +44 [0] (1248) 670489 **W** www.tynrhos.co.uk

217

Once a humble farmhouse, Tyn Rhos has once again become an immaculate country house, under the new ownership of Martin and Janet James. The spacious house has a well furnished lounge, large conservatory and excellent restaurant, with views across the hotel's gardens towards Anglesey. Dinner is the high point of any stay at Tyn Rhos. Starter might be a smoked salmon parcel, filled with trout mousse and served with giant prawns, followed by a fillet of pork tenderloin glazed with Emmental cheese, with a wild berry and raspberry coulis dessert to finish with. This is Taste of Wales cuisine at its very best, based on fresh local ingredients and herbs straight from the garden. Breakfast might include Menai oysters and laverbread. Bedrooms are fresh and individually designed, some ground floor ones opening up on to the spectacular gardens which leads to a carp stocked lake and helipad. There are also three courtyard bedrooms. Tyn Rhos is an ideal touring base, standing between Snowdonia and the sea, close to Caernarfon Castle, Anglesey and the beautiful Lleyn peninsula.

🛏 10 ⚜ 🚫 ♿ ❀ 🎵 🐾 🛏 🈲 ♨ 🍴 40 **P** 30 WIFI

Rates Single room with breakfast from £65; double £85-130.

Meals Garden View Restaurant 3-cse tdh dinner £32.50; spec. diets avail; last orders 2000; bfst fm 0800.

Leisure Breaks 2 nights dinner, b & b £290 standard room/£370 superior king-size; 5 nights, dinner, b & b £625 (standard) - £825 (superior King)

Other activities DVD players. Golf, riding, sailing, squash, tennis, watersports nearby.

 & all major credit cards accepted. Open all year.

(* = Sun-Thurs only)

Low level converted farmhouse with views to Anglesey

Directions
3m S of Bangor on A487 Caernarfon rd, left on B4547, hotel 2m on rt, brown sign

Nearby attractions
Caernarfon & Conwy Castles, Plas Newydd, Snowdonia Nat Park, Bodnant Gdn

Distances
Bangor 5, Caernarfon 6, London 249

Caernarfonshire, Nr. Caernarfon

218

Falcondale Mansion

Falcondale Drive, Lampeter, Ceredigion SA48 7RX
T (0870) 418 8183 F (01570) 423559 E info@falcondalehotel.com
T (International) +44 [0] (1570) 422910 W www.falcondalehotel.com

I knew there was a university college in Lampeter but until now I was ignorant that there is also a very good hotel in this secret Heart of Wales. Falcondale Mansion is owned and run with infectious verve by hands-on hosts Chris and Lisa Hutton. The Mansion is approached from two directions, from the south up the Teify Valley along a mile-long drive flanked by dazzling rhododendrons and azalea bushes when we called in May. Bedrooms are very comfortable with DVD players, modem points, WIFI Internet access and stylish bathrooms en suite. They are furnished with antiques and soft fabrics, most overlooking the lawns and gardens. Fine dining is important at Falcondale and the cuisine has been recognised by an RAC dining award. After dinner, you can relax with a liqueur , play a board game or read a magazine undisturbed in one of the comfortable lounges. Falcondale's central location in this largely undiscovered part of South-West Wales makes it an ideal base from which to explore the rugged mountains to the north and the moor lands and coastal paths around Aberaeron to the west. Red kites have been seen feeding near the hotel and owls can be heard in the evening. A great spot for a break.

Victorian country mansion set in 14 acres of glorious gardens

🛏 20 ✗ ♿ ☺ ⌕ 🐕 (£5 per night) ♨ 60 🅿 60 ⚒

Directions North Drive, approach from Aberaeron A482 tun rt 2m b4 Lampeter. Fm Sth take A475 dir Cardigan, rt at Murco Gar
Nearby attractions Llanerch Aeron NT, Dolaucothi Goldmines, Red Kite Ctre, Nat Botanical Gdns
Distances Aberaeron 13, Brecon 42, London 203

Rates Single room with breakfast from £95; double from £130.
Meals 3-cse tdh dinner in AA ☺ Valley Restaurant £32.50 or informal dining in Peterwells brasserie; spec. diets available; last orders 2100; bfst from 0730.
Leisure Breaks Midseason Breaks available, 3 nights, b & b for price of two. Prices fm £190 per person. Christmas & New Year packages available.
Other Activities Golf, fishing, sailing, game shooting (by arrt), riding nearby.

AMERICAN EXPRESS & major credit cards accepted. Open all year.

Cardiganshire, Lampeter

Royal Oak Hotel

Holyhead Road, Betws-Y-Coed, Conwy County LL24 0AY

T (0870) 860 8467 **F** (01690) 710603 **E** royaloakmail@btinternet.com
T (International) +44 [0] (1690) 710219 **W** www.royaloakhotel.net

219

Privately owned and personally run, The Royal Oak Hotel is a picturesque former Victorian coaching inn overlooking the river Llugwy centrally located in the delightful village of Betws-Y-Coed. All 27 three-star graded ensuite rooms have modern facilities with broadband access, LCD televisions with selected SKY channels. Deluxe 4-posters and family rooms are also available. Guests have a choice of three dining venues: the stylish AA ❀ Llugwy Restaurant, highlighting the best of local Welsh produce, the contemporary vibe of the Grill Bar or the Stables Bistro Bar which hosts regular musical events and has *alfresco* dining. The Royal Oak is the perfect setting equally for sophisticated socialising and casual get togethers. Adjoining the hotel is the Stables Lodge, the perfect choice for walkers, climbers and cyclists, where all rooms are on the same floor with lift access. Guests also have use of a drying room and bike storage facilities as well as complimentary use of the Dukes Leisure Centre nearby. The Royal Oak is the ultimate base for exploring all of Snowdonia's wonders or enjoying multi activity adventures, including the world famous Marin Bike Trail - its all here!

🏷 27 ⊁ ☉ ⌖ ⚞ ⦀ 85 🅿 85 ⚘

Family owned hotel in the centre of the 'capital of Snowdonia'

Rates Single room with breakfast from £65; double from £80. [Ad]

Meals 3-cse tdh dinner fm £17.50; alc, lunch & spec. diets available; last orders 2045 (2100 weekends); bfst from 0745.

Leisure Breaks Lazy Weekend Special - 3 nights, inc Sunday lunch, from £110 per person.

Other Activities Golf, fishing, indoor pool, gym, riding, watersports nearby.

 & major credit cards accepted. Open all year.

Directions
A5 from the East, hotel in centre of village, opp. Railway station and hotel car park.

Nearby attractions
Mt Snowdon, Caernarfon & Conwy cas, Llechwedd slate mines, Swallow Falls.

Distances
Llandudno 23, Bangor 22, London 226

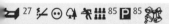

Conwy, Betws-y-Coed

The Groes Inn

Tyn-y-Groes, Nr Conwy LL32 8TN

T (0870) 418 8181 F (01492) 650855 E thegroesinn@btinternet.com
T (International) +44 [0] (1492) 650545 W www.groesinn.com

There has been an inn in this spot since 1573 when The Groes was on the main coach route between London and Holyhead. The Groes Inn is a true family-run hostelry, whose decor reflects the personality of the hosts: from stone cats lounging in the fireplace to the inn's collection of Victorian hats and shields. There is even a display of saucy Victorian postcards, but no jukeboxes or gaming machines! Cuisine specialises in local delights: Conwy crab, mussels and plaice and oysters from the sea around Anglesey. Bread is crusty and homemade. Puddings are another delight with a selection of homemade ice creams. The extensive wine list has a good selection of half bottles. Bedrooms are smartly and individually decorated; some have four-posters, others balconies. All have magnificent views, either of Snowdonia's foothills or of the Conwy valley. The Groes Inn is the perfect spot for a short break, ideally placed for visiting Conwy Castle, Bodnant Gardens & Snowdonia. Recently the self-catering High Cabin - complete seclusion with an outdoor hot tub - opened nearby and this year a luxury cottage '14' has opened in the heart of Conwy town.

Family run hostelry, carrying on tradition of 450 yr-old coaching inn

14 (inc 4 suites) 20 150

Directions From A55 Llandudno Junction, take Conwy signs A547, then left in town onto B5106 Betws Rd; inn 3m on rt

Nearby attractions
Conwy Castle, Bodnant Gardens, Snow-donia, Gwydir Castle, Llandudno Mus.

Distances
Conwy 3, Llandudno 6, London 243.

Rates Single room with breakfast from £79; double from £95. High Cabin £200 per nt. min stay 2 nts.

Meals 3-cse tdh dinner £28; alc, lunch, bar snacks & spec. diets available; last orders 2100; bfst from 0730.

Leisure Breaks 2 nights, dinner b & b, two sharing, from £60 per pers per nt.

Other Activities Golf, fishing, watersports, sailing, shooting, indoor pool, tennis, riding, mountain walking nearby.
& major credit cards accepted. Open all year.

Conwy, Nr. Conwy

Sychnant Pass House

Sychnant Pass Road, Conwy LL32 8BJ

221

T (0870) 418 8182 **F** (01492) 585486 **E** bresykes@sychnant-pass-house.co.uk
T (International) +44 [0] (1492) 596868 **W** www.sychnant-pass-house.co.uk

Set in the foothills of the Snowdonia National Park, Sychnant Pass House is more than just an award winning Country House. It's a home that welcomes guests in a unique way. Lovely sitting rooms with comfy sofas and beautiful pictures delight the eye; wonderful food served in the candlelit restaurant nourishes the body and a warm welcome embraces the spirit. The house stands in three acres of lawns, trees and wild garden with ponds and a stream running through it. It borders the Pensychnant Nature Reserve and enjoys panoramic views in a peaceful setting. Buzzards, herons and foxes are just a few of the regular garden visitors. It is a haven for walkers with the North Wales Coast Path just a stroll away. Other local amenities include five golf courses, sailing, paragliding and horse riding. Two of the comfortable bedrooms are ground floor with their own private terrace (ideal for dogs) and all are named after T S Eliot's *Old Possum's Book of Practical Cats*. There are six suites, some with four-posters and sitting rooms. The 300-strong video library and a new spa complex with salt water pool (no chlorine smells) will round off your stay perfectly. Any Signpost guest is bound to soon feel the Conwy magic here!

 10 (inc 4 suites) 🔥🐎✿🅿🔱🍴🛏🐾🏛🐕

Rates Single room with breakfast from £75; double £95-£180.
Meals 5-cse tdh dinner £30; alc & spec. diets available; last orders 2030; bfst from 0830.
Other Facilities Video, CD players in rooms. Golf, fishing, watersports, riding, nearby.

Visa, Mastercard & Switch accepted. Open all year exc. Christmas.

Enchanting house in unspoiled setting bordering Nature Reserve

Directions
A 547 to Conwy then left after Castle walls, signed Sychnant Pass.

Nearby attractions
Conwy Castle, Bodnant Gardens, Snow-donia, Gwydir Castle, Llandudno Mus.

Distances
Conwy 2, Llandudno 6, London 240.

Conwy, Nr. Conwy

Osborne House

222

17 North Parade, Llandudno, Conwy LL30 2LP

T (0870) 418 8190 **F** (01492) 860791 **E** sales@osbornehouse.com
T (International) +44 [0] (1492) 860330 **W** www.osbornehouse.com

The Osborne is an all-suite townhouse developed by the Maddocks family, who have owned the well known Empire Hotel, Llandudno, for many years. It has taken three years of painstaking renovation to reconstruct this Grade II Listed building as an exclusive all suite Town House Hotel and Restaurant. The suites are exceptionally well appointed: all with four poster beds, fireplaces, DVD players, marble bathrooms with separate WCs and walk-in showers, writing desks with Internet wireless access and comfortable sitting areas. All bedrooms have views of Llandudno Bay and Great Orme's Head. There are six parking spaces (at a premium on the seafront!) behind the hotel. In the stylish Osborne's Cafe Grill, you can get Light Bites at any time of day, maybe hot garlic prawns with noodles, locally caught fish - sea bass or pan fried king scallops, locally reared Conwy Valley Lamb Shank. There is an extensive wine list, with large or small glasses available. The Osborne is within walking distance of the shops and theatre and well placed for visiting the many attractions of the North Wales coast.

Exclusive all-suite town house on Llandudno's Promenade

🛏 6 suites 🔍 ⓡ ☺ 🅿 6

Directions
Follow signs to town centre, then Promenade; hotel at end opp. pier.

Nearby attractions
Conwy & Caernarvon Castles, Bodnant Gdns, Snowdonia Nat'l Pk , Portmeirion

Distances
Bangor 19, Holyhead 43, London 243.

Rates Single/double suite with cont'l breakfast from £145.

Meals Alc restaurant; lunch & spec. diets available; last orders 2200 (Sunday 2100); cont'l bfst from 0700.

Other Facilities DVD players in rooms. Massage, sauna, indoor swimming pool 100 yards.

Awards AA ★★★★ townhouse; AA Hotel of the Year for Wales 2004-2005.

& all major credit cards accepted. Open all year exc 18-30 Dec.

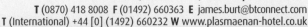

Plas Maenan

Maenan, Llanrwst, Conwy LL26 0YR

223

T (0870) 418 8008 F (01492) 660363 E james.burt@btconnect.com
T (International) +44 [0] (1492) 660232 W www.plasmaenan-hotel.co.uk

High above the Vale of Conwy and overlooking Snowdonia, sits the majestic and elegant Plas Maenan. It was built 100 years ago by th Aluminium Corporation and occupied by its managing director Henry Jack, leading to its pseudonym of *Plas Jack*. Then it was the centre for entertaining in the valley and it reprises this role today, being particularly popular for weddings. New owners Caroline and James Burt are busy putting their mark upon it. Inside it now has the ambience of a welcoming country house, with a comfortable drawing room with log fire and panoramic views. At the front of the building are four spacious suites, with kitchen and dining areas, video and DVD player, a good selection of novels and games and a wide range of toiletries in the spacious bathrooms. The 'small dining room' serves an à la carte menu Tuesdays through Sunday lunchtime, using locally sourced produce wherever possible, including Welsh lamb and beef, crab and mackerel, and game in season. Alternatively The Garden Room, with its topiary and statuary, appeals in the summer and the separate Music Room can be rented for that special occasion.

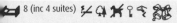 8 (inc 4 suites) 🍴🛏🗡♿♟🎿

Restored boutique hotel with commanding views of the Vale of Conwy

Rates Single room with breakfast from £65; double from £80.

Meals 3-cse tdh dinner £28; alc, lunch & spec. diets available; last orders 2100; bfst from 0800.

Other Facilities Birdwatching, fishing, gym/spa, golf, gardens, riding, sailing, sea, watersports nearby.

 & major credit cards accepted. Open all year.

Directions
Fm Llandudno A470 Sth 10m, turn left opp Dolgarrog Sta, uphill, white pillars

Nearby attractions
Bodnant Gardens, Conwy Cas & Harb'r, Portmeirion, Snowdonia National Park

Distances
Llandudno 10, Betws-y-C 9, London 253

224

The West Arms Hotel
Llanarmon DC, Nr. Llangollen, Denbighshire LL20 7LD
T (0870) 418 8198 **F** (01691) 600622 **E** gowestarms@aol.com
T (International) +44 [0] (1691) 600665 **W** www.thewestarms.co.uk

The West Arms has welcomed travellers from near and far for more than 400 years. It is full of character with slate-flagged floors, large inglenook fireplaces, timberwork, sloping landings and crooked staircases. Cattle drivers from three Welsh valleys used to converge here to take their produce to markets as far afield as London. Today the traffic is the other way around - people flock to the West Arms from all over the world for a spot of superb Welsh hospitality, good food and home spun comfort. New owners Lee and Sian French and award winning chef Grant Williams offer a superb menu featuring fresh local produce prepared to the highest standards. The Welsh breakfast will get you off to a good start for a walk in the surrounding hills, a visit to Rhaeadr Waterfall or Chirk Castle. Or you could fish on the hotel's private 2-mile stretch of the Ceiriog or go pony trekking. There is a four-poster room and new power showers, TVs & radios and a selection of books in rooms. Mountain bikes can also be hired. The Ceiriog Valley is one of the loveliest and most peaceful in Wales. The loudest noise is likely to be the bleating of sheep or the quiet tumbling of the river through lush meadows.

400-year old inn situated at the head of a peaceful valley

🛏 16 (inc 2 suites) ⚒ ☉ ♪ ⚓ 🐾 (£6 per nt fee) ⛊ 60 🅿 20 🐕

Directions
Turn off A5 at Chirk; follow B4500 thru' Glyn Ceiriog to Llanarmon 11 miles.

Nearby attractions
Chirk Castle, Powis Castle, Llanrhaeadr Waterfalls, Erddig Hall, Plas Newydd

Distances
Chirk 11, Shrewsbury 26, London 183

Rates Single room with breakfast £53.50-95; twin/double £87-179.

Meals 3-cse tdh AA ☺ ☺ dinner £28-33; alc, lunch & spec. diets available; last orders 2100; bfst fm 0800.

Leisure Breaks 3 night for price of two, only when booking b & b, subj to avail please call hotel for details.

Awards & accreditations RAC 3 blue ribbons; AA Seafood Pub of the Year 2005 & 2006; AA Courtesy & Care Award 2004

Other Facilities Riding 3m; watersports 10m.
Mastercard, Switch, Solo, Visa accepted. Open all year.

Denbighshire, Llanarmon DC

Wild Pheasant Hotel, Spa & Restaurant

Berwyn Road, Llangollen, Denbighshire LL20 8AD

T (0870) 860 8485 **F** (01978) 861837 **E** wildpheasant@talk21.com
T (International) +44 [0] (1978) 860629 **W** www.wildpheasanthotel.co.uk

225

Set in beautiful pasture land patrolled by wild pheasants, this original 19th century building has been sympathetically updated, retaining the charm and comfort of a country house, whilst providing all the facilities of a modern hotel. The hotel's extension has brought luxury suite accommodation, including a Health Suite with spa & sauna and a Penthouse Suite with a hot tub on the balcony. The 31 bedrooms in the original part of the hotel are more traditionally furnished and two are four-posters. Most rooms offer spectacular views of Castell Dinas Bran, the Berwyn mountains and the Vale of Llangollen. The AA ☺ Cinnamon Restaurant and Bistro Bar is renowned for dishes using fresh local produce: Welsh lamb, Dee salmon, home produced beef, local game, Welsh cheeses and seasonal specialities. Lunch or drinks can be enjoyed in the Chefs Bar and courtyard. The Spa of Tranquillity includes a spa, steam room and treatment room. An extensive range of beauty, health and relaxation treatments are available. Weddings and conferences are also catered for. A good spot for a touch of restorative pampering with lots to see and do in the area.

🛏 48 (inc 15 suites) ⚹ ⚹ ✿ // 🛋 🍽 🎱 ❄ ✆ ⦂⦂⦂ 200 🅿 200 🐎

Rates Single room with breakfast from £42; double from £84. `Ad`
Meals 3-cse tdh dinner £22; lunch & spec. diets available; last orders 2130; bfst from 0730.

Other Facilities Massage. Golf, tennis, riding nearby.

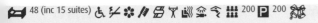

& all major credit cards cards accepted. Open all year.

Modernised hotel with spa, at the foot of the Berwyn Mountains

Directions
A5 to Llangollen. Through town; hotel ¹/₂ mile on left.

Nearby attractions
Valle Crucis Abbey, Llangollen Railway, Plas Newydd, Victorian School & Musm

Distances
Corwen 11, Wrexham 11, London 194

Denbighshire, Llangollen

226

Penhelig Arms
Aberdovey (Aberdyfi), Gwynedd LL35 0LT
T (0870) 418 8186 **F** (01654) 767690 **E** info@penheligarms.com
T (International) +44 [0] (1654) 767215 **W** www.penheligarms.com

Standing beside the Penhelig Harbour, where ocean-going schooners were built many years ago, the Penhelig Arms, with superb views across the Dyfi estuary, is of specific historical interest. The major part was built in the 1700s and was known then as *Y Dafarn Fach* (The Little Inn). In the 19th century, Charles Dickens is reputed to have stayed here. Today the hotel's reputation continues to grow, thanks to its acclaimed cuisine under the supervision of Bronwen Shaw and Jason Griffiths, backed up by proprietor Robert Hughes' carefully chosen wine list. You will quite often find parties of golfers enjoying the fayre! Bedrooms are either 'traditional' in the original inn building or 'large superior' in the recently converted *Bodhelig* annexe. Recently a self-contained apartment sleeping four and a cottage sleeping two have been added. The hotel has retained its essential appeal to locals, too. The Fishermans Bar is always busy! Aberdovey has an 18-hole golf course and the RSPB bird sanctuary across the estuary is home to more than 60 species. It is also a sailing centre where the mountains meet the sea.

Leading waterfront inn specialising in fresh fish with an acclaimed wine list 15 (inc appt & cottage) (not in appt or cottage)

Directions
From the East A493 Penhelig is on rt after railway bridge. Car park opp.
Nearby attractions
Ynis-hir Bird Reserve, Talyllyn Railway, Mawddach Estuary, Harlech Castle.
Distances
Dolgellau 24, Machynlleth 11, London 215

Rates Single room with breakfast from £70; double from £80.
Meals 3-cse tdh dinner ca. £29; bar snacks, lunch & spec. diets available; last orders 2100; bfst from 0800.
Leisure Breaks Dinner, b & b two nights £130 per person. Nov - end March book 2 nts, get 3rd nt free, just pay for dinner.
Awards UK Seafood Pub of the Year 2005.
Other Facilities Fishing, birdwatching, climbing nearby.
CCs Mastercard & Visa cards accepted. Open all year.

Trefeddian Hotel

227

Aberdovey (Aberdyfi), Gwynedd LL35 0SB
T (0870) 418 8185 F (01654) 767777 E info@trefwales.com
T (International) +44 [0] (1654) 767213 W www.trefwales.com

The Trefeddian Hotel, whose family celebrated 100 years at the hotel in 2006, stands in its own grounds one mile west of Aberdovey, a village with many attractions and fast becoming a centre for many outdoor activities. The directors, Mr & Mrs John Cave and Mr & Mrs Peter Cave, run this first class family hotel. They are constantly making improvements. Recently a top floor consisting of eight large new bedrooms was added, landings have been widened and some bedrooms refurbished. The lounges are spacious, relaxing and peaceful and have also been refurbished. The bedrooms, most with views of Cardigan Bay, are comfortable and elegantly decorated. The five course menu offers a good choice of interesting and well presented dishes, complemented by a well chosen wine list, with a good range of half bottles. The Trefeddian faces a four-mile stretch of sandy beach and overlooks the golf course, where the hotel guest can obtain reduced green fees, with the ever changing view of the sea beyond. The courtesy and efficiency of the staff create a happy atmosphere.

🛏 59 (+ 3 s/c appts) 🔼 ♿ 🔺 ⓙ₁₈ 🔍 📺 📞 🍴 🏋 🎾 🎾 🏬 🐾

Family friendly hotel opposite golf course and beach

Rates Bed, breakfast & dinner from £75 per person.
Meals 5-cse tdh dinner £27; childrens menu, lunch & spec. diets catered for; last orders 2045.
Leisure Breaks Spring, Autumn & Winter Breaks available. Festive Season Breaks 23 Dec-2 January. Please ring for details.
Other Facilities Fishing, horse riding, golf, clay shooting, quad biking nearby.

CCs Mastercard,Visa & debit cards accepted. Open all year.

Directions
From the East A493, go through Aber - dovey; hotel up on rt at village end.
Nearby attractions
Ynis-hir Bird Reserve, Talyllyn Railway, Mawddach Estuary, Harlech Castle.
Distances
Dolgellau 24, Machynlleth 11, London 215

Gwynedd, Aberdovey

Palé Hall

Palé Estate, Llanderfel, Bala, Gwynedd LL23 7PS
T (0870) 418 8204 **F** (01678) 530220 **E** enquiries@palehall.co.uk
T (International) +44 [0] (1678) 530285 **W** www.palehall.co.uk

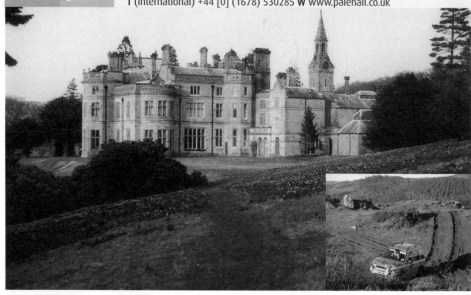

Palé Hall is a delightful discovery for the discerning visitor - a lovingly restored Victorian country manor set in refreshingly tranquil and beautiful surroundings. Queen Victoria herself warmed to Palé's welcome during her visit in 1889 and her bath is still in use today. The present family owners are proud to maintain the Hall's great tradition of hospitality. The elegance and grandeur of Palé remain unchanged while the amenities have been discreetly enhanced to the highest standards. We are sure Her Majesty would have approved. Each individually appointed bedroom overlooks the grounds and bathrooms have been refurbished. With the Land Rover Experience Centre based at Palé, the hotel can offer guests the opportunity to drive off-road in a variety of models around 200 acres of rugged terrain. The Hall lies in an unspoiled area of lush valleys and gentle hills, making it a paradise for many outdoor activities: fishing, shooting, horse riding and mountaineering. Lake Bala is the largest natural lake in Wales (4^1/$_2$ miles long) and it is the only habitat of the trout-like *gwyniaid* and site of a legendary underwater palace. A steam railway runs alongside it.

Victorian country mansion set in 200 acres of parkland near Lake Bala

17 (inc 2 suites + 1 📠) 🥢 🏠 ♟ ❄ 🐟 ♫ ✎ 🅿 40 ♟♟ 22

Directions From A5 Llangollen take A494 twds Bala, 4m left on B4402 for Llanderfel, left after vill, 1st rt Pale, hall on rt.

Nearby attractions
Llangollen Motor Museum, Bala Lake Railway, Blaenau Ffestiniog Railway.

Distances
Corwen 9, Dolgellau 20, London 230.

Rates Single room with breakfast from £85; double from £115.

Meals AA ❀❀ Restaurant; lunch & spec. diets available; last orders 2030; bfst from 0800.

Other Facilities Golf, fitness centre/gym, riding, watersports, sailing nearby. Land Rover Experience Centre.

WTB ★★★★★ Hotel.

CCs All major cards accepted. Open all year.

Sygun Fawr Country House
Beddgelert, Gwynedd LL55 4NE
T (0870) 418 8202 F (01766) 890258 E sygunfawr@aol.com
T (International) +44 [0] (1766) 890258 W www.sygunfawr.co.uk

229

A short walk from the village of Beddgelert , off the A 498 Capel Curig road, across a narrow stone bridge and up a steep lane, in the heart of Snowdonia, you will discover Sygun Fawr - one of North Wales' best kept secrets. It nestles among 20 acres of mountainside and gardens and is the ideal retreat for those wanting a walking holiday or just to get away from the pressures of today's life. There are no TVs or telephones in the individually decorated bedrooms. Ian presides over the cuisine, making full use of local produce such as Welsh lamb, beef and fresh seafood on his daily changing menu, while Chris is 'front-of-house', both patrons having bought Sygun Fawr to 'get away from it all'. There is a TV lounge which has spectacular views down the Gwynant Valley (the best channel!). The new conservatory sitting/dining area takes advantage of the superb view all year round. Portmeirion, Harlech and Caernarfon are all within 30 minutes' drive. Its stunning location makes Sygun Fawr a good base from which to tackle an ascent of Mount Snowdon.

🛏 11 🐦 🦌 🐕 🐾

Former Welsh manor house in breathtaking Snowdonia setting

Rates Single room with breakfast from £51; double from £75.
Meals 4-cse tdh dinner £21.50; alc & spec. diets available; last orders 2000.
Leisure Breaks Two night breaks, dinner, b & b fm £115 pr person weekdays/ £119 pp weekends. Weekly rate, dinner, b & b from £340 per person.
Other Facilities Golf, riding, sea bathing nearby.
Awards *Which?* Hotel of the Year 2002. WTB ★★★★ Country House. AA ◊◊◊◊

CCs Debit cards accepted. Open all year exc. January.

Directions
From Beddgelert A498 Capel Curig Rd, 1/2m right over narrow stone bridge.
Nearby attractions
Welsh Highland Railway, Portmeirion, Caernarfon Castle, Mt Snowdon.
Distances
Caernarfon 12, Betwys y Coed 15, London 230

Gwynedd, Beddgelert

230

Penmaenuchaf Hall
Penmaenpool, Dolgellau, Gwynedd LL40 1YB
T (0870) 418 8187 **F** (01341) 422787 **E** relax@penhall.co.uk
T (International) +44 [0] (1341) 422129 **W** www.penhall.co.uk

The e-mail address says it all - 'relax at Penhall' and I did! My room was called *Vaughan* and as well as a spacious bathroom, it had a tempting minibar, a bed that was hard to get out of and a superb view of the gardens, with not another house in sight! Lorraine Fielding and Mark Watson are 'hands on' hosts, Mark giving advice in the AA ☺☺ oak-panelled restaurant and Lorraine looking after the front of house. Built in 1860, Penmaenuchaf overlooks the Mawddach estuary. A ramble or cycle along the old railway line which used to bring visitors from Euston to Fairbourne is a great way to take in this beauty spot. You can then return to the hotel on the smartly resurfaced drive to explore its own 21 acres of terraced gardens and woodlands and admire the sunken lavender garden. The hall is secluded yet within easy reach of many attractions: historic castles, 'Great Little Trains', gold and slate mines and safe, sandy beaches. Country pursuits abound: 13 miles of fishing on the rivers Mawddach and Wnion, canoeing, birdwatching and golf to name a few. An excellent centre for exploring Snowdonia.

Handsome Victorian mansion over-looking the Mawddach estuary

🛏 14 ⚅ ☉ 🖥 ♘ 🦅 ⛳ 🛁 ♪ ♨ 20

Directions
A493 Tywyn Rd out of Dolgellau, hotel 1m out on left opp Penmaenpool toll br.
Nearby attractions
Blaenau Ffestiniog Rlwy, Portmeirion, Cadair Idris, Harlech Cas, Cymer Abbey
Distances
Caernarfon 50, Betwys y Coed 20, London 230

Rates Single room with breakfast £75-135; double £130-200.
Meals 4-cse tdh dinner £35; spec. diets available; last orders 2130.
Leisure Breaks Two-night breaks, midweek, dinner, b & b per person for two sharing £180-230.
Other Facilities Golf, riding, watersports, birdwatching, canoeing, pony trekking, sailing nearby.
CCs All major cards accepted. Open all year.

Gwynedd, Dolgellau

Hotel Portmeirion
Portmeirion, Porthmadog, Gwynedd LL48 6ET

T (0870) 418 8188 **F** (01766) 771331 **E** hotel@portmeirion-village.com
T (International) +44 [0] (1766) 770000 **W** www.portmeirion-village.com

Portmeirion Hotel and Village was the unique creation of Sir Clough Williams-Ellis 75 years ago. His ambition was to develop a beautiful location without spoiling it. The hotel enjoyed a celebrated clientèle from the start: George Bernard Shaw, Bertrand Russell and H G Wells were habitués; Noel Coward wrote *Blithe Spirit* here during two weeks in 1941. In 1966 it was the setting for the cult television series *The Prisoner*, starring Patrick Mc Goohan. Today the village has matured and brings to mind a piece of Tuscany on the Welsh coast. As such, it provides an enchanting escape from today's busy life. Bedrooms are either in the main hotel or spread throughout the cottages that make up the village. I chose the village and was accommodated in the charming *Neptune 1*, approached up a stone staircase. The village has shops selling pottery, local produce, books and ice cream; *The Gwyllt* nature walk through 70 acres of sub-tropical gardens around the village should not be missed.

40 (inc 12 s'tes +4 ⌁) ☺ ⌖ ⌗ ♫ ⌸ ⌺ ⌾ ⋔ 100

Rates Single room with breakfast from £132; double from £188. **Meals** AA ❀ 3-cse tdh dinner £39; lunch & spec. diets available; last orders 2100; bfst fm 0800.
Leisure Breaks 2 nt breaks, dinner, b & b from £122 pr pers. 3 for 2 avail winter for £300 pr pers the package.
Other Facilities ⌇ ⌁ ⊩ ∪ ⌿ ⌼ nearby.
▦ & all major credit cards accepted. Open all year.

Castell Deudraeth
Portmeirion, Gwynedd LL48 6ET

T (0870) 418 8189 **F** (01766) 771331
E hotel@portmeirion-village.com
T (International) +44 [0] (1766) 770000
W www.portmeirion-village.com

Castell Deudraeth, opened in 2001, is very different. It has 11 bedrooms, two dining areas, a meeting room and walled garden. Beneath its Grade II listed 19th-century exterior, it is bold and contemporary in style. Bedrooms have king or queen size beds, whirlpool baths, real flame gas fires, oak floors with under-floor heating and wide screen TVs with DVDs. The interiors fuse traditional Welsh materials such as slate and oak with cutting edge design featuring unusual finishes such as burnt and fumed oak and acid patinated zinc. This leads to a simple, clean yet high quality finish. Dining choice is either the Castell's informal brasserie or the restaurant at the main hotel (*see above*). It was always part of Sir Clough Williams-Ellis' plan that the Castell would form part of the enchanting village, and this dream has now become a reality. There is nothing quite like it in Wales.

11 (inc 4 s'tes +2 ⌁) ☺ ⌖ ⌗ ♫ ⌸ ⌺ ⌾ ⋔ 25

Rates Single room with breakfast from £176.50; double from £214. **Meals** 3-cse AA ❀ tdh dinner £30; lunch & spec. diets available; last orders 2145; bfst fm 0800.
Leisure Breaks 2 nt breaks, dinner, b & b from £142 pr pers. 3 for 2 avail. winter for £299 pr pers the package.
Other Facilities ⌇ ⌁ ⊩ ∪ ⌿ ⌼ nearby.
Directions From Midlands/Shrewsbury A458/A470 to Dolgellau➜ Ffestiniog, left for Portmadog A487, hotel 8m on left.
Nearby attractions Harlech Castle, Blaenau Ffestiniog Rlwy
Distances Portmadog 3, Betwys 24, Dolgellau 26, London 245

▦ & all major credit cards accepted. Open all year.

Gwynedd, Porthmadog

232

Allt Yr Ynys Country Hotel

Walterstone, Nr Abergavenny (Herefordshire) HR2 0DU
T (0870) 418 8192 F (01873) 890539 E reception@allthotel.co.uk
T (International) +44 [0] (1873) 890307 W www.allthotel.co.uk

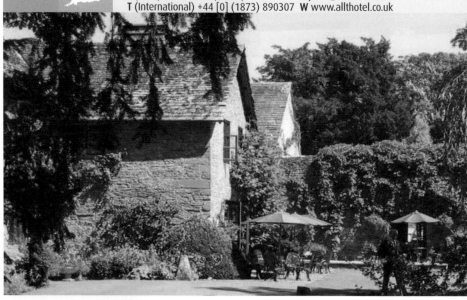

Allt Yr Ynys sits astride the Monmouthshire/Herefordshire border and is centred on a beautifully preserved medieval 16th-century manor house. The Elizabethan Lord Burleigh owned the house at the end of the 16th century and there are many original features still visible: moulded ceilings, oak panelling and beams, a cider press, a walled garden, stone-tiled roof and even a priest's hole. Most bedrooms are in the converted stables and outbuildings and the hotel nestles in stunning countryside at the foot of the majestic Black Mountains and on the fringes of the Brecon Beacons National Park. The award-winning restaurant serves 'modern British cuisine' and, unusually for a country house hotel, there is an indoor swimming pool, sauna and jacuzzi. Outside is a clay pigeon shooting range. When we stayed, there was a 'team building' course in action. I am sure many of the delegates will return as leisure guests to explore further this spectacular Border country. The hotel has a civil wedding licence and its Elizabthan Knot Garden is a romantic place for couples to 'tie the knot'.

Manor House of 16th-century origin straddling the England-Wales border

21 (inc 2 stes & 2 ♨)   ♿ ⊙ ♙ ☂ ♦ / 🛏 📶 ♪ ♨ 120 🐾

Directions
A465 Hereford twds Abergavenny, right 15m at Pandy Inn, under rlwy br bear rt

Nearby attractions
Hereford Cath & Mappa Mundi, Hampton Crt, Nat Mining Mus, Millenium Stad

Distances
Abergav'y 5, Hereford 15, London 230

Rates Single room with breakfast from £65; double from £95.
Meals Alc restaurant; lunch & spec. diets available; last orders 2130.
Leisure Breaks Min two-night break, dinner, b & b for two sharing from £67.50 per person per night.
Other Facilities Massage, aromatherapy, reflexology. Golf, ballooning, cycling, tennis, riding, quad biking nearby.

& all major cards accepted. Open all year.

Monmouthshire, Nr. Abergavenny

The Inn at The Elm Tree
St Brides, Wentlooge, Nr. Newport NP10 8SQ
T (0870) 860 8525 F (01633) 681035 E inn@the-elm-tree.co.uk
T (International) +44 [0] (1633) 680225 W www.the-elm-tree.co.uk

233

The Inn at The Elm Tree, *'The First Five Star Inn in Wales'* is an interesting conception. Originally a 19th century barn, it has been transformed into a celebrated Restaurant with Rooms, under the supervision of chef/patron Shaun Ellis. Some of the bedrooms are classical and some modern - one having a water bed. Some are ground floor, some have four posters and some sitting areas. Some bathrooms have large corner baths, jacuzzis or spas. Cuisine in the intimate restaurant is British with a European influence. Shaun works with the best of Wales' natural produce which can be found on the doorstep: Welsh Black Beef, lobster, oysters and cockles from the nearby coast and game in season form local estates, organic pork and free-range chicken. Bread, cakes and ice cream are home made. The river meadows of the Severn estuary between Newport and Cardiff, known as 'Little Holland' provide a quiet backwater both for business visitors to the two cities, only 15 minutes' away, and for leisure travellers. Small weddings and conferences are also catered for. Golf, trout fishing, carp lakes, shooting and coarse angling are all available nearby.

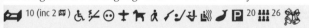 10 (inc 2 🛏) 🚫 ⚶ ☉ ✝ 🐴 🕴 ✓•/⚴ 🏴 ♪ P 20 ⛿ 26 🐎

Restaurant with Rooms between Newport and Cardiff.

Rates Single room with breakfast from £70; double from £90.

Meals Alc restaurant; lunch & spec. diets available; last orders 2200; bfst fm 0700.

Leisure Breaks Two-night break, dinner, b & b for two sharing £220.

Other Facilities Golf, coarse angling nearby.

[Ad]

Directions M4 Junc 28, take A48 signed St Mellons, left at two rdbts till Asda rdbt, rt on Morgan Way 2m on B4239, inn on left

Nearby attractions
Millenium Stadium, Mill'm Centre, Celtic Manor, Big Pit, Tredegar House

Distances
Newport 5, Cardiff 10, London 145

 & all major cards accepted. Open all year.

Glen-Yr-Afon House Hotel

Pontypool Road, Usk, Monmouthshire NP15 1SY

T (0870) 418 8193 **F** (01291) 672597 **E** enquiries@glen-yr-afon.co.uk
T (International) +44 [0] (1291) 672302 **W** www.glen-yr-afon.co.uk

One of the first things that the visitor will notice about the Glen-Yr-Afon is the friendliness and efficiency of owners Jan and Peter Clarke and their staff who believe in a "hands on" approach, and have been anticipating guests' every need for over 32 years. Only five minutes' walk from the pleasant market town of Usk, the hotel has an agreeable river walk opposite. This is an excellent base from which to explore South Wales, being only 15 minutes from the M50 and 10 minutes from the M4. Glen-Yr-Afon is an imposing and elegant Victorian house retaining many original features, yet sympathetically updated. 28 elegant bedrooms enjoy wonderfully large baths to luxuriate in, whilst for the business person, the whole hotel is now a Broadband hotspot. The air-conditioned restaurant offers a range of new menu choices, imaginatively presented with generous helpings and an extensive wine list. Business people and wedding parties are well catered for with a function suite seating 140, whilst the charming Library is the venue for anniversaries, dinner parties and smaller functions for up to 20 people. The hotel makes available to guests, for a small charge, a chauffeur-driven Mercedes Vito seating eight persons.

Family owned hotel fronting the river Usk in market town

🛏 28 ⅍ ♦♦♦ 140

Directions From A40 Monmouth, take A449 twds Newport, turn off at A472 for Usk, hotel on Pontypool Road.
Nearby attractions
Gwent Rural Life Mus, Usk Castle, Blaenavon Ironworks,Caldicot Cas & Cntry Pk
Distances
Newport 10, Monmouth 13, London 136.

Rates Single room with breakfast from £88; double from £123. [Ad]
Meals Alc restaurant; spec. diets available; last orders 2100.
Leisure Breaks Any two-night break, dinner, b & b for two sharing from £135 per person.
Other Facilities Croquet, golf, fishing, tennis, gliding, grass ski-ing nearby.

 & all major cards accepted. Open all year

Monmouthshire, Usk

The Crown at Whitebrook

Whitebrook, Nr. Monmouth, Monmouthshire NP5 4TX

T (0870) 860 8446 F (01600) 860607 E info@crownatwhitebrook.co.uk
T (International) +44 [0] (1600) 860254 W www.crownatwhitebrook.co.uk

235

The Crown has been transformed to produce an interior that injects a fresh contemporary feel into the inn's 17th century shell. The Crown offers eight luxurious and individually styled bedrooms equipped with the latest multi media systems. The rooms boast modern en suite facilities with executive rooms having walk in power showers and some double-ended baths. It has become a romantic *auberge* set in three acres of garden and pasture just one mile from the river Wye. French-influenced modern cuisine is under the supervision of James Sommerin, who prepares mouthwatering dishes making best use of fresh local ingredients, coupled with an imaginative wine list. It has won many plaudits and awards. Whitebrook is the perfect base for exploring this area of outstanding natural beauty, with its rugged limestone outcrops, fast flowing river Wye and Offa's Dyke Path near at hand. The Crown can organise packages to include golf, horseracing, salmon fishing or rugby at The Millennium Stadium. You can be sure of a warm welcome in this valley. Wales Tourist Board ★★★★★ accommodation.

 8 ✂ P 10 ♟ 12

Rates Single room with breakfast from £70; double from £100.

Meals AA ◎◎ restaurant; lunch & spec. diets available; last orders 2130; bfst from 0800.

Other Facilities Riding, golf, walking, fishing nearby.

Visa, Mastercard, Switch cards accepted. Closed two weeks fm December 26.

SE Wales' first 'Restaurant with Rooms' near the Wye Valley

Directions From A40 Monmouth, thru' rd tunnel bear left, 50 yds left at rdbt, approx 500 yds left onto B4293 to Chepstow. 2.7m left brown hotel sign, 2m later Crown on rt

Nearby attractions
Tintern Abbey, Wye Valley, Chepstow Racec'se, Offa's Dyke, Tintern Old Station

Distances
Monmouth 6, Chepstow 11, London 142

Monmouthshire, Whitebrook

Warpool Court Hotel
St David's, Pembrokeshire SA62 6BN
T (0870) 418 8195 **F** (01437) 720676 **E** info@warpoolcourthotel.com
T (International) +44 [0] (1437) 720300 **W** www.warpoolcourthotel.com

The Warpool Court is in a wonderful position overlooking the wild Atlantic and within a few minutes' walk of the famous St. David's Cathedral. This splendid country house hotel, with its unique collection of antique tiles, has been recommended by Signpost for a long time. It is owned by Peter Trier and managed by the very professional and 'hands-on' host Rupert Duffin. You can be assured of good food, gracious living and a warm welcome. The colour schemes are soft and restful and the staff cheerful and efficient. The two ⊕⊕ restaurant has a high repu-tation for good food, backed by a fine selection of well chosen wines. Chef Shaun Ellison has eight years' exper-ience of tempting hotel guests and local diners who come from a wide radius to celebrate 'that special occasion' here. Salmon is smoked on the premises, crab and lobster are caught at the nearby village of Solva. The lounge bar, with its array of antique tiles, provides a relaxed atmosphere for that pre-dinner drink. There are numerous outdoor activities nearby and you can access the Pembrokeshire Coastal Path at one of its most dramatic stretches directly from the hotel's gardens. The spring flowers are not to be missed!

Overlooking the wild Atlantic in Britain's smallest cathedral city

🛏 25 🍴 🐾 🐎 ☉ 🔊 ⚲ ◎ 🧘 ◎ 🎨

Directions
Into centre of St Davids, follow hotel signs from Cross Square, approx ¹/₂ mile
Nearby attractions
St Davids Cathedral & Bishops Palace, Picton Cas & Town Mus, Haverfordwest
Distances
Fishguard 16, Haver'west 16, London 264

Rates Single room with breakfast from £100; twin/double from £150.
Meals 4-cse tdh dinner £39; lunch & spec. diets available; last orders 2115.
Country House Breaks 2-5 nights out of season, dinner, b & b for two sharing from £105 per person per night; 6+ nights from £90 pppn. Full Christmas & New Year packages available.
Other Facilities 9-hole golf course, watersports, riding nearby.

& all major cards accepted. Open all year exc January.

Pembrokeshire, St David's

Penally Abbey

Penally, Nr. Tenby, Pembrokeshire SA70 7PY

T (0870) 418 8194 **F** (01834) 844714 **E** penally.abbey@btinternet.com
T (International) +44 [0] (1834) 843033 **W** www.penally.abbey.com

237

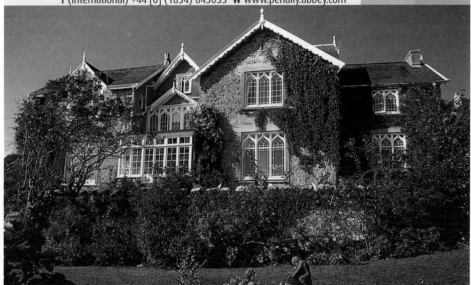

Penally Abbey is a fine country house rich in character and old world charm, where many celebrities have stayed. Standing in five acres of gardens and woodlands with magnificent views over Caldey Island and Carmarthen Bay, it exudes an air of peace and tranquility that belies its monastic past. The hotel stands on the site of a 6th-century abbey and there is a ruined medieval chapel and a wishing well in the garden. Larger and more individual bedrooms in the main house are individually and originally furnished with antiques, many having four posters. St Deniel's Lodge was opened in 2005 to provide five new large rooms with sitting areas, rich wooden furniture and modern marble bathrooms. The rooms' relaxing mellow tones are a fusion of contemporary and classic timelessness. Dining is a romantic candle-lit affair, making use of the best local produce when in season. There is a lot to see and do in this corner of Wales. Tenby has a sheltered harbour, Georgian and Regency houses, medieval castle ruins, town walls and a 13th century church. Tenby golf course is almost opposite the hotel and the Pembrokeshire Coastal Path passes nearby.

 ²²

Rates Single room with breakfast from £120; double £130-160; St Deniel's rooms £134. Dinner, bed & breakfast from £101 per person per night.
Meals 3-cse AA ☺ tdh dinner £34; spec. diets available; last orders 2100.
Leisure Breaks Any two-night break, dinner, b & b for two sharing £198 per night.
Other Facilities Golf, sea bathing, riding, shooting, fishing nearby.

 & all major cards accepted. Open all year

On the site of a former abbey overlooking Caldey Island and the coast

Directions
Take Pembroke Rd A4139 out of Tenby; 1m br rt opp Kiln Park Gar, 1m hotel on rt
Nearby attractions
Carew Castle Tenby, Bishops Palace Lamphey, Pembroke Castle, Tenby Mus
Distances
Tenby 2, Pembroke 11, London 241.

Pembrokeshire, Tenby

238

The Felin Fach Griffin
Felin Fach, Brecon, Powys LD3 0UB
T (0870) 418 8205 **F** (01874) 620120 **E** enquiries@felinfachgriffin.co.uk
T (International) +44 [0] (1874) 620111 **W** www.felinfachgriffin.co.uk

The sign says *EatDrinkSleep* and this is the name of their company but brothers Edmund and Charles Inkin have done much more to the old Griffin Inn than just address these basic functions. It has been developed into a 7-bedroom hostelry of contemporary comfort - crisp Irish linen, goosedown pillows, some Rajasthani beds and furniture, stripped pine floorboards, spacious baths to wallow in after a day in the hills, but no TVs in rooms. Charles trained at the Ballymaloe Cookery School in Ireland. The Dutch head chef produces miracles specialising in local produce - Welsh lamb, beef from the neighbouring farm (organic where possible) and puddings to die for, all with an international twist. Breakfast is taken communally; guests make their own toast on the Aga, and complimentary newspapers are provided. It is all very informal, like a country house. This atmosphere spreads to the bar area where local ales can be sampled in front of a roaring log fire or a liqueur sipped. There is fantastic walking on Llandefalle Hill behind the inn and Offa's Dyke, Kilvert Country and fishing on the Usk and Wye are all nearby. The brothers have just opened The Gurnards Head in St Ives. *(See the Cornwall section of this guide)*

'Modern rustic ' inn with stylish bedrooms and award winning food

🛏 7 (inc 3 🖾) ✶ 🔟 🐕 (£10 fee) ☺ ♀ ☼ 2 🎿 (10/40)

Directions
From East, A40 to just short of Brecon, rt onto A470 signed Hereford, inn 4 m on left
Nearby attractions
Brecon Beacons Nat Park, Offa's Dyke, Dan-Yr-Ogof Showcaves, Hay Lit Festival
Distances
Brecon 5, Hay-on-Wye 12, London 168.

Rates Single room with breakfast from £67.50; double £97.50-£125. [Ad]
Meals 3-cse tdh dinner £25; alc, lunch & spec. diets available; last orders 2130; bfst fm 0730.
Leisure Breaks Discounted rate can be discussed for stays of three nights+.
Other Facilities Fishing, golf, watersports, sailing, shooting, squash all within 10 miles.

Visa & Mastercard accepted. Open all year exc Xmas & Boxing Days.

Caer Beris Manor
Builth Wells, Powys LD2 3NP
T (0870) 418 8196 F (01982) 552586 E caerberismanor@btinternet.com
T (International) +44 [0] (1982) 522601 W www.caerberis.co.uk

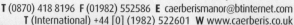

239

Caer Beris was until recently the home of Lord Swansea, although there was a manor on the site as long ago as 1093. Peter and Katharine Smith took over the property in 1987 and have converted it into a secluded country house hotel. It sits in 27 acres of parkland on the banks of the river Irfon and is the perfect escape from the pressures of the modern world. Each bedroom, including four-posters, has its own style. The oak panelling in the award-winning AA ❀ restaurant dates back to Tudor Times. Dishes such as fillet of Welsh black beef with a marrow and tarragon sauce or Canon of Welsh lamb with cranberries and calvados are typical choices. The wine list stretches to over 150 bins and the malt whisky collection is extensive. The hotel has suggested walking routes available. Complimentary salmon trout, grayling and coarse fishing are available on the Irfon from the hotel and the hotel has guest tickets available for the river Wye. Tuition can also be arranged. Riding, birdwatching, golf, horseriding and canoeing as well as the beauties of the Brecon Beacons are all on the doorstep.

 23 🚻 100 P 50

Fishing hotel on the banks of the Irfon with many sporting activities nearby

Rates Single room with breakfast from £64; twin/double from £109. [Ad]
Meals Alc dinner 2-cse ca £20; lunch & spec. diets available; last orders 2130.
Leisure Breaks Any two nights 4-cse gourmet dinner, b & b for two sharing from £57.50 per person.
Other Facilities River bathing, golf, tennis, canoeing, paragliding, off-road driving nearby.

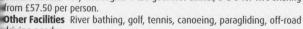 & major cards accepted. Open all year.

Directions
Leaving Builth Wells on A483 for Llan-wrtyd Wells, hotel on left at river bridge.
Nearby attractions
Royal Welsh Showground, Builth. Elan Village. Bronllys Castle, Talgarth.
Distances
Brecon 16, Ross-on-Wye 49, London 171

Gliffaes Country House Hotel
Crickhowell, Powys NP8 1RH
T (0870) 418 8197 **F** (01874) 730463 **E** calls@gliffaeshotel.com
T (International) +44 [0] (1874) 730371 **W** www.gliffaeshotel.com

The clockfaces on the four sides of the Gliffaes' tower show four different times. No, not the hour in Tokyo, London, New York and Sydney, but a symbol of the 'timelessness' of the hotel. Whether you're fishing for a hotel or looking for a hotel that's got some of the best fishing in the UK - Gliffaes has it all. There are stunning walks through the 33 acres of grounds around the hotel and the Brecon Beacons National Park, on the doorstep, offer most outdoor activities. On a fine summer's day, the Italianate terrace will be full of satisfied locals taking afternoon tea, 'a trencherman's dream', with plenty of home made cakes! Bedrooms are priced according to size and views, all being comfortable and full of character. The four largest ones overlooking the river have been refurbished to the highest standard. Gliffaes is a family-run hotel - Susie and James Suter being the third generation. A daily changing menu with good food locally sourced, complemented by a world-wide wine list, a warm fire and a comfortable bed at the end of the day spent outdoors on the hills - what more could one want? Unsurprisingly most people come back for more. The hotel welcomes children and dogs, but does'nt have trouser presses!

Famous family-owned fishing hotel on the banks of the river Usk   🛏 23   🚼 🎣 🐾 🐕 🔦 🏇 ♨ 16

Directions From the East take A40 out of Abergavenny twds Brecon. Hotel on left after A479 branches to rt

Nearby attractions
Abercamlais, Brecon; Tretower Court & Castle; Brecon Beacons National Park.

Distances
Crickhowell 3, Aberg'nny 10, London 171.

Rates Single room with breakfast from £90; twin/double from £95.
Meals 3-cse ◎ tdh dinner £31; late meals by arrangement; lunch, tea & diets available; last orders 2115.

Other Facilities Golf, riding, walking, cycling all nearby.

Major credit cards accepted. Open all year exc. first three weeks Jan.

Lake Vyrnwy Hotel

Lake Vyrnwy, Llanwyddyn, Powys SY10 0LY

T (0870) 418 8200 **F** (01691) 870259 **E** res@lakevyrnwy.com
T (International) +44 [0] (1691) 870692 **W** www.lakevyrnwy.com

241

The Lake Vyrnwy Hotel enjoys one of the best locations in Britain. It sits high in the hills of the Berwyn range, in the midst of a 24,000 acre estate, overlooking the man-made lake, created to supply water to Liverpool in the 19th century. The peace, tranquillity and remarkable views that surround this unique hotel provide the perfect setting for a relaxing stay. Built in 1890 from locally quarried stone, the hotel is full of character, retaining the traditional atmosphere of a country fishing lodge, with expansive armchairs, tables and bookcases. It is a walker's paradise and many other country pursuits are on hand: classic fly fishing on the lake, game and clay shooting and bird watching, to name but a few. After a day's activity, you can enjoy the award-winning cuisine, whose emphasis is on fresh ingredients sourced locally with game and lamb from the surrounding estate. Then retire to your individually decorated and spacious bedroom (some have four posters and some jacuzzis) ready to wake up to the stunning view again in the morning. A new spa and conference wing is due to open in 2007.

🛏 38 ⨝ ⊙ 🦌 ✦ ♪ 🧘‍♂️ 🚲 ◎ 🔍 ⚓ 🏓 120 🅿 70

Sporting hotel enjoying one of the best views in Britain

Rates Single room with breakfast from £90; twin/double from £120.

Meals 3-cse AA ⊛ tdh dinner £33.50; lunch & spec. diets available; last orders 2115; bfst fm 0800.

Leisure Breaks Min two night stay, dinner, b & b for two sharing from £155 per night per couple.

Other Facilities Lake fishing. Golf 10m.

& major cards accepted. Open all year.

Directions From Shrewsbury take A458 twds Welshpool. After 3m turn rt B4393 signed Lake Vyrnwy 28m.

Nearby attractions
Andrew Logan Mus & Powis Cas Welshpool, Bala Lake Rlwy, Snowdonia.

Distances
Llanfyllin 10, Shrewsbury 35, London 204

Powys, Lake Vyrnwy

242

The Lake Country House & Spa
Llangammarch Wells, Powys LD4 4BS
T (0870) 860 8449 **F** (01591) 620457 **E** info@lakecountryhouse.co.uk
T (International) +44 [0] (1591) 620202 **W** www.lakecountryhouse.co.uk

This welcoming Welsh country house is set in 50 acres, with rhododendron-lined pathways, riverside walks and a well stocked trout lake. The grounds are a haven for wildlife: herons, dippers and kingfishers can often be seen skimming over the water. There are resident badgers regularly spotted by guests, while swans and waterfowl abound. Overlooking these lovely surroundings, the hotel rooms are filled with antiques, paintings and fresh flowers. Each bedroom and suite is furnished with thoughtful attention to detail. From the windows, ducks and geese can be glimpsed wandering in the garden - carpeted with daffodils in the Spring - which cascade down to the river. Guests can fish for trout or salmon on four miles of the river Irfon and on the three acre lake. The new spa is a haven of luxury and relaxation. It boasts a 50ft indoor pool, a fully equipped gym, sauna and hot tub with fabulous views over the lake. Qualified therapists offer a range of health and beauty treatments. There is a 9-hole golf course in the grounds, and a tennis court. For the less active, a delicious afternoon tea trolley is on offer. Attractions in the area include the Black Mountains and several historic castles.

Comfortable mid-Wales hotel with new suites and state-of-the-art spa

31 (inc 21 suites)

40 P

Directions
A40 to Brecon, then B4520 to Upper Chapel. In vill. branch left B4519, hotel signed 7m

Nearby attractions
Elan Valley, Hay, Brecon Cath & Mus, Nat Bot Gdn Wales, Dolaucothi Gold Mines

Distances
Llanwrytd Wells 3, Builth 6, London 200

Rates Single room with breakfast from £110; twin/double from £160.
Meals 4-cse tdh AA ☺ ☺ dinner £39.50; lunch & spec. diets available; last orders 2115; bfst fm 0730.
Leisure Breaks Special breaks available. Please call for details.
Other Facilities River bathing.

 & all major credit cards accepted. Open all year

Lasswade Country House Hotel
Llanwrtyd Wells, Powys LD5 4RW

243

T (0870) 418 8199 F (01591) 610611 E info@lasswadehotel.co.uk
T (International) +44 [0] (1591) 610515 W www.lasswadehotel.co.uk

Lasswade is a period country house hotel in the foothills of the Cambrian mountains. The emphasis here is on quality food, comfort and personal service, along with care of the environment. Guests return to sample the warm hospitality emanated by hosts Roger and Emma Stevens. Lasswade offers commanding views of the lovely Welsh countryside and an aura of peace. En suite bedrooms are light, spacious and comfortable with attention to detail on organic toiletries, soft towels and single estate/fair trade teas and coffee. The restaurant specialises in locally produced food with the emphasis on organics. With an AA ☺, the ever changing menu might include locally produced mutton, slow roast belly of free range pork, wild venison (a hit with the Good Food Guide 2007 inspector). Dessert might be plums in mulled wine with a zabaglione sauce, a fluffy cognac crème brûlée, or a filo basket of wild hedgerow fruits in season with organic crème fraiche, to cap the eating experience. Llanwrtyd Wells is the smallest Spa town in Britain and is the home of many unusual events. Lasswade is the perfect base from which to explore the secrets of mid-Wales, visit historic houses or gardens or simply walk in the pure air and take in the beautiful scenery.

⊨ 8 ⅋ 🛏 ⋕⋕⋕ 12 🅿 8

Small hotel in heart of Cambrian Mts, 20 miles from Brecon Beacons

Rates Single room with breakfast £55; twin/double £75-95.
Meals 3-cse dinner £28; spec. diets available; last orders 2130.
Accreditations Hospitality rating 79%. AA ☺ cuisine. Good Food Guide listing.
Leisure Breaks Available late autumn, winter and early spring. Please contact hotel for details.
Other Facilities Cycling, golf, fishing nearby.

Visa, Mastercard, JCB & Maestro cards accepted. Open all year.

Directions A40 via Brecon to Llandovery, then A483 12m to Llanwrtyd Wells. rt in centre into Station Rd, hotel on rt.
Nearby attractions
Lost Gardens of Aberglasney, Red kite Feeding Ctre, Lakes & Dam of Llynbryann
Distances
Llandovery 12, Builth 12, London 185

Powys, Llanwrtyd Wells

The Three Cocks Coaching Inn
Three Cocks, Nr. Brecon, Powys LD3 0SL

T (0870) 418 8085 F (01497) 847339 E info@threecockshotel.com
T (International) +44 [0] (1497) 847215 W www.threecockshotel.com

Roy and Judith Duke took over the Three Cocks in 2006 and are busy returning it to its traditional role: a characterful hostelry on a well established coaching route, that has been welcoming travellers for 400 years. Arguably one of the best known little inns of Wales, you can't miss its hanging baskets, tubs of geraniums in season and cobbled courtyard as you pass through the hamlet of Three Cocks between Hereford and Brecon. Upstairs the floors may be crooked and there may be no TVs in rooms, but the seven individual bedrooms are clean, furnished with antiques and very cosy. Downstairs there is a pleasant bar area, an open brazier and a limed-oak panelled drawing room where guests can watch a wide-screen TV, a video or just chat with a liqueur in front of a roaring log fire. Dinner is served in the spacious restaurant which overlooks the rear gardens. This is fascinating border country with the Black Mountains and Hay Bluff just to the South, the Brecon Beacons to the Southwest and the beautiful Wye Valley to the North. If you want to sample old fashioned hospitality in beautiful surroundings, the Three Cocks is definitely for you.

Charming L-shaped former coaching inn on Brecon-Hereford road

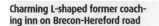 7 (1 ⦿ only) ⚬ ⅍ 🅿 10

Directions
From East A438 fm Hereford, 4m after Hay-on-Wye, inn on left nr A4079 turn.
Nearby attractions
Hay-on-Wye, Brecon Beacons Nat'l Park, Black Mts, Llangorse Lake, Offas Dyke Pa
Distances
Hay-on-Wye 4, Brecon 12, London 160

Rates Single occupancy with breakfast from £65; twin/double from £75.
Meals Alc & tdh dinner avail; lunch & spec. diets served; last orders 2100; bfst fm 0730.
Leisure Breaks Contact hotel for Christmas offers
Other Facilities Riding, golf, fishing, shooting, aero-gliding, watersports nearby.

Visa, Mastercard, JCB & major cards accepted. Open February to December

Signpost Guide 2007
Scotland

Fact File
Illustrated Guide to
Historic Houses and Gardens,
Walks and Attractions

Scotland

Scotland is a proud nation that has much to be proud about....famous inventors, writers, politicians, beautiful countryside that is a playground for the sportsman. Golf, sailing, fishing, shooting, stalking are all available in abundance. Golf was invented at St Andrews four centuries ago. With cheap flights now available from the South, all this is easily within range for a weekend or short break.

Hotels guide

Further information
Visit Scotland
Ocean Point One, 94 Ocean Drive,
Edinburgh EH6 6JH
Tel: 0131 332 2433

www.scotexchange.net

Eilan Donan Castle, Highland

Scotts View, River Tweed

Blaircastle

246

| TOP 10 | Historic Houses Gardens and Parks |

Glasgow

David Livingston Centre, Blantyre
Glasgow Botanic Gardens
Glasgow Cathedral
Greenbank Garden, Clarkston
Holmwood House, Cathcart
Hutchesons Hall, Glasgow
Newark Castle, Port Glasgow
New Lanark Mills, Lanark
Pollok House, Pollokshaws
Colzinium House & Walled
  Garden, Kilsyth

Glasgow

Glasgow Cross

Piper at St. George's Square

| TOP 10 | Attractions |

The Burrell Collection
Gallery of Modern Art
Glasgow Science Centre
Hunterian Gallery
Kelvingrove Art Gallery &
  Museum
Motherwell Heritage Centre,
Museum of Scottish Country Life
Museum of Transport
The Peoples' Palace
The Tenement House Museum

Charles Rennie Mackintosh souvenirs

Glasgow, Scotland's 'Second Capital' and largest city is one of the liveliest and most cosmopolitan destinations in Europe. It has been reborn as a centre of style and vitality, set against a backdrop of outstanding Victorian architecture. It was European City of Culture 1990 and UK City of Architecture and Design in 1999.

Glasgow boasts world famous art collections, some of the best shopping in the UK and the most vibrant nightlife in Scotland. A 'must see' is the *Art Nouveau* splendour of Scotland's best known architect **Charles Rennie Mackintosh**, whose inimitable style adorns attractions such as **The Lighthouse**, **Glasgow School of Art**, **House for an Art Lover** and the **Hunterian Gallery**. **Glasgow Art Gallery and Museum** displays a unique collection of European art and a famous array of European arms and armour.

St. Mungo's Tomb

Art and Culture are important in Glasgow life with its many galleries and museums - most with free admission. The choice of over 20 includes the world's first **Museum of Religion**, the renowned **Burrell Collection** and the contemporary **Gallery of Modern Art**. **Glasgow Cathedral** is built near the church site said to have been built in the 6th century by the city's founder, St Mungo. The **Museum of Transport** has a showroom of Scottish-built cars and the Clyde Room of ship models. The **Peoples' Palace**, in Glasgow's East End, is a social history museum covering the city's history since 1175. It has a purse and ring which once belonged to Mary, Queen of Scots.

Glasgow's revitalised riverside offers numerous options for leisure and entertainment, including the city's newest attraction, the £75m **Glasgow Science Centre**. This exciting development is an attractive titanium-clad complex which includes an IMAX cinema, a science mall and the unique engineering feat of the 100m tall **Glasgow Tower**, Scotland's tallest building, with panoramic views of the city.

Edinburgh

Holyrood House

View over Edinburgh

Edinburgh Castle

Edinburgh is the jewel in Scotland's crown. The jewel has many facets: fortified hilltop architecture, sweeping Georgian crescents, tree-filled valleys, medieval cobbled crescents, graceful bridges soaring across chasms and green parks.

Its centrepiece is **The Castle** which dominates the city form its volcanic rock. It was the traditional home of Scottish kings and queens and now the Scottish Crown Jewels are kept in the **Old Royal Palace** where Mary, Queen of Scots gave birth to the future James VI of Scotland, James I of England. At the other end of **Royal Mile** is **Holyroodhouse**, Her Majesty the Queen's official residence when in Edinburgh. Mary, Queen of Scots, lived here from 1561-1567 and today the picture gallery has portraits of 89 Scottish kings. Also in the **Old Town** is **John Knox House**, former home of Scotland's religious reformer and **St Giles Cathedral**, the high kirk of Edinburgh, with its famous Crown Spire, dating from the 15th century.

The 18th century **New Town**, north of Princes Street, is the largest single area of Georgian architecture in Europe, officially recognised by the EU. Numerous architects in the 18th & 19th century endowed the city with a wealth of meritorious buildings, both private and public. **Georgian House**, in Charlotte Square, has rooms furnished as they might have been in the city's Golden Age, 1796. Nearby the **West Register House** has a fascinating collection of documents from Scotland's past.

Today the highlight of Edinburgh's cultural year is the **Festival** in August, which is the largest pan-arts festival in the world. As well as the official festival, there are over 500 'fringe events' where many of today's leading actors, comedians and writers have cut their teeth, and also a film and literary festival. The **Scottish Parliament**, the first devolved one for 300 years, opened in the new over-budget **Holyrood House** in 1999.

Historic Houses
Gardens and Parks

The Lowlands

Auchinleck House, Ochiltree, Ayrs.
Broughton House & Garden,
  Kirkcudbright
Castle Kennedy Gdns,
  Rephad, Stranraer
Culzean Castle & Country Park,
  S. Ayrshire
Drumlanrig Castle & Country
  Park, Dumfries
Lennoxlove House,
  Haddington, E Lothian
Logan Botanic Garden, Stranraer
Maxwelton House, Nr. Dumfries
Meadowsweet Herb Garden,
  Nr. Stranraer
Threave Garden, Castle Douglas

Attractions

Blairquhan Castle, Maybole, Ayrs.
Bowhill House & Country Park,
  Selkirk, Borders
Brodick Castle & Country Park,
  Isle of Arran
Burns Centre, House &
  Mausoleum, Dumfries
Caerlaverock Castle,
  Glencaple, Dumfries
Dirleton Castle & Gardens,
  E. Lothian
Ferniehurst Castle, Jedburgh, Bders.
Floors Castle, Kelso, Borders
Manderston, Duns, Borders
Peter Anderson Cashmere Woollens
  Mill & Museum, Galashiels, Bdrs.

**Walks and
Nature Trails**

Abbey St Bathan's > Edins Hall
  Fort & Moorhouse, Duns, Borders
Grey Mare's Tail > Firthybrig Head
  >White Comb, Nr. Moffat
Jedforest Deer & Farm Park, Borders
Maidens > Culzean Castle >
  Croy Bay, Ayrshire
Muirshiel Country Park, Paisley
Portpatrick > Dunskey Castle
  > Knockinaam Lodge > Portree
Raiders Road.
  Nr New Galloway, Dumfries
Southern Upland Way. Portpatrick
  > Cockburnspath (Dunbar)
Stroan Bridge Forest Trail,
  Nr. Newton Stewart
Wallace's Seat near Ayr

Floors Castle

Gretna Green

St. Mary's Loch

Rich, rolling farmland, rugged
sea coasts and Clyde coast
islands characterise the **South
of Scotland**. It is a land of
ancient abbeys, castles and
historic houses and also boasts
strong literary connections,
with both **Robert Burns** and
Sir Walter Scott having lived
here. Robert Burns around
Dumfries where his house and
favourite drinking haunt, **The
Globe Inn**, still stand and Scott
in the **Lammermuirs** of **East
Lothian**, where sheep now
graze and skylarks soar where
bitter battles once raged.

The **Tweed** meanders from the
coast along the border to rise in
the **Pentland Hills**, whereas the
coast of **East Lothian** is dotted
with castle remains, golf
courses and looks out to the
bird sanctuary of the **Bass
Rock**. **Stranraer** is the gateway
to Northern Ireland and the
A75 streaks through Dumfries
& Galloway bearing freight to
its port.

The real Scotland starts right at
the border. Different accents in
the shops, different beer names
in the pubs and different money
notes are just three of the ways
in which Scotland stamps its
personality straight away. Even
the scenery changes and the
hazy blue peaks of the **Cheviot**
and **Elidon Hills** have lifted the
hearts of many a traveller
crossing **Carter Bar** on the A68.
Crossing from Carlisle towards
Edinburgh the traveller passes
Bruce's Cave and there are
numerous castle remains where
he fought the English. The A7
scenic route passes through the
gentle hills of **Eskdale** and the
Moorfoots.

Then there are the forests and
wild moors of upland **Galloway**
and the vivid greens of
Ayrshire's rich pastures, with
the steep mountainous profile of
Arran as a backdrop. Wherever
you travel here, you can be sure
of a real Scottish welcome.

Highland Games

Central Scotland

Duart Castle, Mull

St. Andrews Old Course

Argyll, the Isles, Loch Lomond, Stirling & the Trossachs form the birthplace of Scotland and are the cradle of its Christianity and nationhood as well as the focal point of much of its dramatic history. Here you can savour the atmosphere of the Hebridean Islands, the charm of rural villages, and trace the footsteps of heroes like St Columba, Sir William Wallace, Robert the Bruce, Mary, Queen of Scots and Rob Roy.

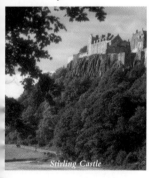

Stirling Castle

These are lands where you can glimpse an eagle, an osprey, a wildcat, a fine antlered stag, or even whales and dolphins. And if the fancy takes you, you can enjoy the spectacle of Highland Games, the warmth of a traditional Celtic folk night or the flavour of a local food festival.

Skye, in the West is a magical island of mountains (The Cuillins), deep lochs and Iron Age forts. It is now linked to the mainland by a (free-of-charge) road bridge. The islands have a harsh history, with Norse invasions, fierce clan feuds and the Highland Clearances that followed Culloden. Argyll and Bute, warmed by the Gulf Stream, have many spectacular gardens whereas Stirling and the Trossachs are Scotland's first National Park, encompassing 720 square miles of superb walking country. Rob Roy's grave can be seen at Balquhidder on Loch Voil and Inchmahone Priory, Port of Menteith was once the childhood home of Mary, Queen of Scots. Stirling was the site of Wallace's famous victory over the English in 1297.

From the heather moorland around Loch Rannoch in West Perthshire and the Pitlochry Drama festival to the well manicured golf courses of St Andrews in Fife, where golf was invented 400 years ago, there is always plenty to do and see in this Central Scottish belt.

Sidebar

TOP 10 — Historic Houses Gardens and Parks

Achamore Gardens, Isle of Gigha, Argyll
Ardenvraig Gardens, Rothesay, Bute
Ardanaisieg Gardens, Loch Awe, Argyll
Arduaine Garden, Nr. Oban, Argyll
Blair Castle, Pitlochry, Perthshire
Dunstaffnage Castle, by Oban
Inveraray Castle, Jail & Gardens, Argyll
Kilmory Gardens & Woodland Park, Lochgilphead
Stirling Castle, Stirling
Torosay Castle & Gardens, Isle of Mull

TOP 10 — Attractions

Argyll Wildlife Park, Inveraray
Armadale Castle Gardens & Museum of the Isles, Skye
Bannockburn Heritage Centre, Stirling
Duart Castle, Isle of Mull
Dunvegan Castle, Isle of Skye
Glamis Castle, Angus
Inchmahome Priory, Port of Menteith
Rob Roy & Trossachs Visitor Centre, Callander, Perthshire
Scone Palace, Nr. Perth
St Andrews Castle & Cathedral, Fife

TOP 10 — Walks and Nature Trails

Carsaig Arches, Carsaig, Isle of Mull
The Hermitage Woodland Walk, Dunkeld, Perthshire
Kings Cave Shore, Blackwaterfoot, Arran
Lauder Forest Walks, Strachur, Argyll
Prince Charlie's Cave > Dalwhinnie, Perthshire
Rannoch Station > Loch Spean > Fort William
Queens View Centre, Loch Tummel, Nr. Pitlochry
Scottish Deer Centre, Cupar, Fife
Tulliebaccart to Lundie Crags, Nr. Coupar Angus, Perthshire
West Highland Way. Glasgow (Bearsden) to Fort William

The Highlands

Glenlivet Distillery and Blairfindy Castle

Balmoral Castle

Sutherland and the far **North** of Scotland have some of the most unspoiled terrain in Europe. They have much to offer - spectacular mountains, majestic glens and mirror-like lochs form the backdrop to picturesque towns, isolated crofts, towering castles and pagoda-topped distilleries. A startling variety of wildlife also makes its home in the sea lochs and glens where an unbroken thread of human history reaches back into the mists of time. There are ruined brochs of the Iron Age people and carved stones left by Dark Age picts. Nowhere else in the British Isles are you able to drive for 30 miles without seeing a habitation or another car, but beware, the single track (with passing places) roads of the north west are unsuitable for trailers or caravans.

This is some of Britain's best walking and climbing country; also the land of the **Helmsdale**, arguably Britain's best salmon river. History, legend and romance and the great outdoors combine seamlessly here to guarantee visitors a warm Highland welcome and a truly memorable holiday.

The **North-East** of Scotland likewise is blessed with outstanding scenery. The majestic **Grampian** mountains dominate the skyline to the **West** whilst **Aberdeen**, Scotland's third largest city, has a vibrant, prosperous air.

Stacks near John O'Groats

The Malt Whisky Trail from, **Aviemore**, through **Speyside** to **Huntly**, takes in eight major distilleries and cooperage, all open to the public. There is also the **Castle Trail** on **Royal Deeside** which takes in 11 of the finest gems the region has to offer, including **Balmoral**. On the **coast** are empty beaches, interspersed with picturesque fishing villages and dramatic clifftop scenery waiting to be explored. The ski slopes of **Glenshee** and **Aviemore** are readily accessible, championship golf courses are there to be played.

Banchory Lodge Hotel
Banchory, Aberdeenshire AB31 5HS

251

T (0870) 860 8451 F (01330) 825019 E enquiries@banchorylodge.co.uk
T (International) +44 [0] (1330) 822625 W www.banchorylodge.co.uk

Privately owned and run, Banchory Lodge Hotel offers superior accommodation in a riverside setting. The elegant, flower-filled public rooms are enhanced by a considerable collection of pictures and antiques and the comfortable bedrooms include four-posters and family rooms, most with river views. The hotel bar, dominated by an ornate carved counter, serves a good range of malts as well as wines and spirits. The freshly prepared, imaginative dishes are served in the Riverview restaurant and created by an award winning chef and team including *Grampian Seafood Chef of the Year 2005*. The daily changing menus include fresh Scottish salmon and Aberdeen Angus beef. There is fishing directly from the hotel's lawn or nearby beats can be rented daily or weekly. Drying and freezing facilities are provided; a ghillie is available and equipment can be hired locally. Royal Deeside has much to offer the visitor, including the Castle Trail, The Whisky Trail and the Victorian Heritage Trail. There is golf in the village, splendid walks and other activities near at hand: shooting, pony-trekking, bird-watching and sailing to name a few.

⊨ 22 ⚥&♨♫♙ ♖♞ 3x ♟♟♟100 P 50 🐎

Family owned fishing hotel on the banks of the Dee

Rates Single room with breakfast from £85; double from £150.
Meals Alc dinner. Lunch & spec. diets available. Last orders 2100; bfst fm 0700.
Leisure Breaks Three nights for the price of two; spring & autumn breaks.
Other Facilities Golf, watersports, squash, shooting, tennis nearby.

[Ad]

Directions
Entering Banchory from East, turn left at taffic lights in centre, hotel 150 yds on left
Nearby attractions
Crathes, Drum, Balmoral & Craigevar Castles, Falls of Feugh salmon leap.
Distances
Aberdeen 17, Dundee 55, Edinburgh 118

& major credit cards accepted. Open all year.

Aberdeenshire, Banchory

Abbots Brae
West Bay, Dunoon, Argyll PA23 7QJ
T (0870) 860 8450 F (01369) 701191 E info@abbotsbrae.co.uk
T (International) +44 [0] (1369) 705021 W www.abbotsbrae.co.uk

The Cowal peninsula is one of Scotland's hidden treasures. It has picturesque freshwater lochs, stunning sea lochs, glorious views over the Firth of Clyde to Ayrshire and to distant Ben Lomond. Dunoon is the Western gateway to Loch Lomond & Trossachs National Park. Close to Dunoon is Scotland's most magnificent Benmore Botanic Garden and a delightful small hotel called Abbot's Brae. This 'house on a hill' was built in the 1800s by a Glasgow glass merchant. Fine trees were planted around the house but the view was left unimpaired. This year Colin and Christine Macpherson have taken over the hotel. With a hospitality background, they are building on the previous owners' reputation and giving personal attention to detail and good food. They have the confidence and natural ease to treat their guests as special. Bedrooms are individually decorated with great style and comfort and most have wonderful views. Bathrooms are modern with a Victorian touch. All rooms are named after local villages and a guest folder relates the history of each place, encouraging guests to leave their 'rooms with a view' for a bit of local exploring.

Small family owned hotel with views over the Firth of Clyde

Directions
From Glasgow M8/A8 ferry from Gourock. Hotel at s'th'n end of town on Bullwood Rd
Nearby attractions
Benmore Botanic Gdn, Mt Stewart Hse Gdns, Quadmania, River Rocket
Distances
Glasgow 27, Oban 77, Edinburgh 73.

Rates Single room wth breakfast from £55; double from £70.
Meals 3-cse tdh dinner £23; spec. diets avail; last orders 2030; bfst from 0800.
Leisure Breaks Romantic Breaks, Two nights, dinner, bed & breakfast with a bottle of champagne & box of chocolates in room from only £219 per couple.

Other Facilities Fishing, golf, watersports, sailing, shooting, riding nearby.

Visa & Mastercard accepted. Open all year.

Argyll & Bute, Dunoon

The George Hotel
Main Street East, Inveraray, Argyll PA32 8TT

T (0870) 860 8453 **F** (01499) 302098 **E** info@thegeorgehotel.co.uk
T (International) +44 [0] (1499) 302111 **W** www.thegeorgehotel.co.uk

253

The present George Hotel was originally two Georgian private houses, part of a project by the third Duke of Argyll in 1774 to build a New Town at Inveraray. In 1860 these were acquired by the Clark family, the seventh generation of whom are now in residence. The George today has fifteen bedrooms, refurbished in country house style and in keeping with the building's history and contours, some with large bathrooms, some with jacuzzis or Victorian roll-top tubs. Its strength has always been its ambience, cuisine and warmth of welcome - a perfect setting for good food and company. The two bars are lively haunts for local and visitor alike, with a wide choice of real ales and over 100 malt whiskies. The emphasis in the dining room is on using the very best of local produce - well hung West Highland beef and lamb from the market, seafood and fish from the local port of Tarbert and Loch Fyne salmon. Inveraray is the perfect centre for touring Argyll. It has its own castle and jail, walks on the Argyll estate, Crarae Gardens and Ardkinglas Gardens, a farming museum and fishing and golf nearby. Helpful staff at the George will be pleased to advise on how to get the best out of this fascinating area.

 15 🐾 🐕 👥 40 🅿 12

Rates Single room with breakfast from £35; double £70-135.
Meals Conservatory/Cocktail Bar/Public Bar. Alc, lunch & spec. diets avail; last orders 2100; bfst from 0800.

Other Facilities Golf, sea/river bathing, tennis, riding nearby.

 & major credit cards accepted. Open all year exc 25 Dec & 1st Jan.

Family run inn in centre of historic 'capital' of the West Highlands

Directions
From Glasgow A82/A83 to Inveraray. Hotel in centre opposite church

Nearby attractions
Inveraray Castle & Jail, Crarae Gardens, Auchindrain Township.

Distances Arrochar 21, Lochgilphead 24, Oban 38, Glasgow 60, Edinburgh 99

Argyll & Bute, Inveraray

Ardanaiseig Hotel

Kilchrenan, Taynuilt, Argyll PA35 1HE

T (0870) 418 8218 **F** (01866) 833222 **E** ardanaiseig@clara.net
T (International) +44 [0] (1866) 833333 **W** www.ardanaiseig.com

The ten mile journey from Taynuilt down a single track road to Loch Awe may seem long but the moment one enters the lime tree lined drive of this Victorian country house , the sense of anticipation quickens. Tall astricalled windows, more reminiscent of the Georgian period, allow light to flood into the handsome rooms and guests to lose themselves in the haunting views. Bedrooms are decorated with singular style and strong colours, which along with the eccentric collection of oriental antiques and paintings, make this hotel a delight to visit. This year a one-bedroom suite, *The Boatshed*, down by the jetty, has been added to the room inventory - the ultimate hideaway. Chef Garry Goldie, makes best use of local produce in the AA ❀❀ restaurant. Fresh water comes in old-fashioned 'pop' bottles, straight from the hills. We strolled through the estate's famous 100 acre gardens, saw the 130-ft high and 20ft girth fir tree, the restored wall garden and went down to the loch, with its mystical outlook over wooded islands to the mountains beyond. Quality of light and constant colour changes in this part of the Highlands are always dramatic.

Victorian country house with fantastic views over Loch Awe

🛏 16 🍴 ♿ ✿ ☉ ♟ ⚒ 🏮 △ ✓ ✇ ⚖

Directions
From East A85 to Taynuilt, then B845 signed Kilchrenan. Turn left at lochside.

Nearby attractions
Ardanaiseig Gardens, Arduaine Gdn
Oban, Kilmartin Glen, Achnacloich Gdn.

Distances
Oban 18, Glasgow 87, Edinburgh117

Rates Single room wth breakfast from £76; double from £138. [Ad]
Meals Tdh 3-cse dinner £42; lunch & spec. diets avail; last orders 2045; bfst fm 0800
Leisure Breaks spring & Autumn Breaks - stay three nights for price of two.
Other Facilities Loch bathing. Golf 6m, riding 10m.

 & major credit cards accepted. Open all year exc Jan 3rd-Feb 10th.

Greywalls Hotel

Muirfield, Gullane, East Lothian EH31 2EG

T (0870) 418 8215 F (01620) 842241 E hotel@greywalls.co.uk
T (International) +44 [0] (1620) 842144 W www.greywalls.co.uk

255

This lovely hotel enjoys views over the Firth of Forth and Muirfield Golf Course. Its architecture, history, atmosphere and award-winning restaurant combine to make a stay at Greywalls a very pleasurable experience. The then holiday home was created by the architect of New Delhi, Sir Edwin Lutyens, in 1901 and later the leading Scottish architect Sir Robert Lorimer added a wing, making Greywalls a unique co-operation between two eminent designers, as well as being the only complete Lutyens house in Scotland. The beautiful walled garden has been attributed to Gertrude Jekyll. One famous visitor was King Edward VII and his outside lavatory is now a charming bedroom aptly named *The King's Loo*. Greywalls became an hotel in 1948 and the same family, which has now owned it for over 75 years, continue to impart the atmosphere of a private house to their guests. This shows in the bedrooms and the wood panelled library with its open fire. The bar is cosy and the sun room a delight. David Williams presides over the acclaimed restaurant, specialising in British cuisine using the best of Scottish produce. Greywalls is an enchanting place and the hotel's particular magic has few equals.

🛏 23 ⚡ 🎣 ❄ 🔟 ▶₁₈ ♒ ⋕ 20 🅿 20

Enchanting Lutyens-designed hotel facing Muirfield golf course

Rates Single room with breakfast from £140; double from £280.
Meals Last orders 2130. Bfst from 0700.
Leisure Breaks Spring and Autumn Breaks available.
Other Facilities Airport pick-up can be arranged.

[Ad] **Directions**
From Edinburgh take A1/A198 for Gullane.
At end of village, brown hotel sign to left.

Nearby attractions
Bass Rock, Lennoxlove Hse Haddington, Mus of Flight Nth Berwick, Winton Hse

Distances
Haddington 7, Berwick-u-T 45, Edinburgh 18

& major credit cards accepted. Open March - December.

East Lothian, Gullane

Royal Marine Hotel

Golf Road, Brora, Sutherland KW9 6QS

T (0870) 860 8458 **F** (01408) 621181 **E** info@highlandescape.com
T (International) +44 [0] (1408) 621252 **W** www.highlandescapehotels.com

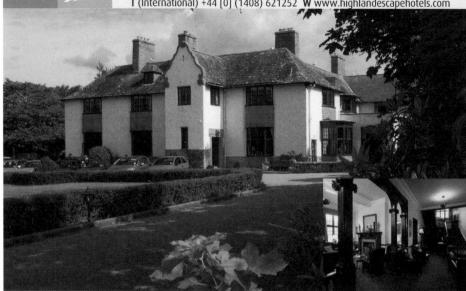

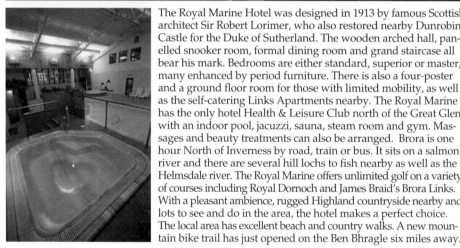

The Royal Marine Hotel was designed in 1913 by famous Scottish architect Sir Robert Lorimer, who also restored nearby Dunrobin Castle for the Duke of Sutherland. The wooden arched hall, panelled snooker room, formal dining room and grand staircase all bear his mark. Bedrooms are either standard, superior or master, many enhanced by period furniture. There is also a four-poster and a ground floor room for those with limited mobility, as well as the self-catering Links Apartments nearby. The Royal Marine has the only hotel Health & Leisure Club north of the Great Glen with an indoor pool, jacuzzi, sauna, steam room and gym. Massages and beauty treatments can also be arranged. Brora is one hour North of Inverness by road, train or bus. It sits on a salmon river and there are several hill lochs to fish nearby as well as the Helmsdale river. The Royal Marine offers unlimited golf on a variety of courses including Royal Dornoch and James Braid's Brora Links. With a pleasant ambience, rugged Highland countryside nearby and lots to see and do in the area, the hotel makes a perfect choice. The local area has excellent beach and country walks. A new mountain bike trail has just opened on the Ben Bhragle six miles away.

A 'resort' hotel and golf course on Scotland's north-eastern coast

22 (inc 1 🛏) 👤 ☉ 🐟 ⛴ 🎣 🍸 🍴 ⛳ 🏌 (£5 stay) ♨ 70 **P** 40 🐾

Directions
A9 from Inverness into centre of Brora, take sign twds sea, saying 'golf course'

Nearby attractions
Dunrobin Cas, Castle of Mey, Falls of Shin, Clynelish Distillery, Timespan Her Centre

Distances
Wick 49, Inverness 78, Edinburgh 234.

Rates Single room with breakfast from £79; double/twin from £130.

Meals Lorimer Restaurant, Hunters Bistro, Garden Room Cafe Bar; alc, lunch & spec. diets available; last orders 2045; bfst fm 0730.

Other Facilities Fishing 2m. Sea & river bathing.

[AMERICAN EXPRESS] & major credit cards accepted. Open all year.

Highland, Brora

Flodigarry Country House Hotel

Flodigarry, Staffin, Isle of Skye IV51 9HZ
T (0870) 418 8209 **F** (01470) 552301 **E** info@flodigarry.co.uk
T (International) +44 [0] (1470) 552203 **W** www.flodigarry.co.uk

257

Flodigarry sits at the northeast corner of Skye in splendid isolation, with the Quiraing as backdrop and views over Staffin Bay. It is exceptionally situated for those who wish to spot golden eagles, whales and basking sharks, otters and seals. The hotel can organise wildlife expeditions together with a choice of walks, some easy, some more challenging! There are 11 bedrooms in the main house and a further seven in Flora Macdonald's Cottage (*pictured top right*), situated in the grounds. These are cosy with low ceilings in character, some with direct garden access. Flora lived here after she had helped Bonnie Prince Charlie 'over the sea to Skye' and ultimately to escape to France. Today the fine dining menu might start with crab claws, Skye mussels or marinated duck, followed by baked monkfish or best end of Highland lamb, local ingredients being used wherever possible. A bistro menu can be served in the conservatory, with its fabulous bay views. Savoury bar snacks are also available. Your host Robbie Cairns and his friendly staff will make you feel especially welcome in this breathtaking spot.

🚗 18 ⚌ ♿ 🐎 🦌 🏹 📻 🎣 🔍 ♨ 30 🅿 40 🐎

Splendidly isolated comfortable hotel next to Flora Macdonald's cottage

Rates Single room with breakfast from £100; double from £130. [Ad]
Meals 4-cse tdh dinner £36; alc, bar, bistro, lunch & spec. diets available.
Leisure Breaks Log fire Winter Breaks from £30 per person, b & b; Spring Break and Autumn Gold Break from £35 per person b & b.
Other Facilities Guided wildlife walks, sea fishing. Golf, shooting, squash, tennis, riding nearby.

Visa & Mastercard accepted. Open all year.

Directions
From Portree take A855 through Staffin. Hotel on right 1¹/₂ m after Digg.
Nearby attractions
Skye Mus of Island Life, Dunvegan Cas, Cuillin Hills, Quiraing, Dinosaur footprints
Distances
Portree 20, Skye Bridge 53, Edinburgh 240

Highland, Isle of Skye

Greshornish House Hotel
Edinbane, by Portree, Isle of Skye IV51 9PN
T (0870) 418 8237 **F** (01470) 582345 **E** info@greshornishhouse.com
T (International) +44 [0] (1470) 582266 **W** www.greshornishhouse.com

Dating from the mid-18th century, Greshornish occupies a secluded site up a single track road on the shores of Loch Greshornish, between Portree and Dunvegan on the beautiful island of Skye. This warm and friendly family run hotel is the ideal place to enjoy the gentle pace of Skye life. Situated within 10 acres of gardens and wooded grounds, including possibly the only hard tennis court on the island, the hotel has nine bedrooms, each of varying size and including four posters, doubles and twins. Food is sourced locally, with an abundance of local seafood, Skye lamb and Scotch beef on the menu as well as an exceptional range of Scottish cheeses. Non-residents are welcomed and there are anchorages, moorings and a jetty within yards of the hotel. A walk along the shore might reveal otters, seals, eider, heron, curlew or a glimpse of the sea eagle soaring overhead. Greshornish's location, with views across to the Trotternish peninsula, make it an ideal base from which to visit Skye's many attractions, including Dunvegan Castle, Skyeskyns Tannery and the Talisker distillery.

Charming family run small hotel on the shores of Loch Greshornish 🛏9 🍴 ☺ 🪑 🔟 ♻ 🎵 🐾 (£4 fee) **P**

Directions
Right off Portree-Dunvegan rd, single track 2 m, then drive on right. Watch for sheep!

Nearby attractions
Dunvegan Castle, Edinbane Pottery, Talisker Distillery, Neist Pt Lighthouse

Distances
Portree 17, Skye Bridge 45, Edinburgh 197

Rates Single room with breakfast from £70; double from £140.
Meals 3-cse tdh dinner fm £32.50; lunch & spec. diets available.
Other Facilities Golf, sea bathing, horse riding, sailing nearby.

 Visa, Maestro, Mastercard accepted. Closed Xmas/part Nov. & part Feb.

Highland, Isle of Skye

Viewfield House

Portree, Isle of Skye, Highland IV51 9EU

T (0870) 860 8526 **F** (01478) 613517 **E** info@viewfieldhouse.com
T (International) +44 [0] (1478) 612217 **W** www.viewfieldhouse.com

Viewfield House offers a unique opportunity to stay in style and comfort in what has been the home of the Macdonald family for over 200 years. The house stands in extensive wooded grounds on the outskirts of Portree, overlooking Portree Bay and within easy walking distance of the centre. The house has retained many of its Victorian features. Guests eat in Victorian splendour beneath family portraits or mementoes from India. The 10 en suite bedrooms are tastefully decorated, each in their own style, with several overlooking the bay. There is plenty to do on Skye: boat trips to Gairloch, Raasey or round the harbour, fishing, sailing, walking in the Cuillin Hills, pony trekking and golf. Or you could visit the otter haven at Kylerhea or take a scenic drive around the coast admiring the striking scenery and visiting Dunvegan Castle, home to the MacLeod Clan since time immemorial. When you return exhausted after your excursion, sit down in peace and quiet in the spacious drawing room with a cup of tea or a wee dram by the open fire. Host Hugh Macdonald will be able to recommend you several eateries in the nearby town of Portree.

🛏 10 ✂ ♿ ❀ 🦃 🔟 🕺 ✔ 🐕 🅿 WIFI

Victorian house on the outskirts of Portree, offering quality bed & breakfast

Rates Single room with breakfast from £55; double from £100.
Meals No evening meal but many restaurants within walking distance.
Other Facilities Fishing 2m, golf 9m, riding 3m. Sailing, squash, shooting, indoor pool within 1 mile.
Leisure Breaks 3 days b & b gets 5% discount + free bottle of house wine.

Visa & Mastercard accepted. Open April-October.

Directions
Fm Skye roadbridge (allow one hour) A850 to Portree, drive on left opp. BP garage
Nearby attractions
Dunvegan Castle, Armadale Cas/ Grds, Talisker Distillery, The Cuillins
Distances
Skye Br. 32, Mallaig ferry 44, Edinburgh 184

Highland, Isle of Skye

260

Pool House
Poolewe, Wester Ross IV22 2LD
T (0870) 860 8457 F (01445) 781403 E enquiries@poolhousehotel.com
T (International) +44 [0] (1445) 781272 W www.poolhousehotel.com

Pool House is an unashamedly luxurious all-suite hotel on the shores of Loch Ewe, in one of the most remote and beautiful locations of Wester Ross, dubbed by the Sunday Times *'the most romantic hotel in Scotland'*. The original 17 bedrooms have been transformed into eight luxury suites. One, *The Diadem*, has a tile from the Titanic on its wall as well as a replica of one of the ship's china services. A two-bedroom/two bathroom suite *The Nairana*, and a residential boathouse with hot tub are due to open soon. The Harrison daughters scour the world for antiques, nautical relics and reproductions to put in these sumptuous rooms. Bathrooms have free standing Victorian baths and large power showers; log fires burn in the sitting areas; magazines, books, fruit and flowers abound. The indulgence continues in the dining room, whose ceiling bears a hand painted gold leaf compass. Cuisine is supervised by chef John Moir who makes best use of his own vegetables and locally caught salmon and scallops, Scottish beef and venison. Inverewe Gardens are next door and Scotland's Gulf Stream-warmed northwest coastline all around. Only one and a half hours' drive from Inverness Airport, Pool House is the ultimate venue for a romantic, self-indulgent break.

Luxurious all-suite hotel on the shores of Loch Ewe	🛏 8 suites ✗ ❀ 🍴 🎵 P 20

Directions
Fm Inverness A835 twds Ullapool. At Garve take the A832 for Gairloch. Hotel 6m north.

Nearby attractions
Inverewe Gardens, Highland Hawking, Beim Eighe Nature Reserve.

Distances
Ullapool 50, Inverness 78, Edinburgh 234

Rates Double inc. breakfast from £250.
Meals 5-cse tdh dinner £45; spec. diets avail; last orders 2145; bfst fm 0800.
Leisure Breaks If staying both Friday & Saturday nights, Sunday b&b charged ¹/₂ price.
Other Facilities Indoor swimming pool ¹/₄ mile (fee payable). Golf, sea bathing, sailing, squash, tennis, riding, nearby.

 & Visa, Mastercard, JCB accepted. Open all year exc. January.

Highland, Poolewe

Eddrachilles Hotel

Badcall Bay, Scourie, Sutherland IV27 4TH

T (0870) 418 8225 **F** (01971) 502477 **E** enq@eddrachilles.com
T (International) +44 [0] (1971) 502080 **W** www.eddrachilles.com

261

Presbyterian ministers had a knack of choosing perfect sites for their Manses and Eddrachilles is no exception. Sheltered by gentle hills and with stunning views, this is a place to escape to. The new owners are enthusiastic about their new home and enjoy sharing it with their guests. Everything is home produced with a selection of home made chutneys and conserves available to buy. The menu changes daily and there is a good wine list and over 116 malt whiskies in the bar. The seafood is outstanding and the beef, venison and lamb from Highland farms unsurpassed. Bedrooms are freshly decorated and the conservatory has huge wicker chairs in which to relax. The North of Scotland is unique. Its remote and untouched beauty can be best explored on quiet single-track roads, or by one of numerous scenic walks and climbs over beach, cliff and hill. The hotel has an excellent list of walks both from the hotel, in the local area and further afield such as around Sandwood Bay and the Bone Caves. Handa Island, the famous bird sanctuary, can easily be visited by boat from nearby Tarbet. Fishermen have no restriction on the number of brown trout they may catch on nearby hill lochs.

Former manse with stunning views of Scourie Bay and Handa Island

Rates Single/double room with breakfast from £45; dinner, room & breakfast from £57.
Meals Last orders for dinner 2000; bar lunches & special diets available.
Leisure Breaks Reduced rates for stays of 3, 6 or10 days.
Other Facilities Children of three+ welcome.

Switch, Visa & Mastercard accepted. Open March-October.

Directions
From Inverness A9/A835 via Ullapool to Ledmore, then rt A894 Durness Rd to Badcall
Nearby attractions
Handa Island, Ardvreck Castle, Aluinn Falls, Cape Wrath, Kerracher Gardens
Distances
Ullapool 40, Inverness 98, Edinburgh 245

Highland, Scourie

Tigh an Eilean Hotel

262 Shieldaig on Loch Torridon, Ross-shire IV54 8XN

T (0870) 860 8459 **F** (01520) 755321 **E** tighaneileanhotel@shieldaig.fsnet.co.uk
T (International) +44 [0] (1520) 755251 **W** www.signpost.co.uk/tighaneilean

Shieldaig is an unbelievably beautiful spot on the West coast of Scotland, facing its own sheltered loch, part of the larger Loch Torridon, and with the Torridon mountains rising behind. It is a white painted fishing village with no modern buildings, the hubs being the hotel, the pub and the shop. Christopher and Cathryn Field left London eight years ago to fulfil their dream of running a small Highland hotel and Tigh an Eilean (*The House of the Island*) is the triumphant result. The eleven bedrooms, most with sea views, are individually decorated in restful greys and greens with pretty wallpaper and curtains. The airy dining room looks out to sea and sports modern pottery and driftwood sculptures on its walls. Its award winning cuisine specialises in the finest from the sea, river and hill cooked with flair and imagination. There are no TVs or telephones in rooms but there is a TV lounge and Internet access. The surrounding mountains make for one of the most dramatic landscapes in the Highlands, ideal for hill walkers. Fishermen will find the hill lochs stuffed with brown trout and there are sandy beaches, rock pools and two golf courses nearby. If you want to forget yourself in the West Highlands, then this is the place for you.

Exceptionally peaceful small hotel on Loch Torridon

🛏 11 🍴 ⛰ 🏃 🎿 🐾 🅿 🎪

Directions From Inverness take A9/A832 to Kinlochewe, then A896 to Torridon & Shieldaig. Hotel in middle of village on sea
Nearby attractions Inverewe Gardens, Beinn Eighe Nature Reserve, Applecross, Eilean Donan Cas.
Distances Inverness 68, Skye Bridge 37, Edinburgh 237

Rates Single room with breakfast from £68; double from £144.
Meals 3-cse dinner £38 (£42 non-residents); lunch (bar only) & spec. diets available; last orders 2030; bfst fm 0800.
Leisure Breaks Special dinner, b & b packages available for stays of 5+days; (3 days March/April & Oct).
Other Facilities Golf 17m. Fabulous varied hiking, fishing, beaches & sea bathing nearby.
Visa & Mastercard accepted. Open mid-March to end October.

Highland, Shieldaig

Dunalastair Hotel

The Square, Kinloch Rannoch, Pitlochry, Perthshire PH16 5PW

T (0870) 860 8452 **F** (01882) 632371 **E** info@dunalastair.co.uk
T (International) +44 [0] (1882) 632323 **W** www.dunalastair.co.uk

263

The Dunalastair is the Warm Heart of the Highlands, amidst layers of highland lochside forest and mountain scenery right in the middle of Scotland, yet near Pitlochry and Perth, thus very accessible by road and rail. The hotel specialises in activity holidays organised in conjunction with Activity Scotland ranging from pony trekking to white water rafting. Otherwise there are great walks around the hotel or a visit to a whisky distillery can be arranged. Bedrooms have been recently refurbished and their individual decor combined with classic furniture make them veritable 'comfort zones'. The Rob Roy four-poster room, where Liam Neeson stayed during location work, must be the *pièce de résistance*. Cuisine is classic Scottish - well presented with full use made of Scotland's larder on the doorstep. House wines are excellent value and the hotel is an outlet for Ian Mellis specialist cheeses. The Dunalastair's mission is to provide the most complete Highland Experience and the friendly staff strain every sinew to achieve this. Once sampled, you will want to go back for more!

Comfortable family-owned hotel at the 'Warm Heart of the Highlands'

🛏 28 ⊁⊙♨♪✓▲🐎 (£5 per night) 3x ♦♦♦ 102 P 50 ⛳

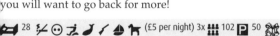

Rates Single room with breakfast from £45; double from £80. [Ad]
Meals 3-cse tdh dinner in AA ☺ Schiehallion Restaurant £27.50; alc, lunch & diets available; last orders 2100; bfst fm 0730. Stables, Cocktail & Whisky Bars.
Leisure Breaks Weekday breaks fm £99 per pers for 2 nts dinner, b & b. Weekend breaks fm £109 per pers 2 nts dbb. Whisky Weekends, Activity, Spa, Xmas, Valentines etc breaks available
Other Facilities Outdoor activity centre. Fishing, golf & riding nearby.

& major credit cards + Switch accepted. Open all year.

Directions
A9 Pitlochry then B8019/B846 to Kinloch Rannoch. Hotel in centre on square

Nearby attractions
Blair Castle, House of Bruar, Pitlochry Theatre, Edradour Distillery, Queens View

Distances
Pitlochry 21, Rannoch ⇌ 20, Edinburgh 92

Perth & Kinross, Kinloch Rannoch

264

Loch Tummel Inn

Queens View, Strathtummel, Pitlochry, Perthshire PH16 5RP

T (0870) 860 8527 **F** (01882) 634272 **E** info@lochtummelinn.co.uk
T (International) +44 [0] (1882) 634272 **W** www.lochtummelinn.co.uk

Just past the famous Queens View, 10 miles from Pitlochry, on a stunning scenic road along the banks of Loch Tummel, The Inn presents a quite charming taste of glorious Highland hospitality, quintess-entially Scottish in an unmistakeable unspoiled traditional country inn style. Now under the same ownership as The Dunalastair (*see previous page*), Loch Tummel Inn is a romantic getaway, steeped in olde worlde style, in a spectacular lochside position with seven delightful bedrooms, many with their original fireplaces. Guests start the day with a hearty Scottish breakfast in the Hayloft Restaurant, and usually return for a delightful evening meal, accompanied by fine wines. Alternatively guests can eat in the bar/bistro and sit at the wooden tables outside and drink in the marvellous views. Inside there are wood burning fireplaces, antique fixtures and fittings, two residents' lounges well stocked with books, games and magazines for wet days - you'll never want to leave. Pitlochry has Highland Games, a Drama Festival, a distillery and the House of Bruar just up the road.

Lochside inn in the Heart of the Highlands, with superb views

Directions
A9 Pitlochry then B8019 twds Kinloch Rannoch. Hotel 5m on right side of rd.

Nearby attractions
Blair Castle, House of Bruar, Pitlochry Theatre, Edradour Distillery, Queens View

Distances
Pitlochry 5, Rannoch ⇌ 32, Edinburgh 76

(£5 per night) 20 **P** 30

Rates Single room with breakfast from £40; double from £70.

Meals 3-cse tdh dinner in Hayloft Restaurant £26; alc, lunch & diets available; last orders 2100; bfst fm 0730.

Leisure Breaks Weekday breaks fm £100 per pers for 2 nts dinner, b & b. Weekend breaks fm £110 per pers 2 nts dbb.

Other Facilities Golf, tennis & riding nearby.

 & major credit cards + Switch accepted. Open all year

265

Signpost Guide 2007
Channel Islands

Fact File
Illustrated Guide to
Historic Houses and Gardens,
Attractions and Walks

Channel Islands

Britains' southernmost islands lie some 14 miles off the French coast, yet despite many French place names, they have not been owned by France since William the Conqueror. Each has its own appeal: Alderney's St Annes has the character of a Normandy village, Guernsey has strong links with fishing and the sea; Jersey is a cosmopolitan offshore financial centre; Herm and Sark are car-free zones.

Hotels guide

Guernsey	page 269
Herm	page 271
Jersey	page 272
Sark	page 275

Further information:
Visit Guernsey
PO Box 23, St. Peter Port GY1 3AN
Tel: 01481 723 552

www.visitguernsey.com

Jersey Tourism
Liberation Square, St. Helier, JE1 1BB
Tel: 01534 500 700

www.jersey.com

Historic Houses Gardens and Parks

Candle Gardens, St Peter Port
Castle Cornet Specialist Gardens
Chateau de Marais, St Peter Port
Lihou Island Chapel
Le Friquet Flower
& Butterfly Centre
Little Chapel, Les Vaubelets
Oatlands Craft Centre, St Sampson
Royal Court Parliament Bldg,
St Peter Port
Sausmarez Manor, St Martins
Vale Castle, St Sampson

Attractions

Castle Cornet Museum
Folk Museum, Cobo Bay
Fort Grey Maritime Museum
German Occupation Museum
German Underground Hospital
Guernsey Aquarium, Havelet Bay
Guernsey Bird Sanctuary,
St Andrew's
Guernsey Museum & Art Gallery,
St Peter Port
Guernsey Zoo
Victor Hugo's House, St Peter Port

Victor Hugo's House

Walks and Nature Trails

Fort Pembroke > Beaucette Marina
Fort Pembroke > Les Fouaillages
ruin, Grande Havre Bay
Grandes Rocques
Guernsey Cliff Path (west)
Pezeries Point > Icart Point
Guernsey Cliff Path (east)
Icart Point > St Peter Port
Perelle Bay
prehistoric ruins & fort walk
Port Soif Nature Trail
Sausmarez Nature Trail & Park
Walk, starting at Cobo Bay
St Peter Port Harbour Walk
St Peter Port >
St Martin's Point Walk

Guernsey

Harbour, St Peter Port

Guernsey is a veritable haven for the holiday maker with a modern airport, excellent harbour and a wide range of available accommodation. Street names are displayed in both English and French.. Now and again you catch a snatch of conversation between islanders in *patois* - a halfway dialect.

The island was once under the domination of the Norman dukes, then vassals of the French king. William II of Normandy, crowned William I of England in 1066, established the connection with England and ever since the Islands have been part of the *dominion* of the Kings of England, but never part of their kingdom. **St Peter Port**, the capital, is a flourishing commercial centre with a busy harbour. From the castle ramparts throughout the summer, there booms the noonday gun - shades of the old Hong Kong.

Guernsey has many unique attractions for the visitor. The **Little Chapel** is the smallest in the world, lavishly decorated with pottery and shells and with room for only five worshippers at a time. **Victor Hugo** lived in exile in the town for 15 years and his former house is now a museum. There are a host of museums, a zoo, a butterfly centre and a variety of archeological sites; also spectacular cliff walks and beautiful countryside to explore.

The island is famous for its delicacies, not least *Guernsey Gache,* a sort of fruit loaf. A good place to buy some would be the Thursday **Old Guernsey Market**. Traditionally dressed stall holders sell all manner of island produced wares from freesia corms to the famous eponymous sweaters. There is much to fascinate the holiday maker on Guernsey. The islanders, proud of their heritage, will afford the warmest of welcomes.

Sausmarez Manor

Jersey

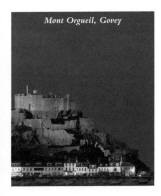

Mont Orgueil, Govey

Jersey is the largest and most southerly of the Channel Islands, 100 miles south of England, yet only 14 miles from the French coast. Measuring just 45 square miles, it's an island big enough to lose yourself in, yet small enough to feel at home.

Leave the car behind and make tracks on foot or pedal along green country lanes for a breathtaking discovery of the island. The 96-mile cycle network has been designed to give precedence to pedestrians and cyclists, allowing you to discover new sights and experiences.

Jersey fits an encyclopaedic amount of history into its pocket book size and it comes to life everywhere. In just a short distance, it is possible to travel from prehistoric to post-war times. In the East is **Mont Orgueil Castle**, overlooking Grouville Bay. Originally built in the 13th century as a first line of defence against the French, it has recently

undergone a five-year programme of repair and reconstruction.

The Maritime Museum uses state-of-the-art interactive displays to celebrate Jersey's long association with the sea. **The Jersey War Tunnels** record the occupation of Jersey during the second world war.

The Durrell Wildlife Conservation Trust is a 'must-see' for any visitor to the island. First established nearly 50 years ago by Gerald Durrell, it is set in 40 acres of parkland and aims to save as many threatened species as possible from extinction.

Jersey may measure just nine miles by five, but it is packed with interesting things to see and do. Whatever your age and whatever time of year you visit, you will be assured of a warm welcome.

Le River Tower

Bohemia, St Helier

Alderney, Herm and Sark

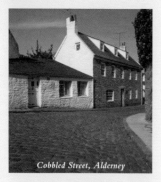

Cobbled Street, Alderney

Alderney Society Museum
The Alderney Railway
The Alderney Lighthouse
Burhou Bird Sanctuary, Alderney
St Anne's Church, Alderney

Herm Harbour

St Tugal Church, Herm
Coastal Walk around Herm
Shell Beach, Herm
La Seigneurie, Sark
Fairy Grotto, Sark

The Sark Seigneur, John M Beaumont

Alderney is the third largest Channel Island, just 1.5 miles wide and 3.5 miles long, yet with 3000 friendly and welcoming inhabitants. It is only eight miles from France yet is known as 'the most English' of the islands, with a fledgling off-shore finance and E-commerce sector. It has an abundance of flora, fauna and wildlife, including black rabbits and white hedgehogs, beautiful beaches and a relaxed friendly lifestyle.

Sights include **St Anne's Church**, often referred to as *The Cathedral of the Channel Islands*, the **Alderney Society Museum**, covering the island's history and development, the cinema, library and **Alderney Railway**, the only one in the Islands, dubbed The Orient Express, running at weekends and Bank Holidays in the summer and a favourite for railway enthusiasts and children alike. The **Alderney Lighthouse**, which was automated in 1997, is open to the public.

Herm is three miles from the Guernsey coast and is reached by a daily 20-minute catamaran service. There is a regular boat connection (20 minutes) to the nearby island of Sark. 200 years ago 400 people lived on Herm,

largely employed in quarrying stone which was subsequently used to build St Peter Port Harbour, Guernsey. The island was purchased by the States of Guernsey after the war and leased out to the late Major Peter Wood. His family still own the **White House Hotel** *(see page 266)*. Herm measures just half a mile square, and the island can be covered on foot within a couple of hours. It has unspoilt beaches and a clean, unpolluted environment, with no cars. The neighbouring island of **Jethou** is now owned by the reclusive Barclay brothers.

Sark is the smallest of the main Channel islands, located some 80 miles off the south coast of England. Although only three miles long and half a mile wide, it boasts 40 miles of picturesque coastline. There are no cars; travel is by bicycle or horse-drawn cart. Sark used to have the last feudal constitution in the Western world, being governed by a seigneur, who held the island in perpetuity from the monarch. In 2007 the island's parliament, *The Chief Pleas*, will be made up for the first time of elected representatives drawn from the island's 600 residents. **The Seigneurie** is open to the public and its beautiful walled gardens are one of Sark's most popular attractions. More recently the island has been in the news as the yacht **The Spirit of Sark** won the Round Britain and Ireland Challenge in 2005, sailing in very difficult conditions.

La Grande Mare Hotel, Golf & Country Club
Vazon, Castel, Guernsey GY5 7LL

T (0870) 418 8231 **F** (01481) 256532 **E** hotellagrandemare@cwgsy.net
T (International) +44 [0] (1481) 256576 **W** www.lgmguernsey.net

Whatever your reason for visiting Guernsey - business, pleasure, a short break or a family holiday, La Grande Mare, with its beachside location and multiple leisure activities, should be high on your short list of places to stay. The hotel, spa and golf courses are family owned and run with attention to detail and guests' comfort and enjoyment the top priority. Spacious bedrooms have the finest linen sheets and are fitted out to a high standard. Dinner can either be taken in the formal restaurant or during the summer *al fresco* on the timber balcony beside the pool. Alternatively a snack meal is available in the conservatory. Within yards of the hotel is recreation of many kinds: a leisurely picnic by the lake, a walk or jog on the Vazon bay beach, a supervised workout in the gym, a swim, a game of tennis, a sauna, jacuzzi, or any form of water-sport. For the golfer, there is an 18-hole course set in 110 acres of parkland. It also caters for Corporate and Society Days with PGA tuition and a very well-stocked tax-free golf shop. Just 15 minutes from the airport and St Peter Port, La Grande Mare is a hotel with a lot to offer in comfort and style to visitors of all ages.

25 (inc 14 suites) ⊙ ♿ ✂ 📞 🏌 🛋 🍴 🍷 🎱 🔍 🧖 🏊 🚣 ⚓ ⛵ ♨ 30

Resort hotel on Vazon Beach, one of the longest on the island

Rates Single/double/twin inc breakfast from £84. [Ad]
Meals 3-cse tdh dinner £19.95; alc, lunch & spec diets avail; last orders 2100
Leisure Breaks of many sorts available - gourmet, golf, romantic, chill-out. See our tariff for details.
Other facilities Golf, watersports, sailing, tennis 3m, sea ¹/₂m.

 & all major credit cards accepted. Open all year.

Directions
From St Peter Port, follow signs to Castel & Sausmarez Park, branch left to Vazon Bay
Nearby attractions
Sausmarez Manor, Castle Cornet Gdns, Fort Grey Shipwreck Museum
Distances
St Peter Port 4, St Saviour 1, Airport 2

[Ad] after prices signifies that the hotel accepts the Signpost Advantage Card - see back of book for details. **Guernsey**, Castel

270

Guernsey

La Frégate Hotel
Les Cotils, St Peter Port, Guernsey GY1 1UT
T (0870) 418 8227 **F** (01481) 720443 **E** enquiries@lafregatehotel.com
T (International) +44 [0] (1481) 724624 **W** www.lafregatehotel.com

La Frégate was recommended to me by the owner of another Channel Islands hotel, based on the excellent reputation of its restaurant. What a discovery! This is certainly some hotel - it combines the charm and character of an 18th century Manor House with the chic style of a boutique hotel where accommodation, cuisine and service are the focus of attention. Located just a few minutes from St Peter Port's shopping and financial centres and set in its own secluded grounds, it occupies an enviable elevated position overlooking Guernsey's capital and harbour. Renowned for its excellent AA ©© restaurant, the mainly French cuisine features locally caught seafood and fresh vegetables from the hotel's own garden, a fine wine list and has spectacular sea views. The same view is enjoyed by 11 of the 13 bedrooms, many of which also have balconies, some of the 'Bay' rooms including a telescope. La Frégate is a little bit different - it is for the discerning guest who expects and appreciates real quality.

18th century manor house with the style of a boutique hotel

🛏 13 ⊙ ✗ 🏠 🄰 ♨ 32

Directions From St Peter Port harbour, take St Julian's Avenue, rt by Candie Gdns into Vauxlaurens, rurn right, hotel on right
Nearby attractions Sausmarez Manor, German Occupation & La Valette Underground Museums
Distances St Saviour 2, Airport 3.

Rates Single room with breakfast from £85; double from £135.
Meals 3-cse tdh dinner £26.50; alc, lunch & spec diets avail; last orders 2130; bfst from 0715.
Other facilities Fishing, sailing, watersports 300 yards.

 & all major credit cards accepted. Open all year.

Guernsey, St Peter Port

The White House Hotel
Herm Island, via Guernsey GY1 3HR

T (0870) 418 8232 **F** (01481) 710066 **E** hotel@herm-island.com
T (International) +44 [0] (1481) 722159 **W** www.herm-island.com

Herm is a 20-minute boat journey from Guernsey and is the smallest of the Channel Islands. There are no cars and Herm's magic starts to work as soon as you are greeted on the quayside: the pretty harbour houses the island's three shops and the Ship Inn. Nearby is the island's school, 10th century chapel and castellated manor, where the owners of the island, the Heyworths, live. There are bracing cliff walks and beautiful unspoiled beaches, wild flowers and clear landscapes for painting. As the gentle chugging of a tractor heralds the arrival of your luggage, you know the White House Hotel is special. How many hotels can boast an island as their garden, a harbourside setting and such spectacular sea views? Where else could you enjoy shellfish so fresh in the award-winning restaurant? You are assured of a warm and friendly welcome from Jonathan Watson and his staff. In the 40 delightful bedrooms, you'll find private bathrooms and baby listening but no televisions, clocks or telephones. Children have always been welcome, with a popular high tea for junior diners. The hotel encourages you to unwind and the island is perfect for that away-from-it-all break.

🛏 40 🍴 🛒 🚬 🍹 🐾 ⛵ ☂

Family friendly hotel overlooking Herm harbour

Rates Dinner, bed & breakfast from £76 per person per night.
Leisure Breaks £168 pp for two nights inc boat fare, wine, cookies & fudge.
Sunset September Break - 2 nights Sun-Wed £168 per person; 3 nights £226 per pers, inc boat fare, sparkling wine & chocolates on arrival.

Directions
Track up from the harbour.
Nearby attractions
Coastal Walk, St Tugal Church, Shell Beach.
Distances
St Peter Port, Guernsey 4m.

 & Visa, Mastercard, Euro, Switch accepted. Open April 2nd-October 10th.

Herm

272

The Club Hotel and Spa

Green Street, St Helier, Jersey JE2 4UH

T (0870) 860 8528 **F** (01534) 720371 **E** reservations@theclubjersey.com
T (International) +44 [0] (1534) 876500 **W** www.theclubjersey.com

The in-house newsletter for the Club Hotel & Spa is called *Indulgent Times*, and no title could better describe the experience awaiting you when you stay at this new modern boutique style hotel. In the heart of St Helier, its location is excellent for both business and leisure guest and its accommodation, restaurant and facilities are top class. Its contemporary elegance is reflected throughout the hotel - public areas are wonderfully bright and cheerful, and each of the 30 bedrooms and eight suites is luxuriously furnished to an extremely high standard. The exclusive Club Spa has attentive, professional staff offering an outstanding variety of treatments and its relaxing soft lighting and facilities are first class in promoting that feel-good factor - the salt water pool, the innovative Rasul room, the salt cabin, herbal steam room and sauna all beckon those who wish to relax and revitalise. And, after such an experience, you must complete your indulgence in the hotel's Bohemia restaurant. With four AA rosettes and a Michelin star, chic and sophisticated ambience and excellent service, this is fine dining at its very best.

Sophisticated town house hotel and spa in the centre of St Helier

38 (inc 8 suites) 🛏 ⊙ ✂ ♿ ♻ ± ≋ ☐ ♫ ♟ 🎱 ⬆ ✆
🍴 ♨ 20 🅿 28 WIFI

Directions On corniche pass under Fort Regent tunnel coming fm West, left at rdbt Green St, hotel 50m on left.

Nearby attractions
Elizabeth Cas, War Tunnels, German Occupation Museum, Durrell Cons Tst

Distances
Gorey 3, Airport 3, Rozel 6.

Rates Single/double room inc. continental breakfast from £195.
Meals Club Cafe 3- cse tdh £30; Bohemia fm £45; alc, lunch & spec diets avail; last orders 2200; bfst fm 0730.
Leisure Breaks See website for current offers.
Other facilities Massage. Riding, golf, fishing, squash, tennis, watersports nearby.

 & major credit cards accepted. Open all year.

Greenhills Country Hotel & Restaurant
St Peter's Valley, Jersey JE3 7EL
T (0870) 418 8233 **F** (01534) 485322 **E** greenhills@messages.co.uk
T (International) +44 [0] (1534) 481042 **W** www.greenhillshotel.com

273

When I first discovered this 17th century country house hotel in 1999, I described it as *'one of Jersey's best-kept secrets'*. Well, the secret is very definitely out and it is now well known as simply one of the best hotels in Jersey. Owner Peter Bromley and his excellent staff provide personal and unpretentious hospitality to ensure that service matches the high standards of the hotel's accommodation, cuisine and facilities. Set in award winning gardens and nestled attractively in the tranquil heart of St Peter's Valley, the hotel has retained its character and features to ensure that guests experience the unique atmosphere and intimacy of a period country house. The 31 comfortable and traditionally styled bedrooms have a 'cottagey' atmosphere but with all modern amenities. Cuisine is British with continental influences, the accent being on fresh local seafood. Add to this comfortable public rooms and a sheltered swimming pool and you can see why Greenhills is so highly regarded by all those who have had the pleasure of staying there, and why so many guests return.

30 (inc 2 suites) 🛁 ❀ 🛗 ♞ ♖ ☇ 🐎 ♨ 45 **P** 40 🚴

Country hotel of 17th century origins, set in delightful gardens

Rates Single room with breakfast from £50; double from £100.
Meals 4-cse tdh dinner from £22.50; alc, lunch & spec diets available; last orders 2130.

Directions Fm St Helier take A1, then A11 to St Peter's Valley. 4m out turn rt onto C112; hotel signed on left.

Nearby attractions
Jersey Heritage Trust, Jersey Lavendar St Brelade, Judith Queree's Gdn St Ouen

Distances
St Ouen's 3, St Helier 4, Airport 2.

& major credit cards accepted. Open 9 February - 16th December.

Jersey, St Peter's

274

Jersey

Longueville Manor

St Saviour, Jersey JE2 7WF

T (0870) 418 8236 **F** (01534) 731613 **E** info@longuevillemanor.com
T (International) +44 [0] (1534) 725501 **W** www.longuevillemanor.com

RELAIS & CHATEAUX

Longueville Manor has for some time been regarded as the flagship quality hotel of the Channel Islands. Now it is one of Europe's most celebrated hotels and remains one of the most popular in *Signpost*. Standing in 15 acres at the foot of its own private wooded valley, this 13th century Norman manor house provides the very best of courteous service, accommodation and cuisine. With over 50 years of family run experience Malcolm Lewis and his friendly professional staff provide a warmth of welcome and service which will remain throughout your stay. In each of the luxurious individually styled bedrooms you will find resplendent decor, fine antique furnishings, elegant fabrics, fresh flowers and fruit, blending successfully with modern facilities like satellite digital TV, DVD and CD players. The finest food and wine is served in the award winning Oak Room and Garden Room. Outside there is tennis and a pool or why not take a stroll to the lake to inspect the black swans and mandarin ducks? Wherever you are in this magnificent hotel, you will always feel special.

Former 13th century manor house, now one of Europe's most celebrated hotels

🛏 30 (inc 2 suites) ♿ ❀ ♨ ♟ ⤳ ♘ ♞ ⅲ 45 🅿 40 🐎

Directions
A3 East from St Helier twds Gorey; hotel in St Saviours 1m on left

Nearby attractions
Jersey Museum, Jersey Zoo, Samares Manor, German Occupation Museum

Distances
Gorey 3, St Helier 1, Airport 5.

Rates Single room with breakfast from £170; double from £210.

Meals 3-cse tdh dinner from £40; alc, lunch & spec diets available; last orders 2200; bfst fm 0700.

Leisure Breaks Min. two nights dinner, b & b + Group A car hire from £300 per room, per night.

Other Facilities Satellite TV/DVD/CD players in rooms. Self-catering cottage.

Accreditations AA Top 200 ★★★★ ☺☺☺ Hotel. Relais et Châteaux member.

& all major credit cards accepted. Open all year.

Jersey, St Saviour

Hotel Petit Champ
Sark, Channel Islands GY9 0SF

275

T (0870) 418 8235 F (01481) 832469 E info@hotelpetitchamp.co.uk
T (International) +44 [0] (1481) 832046 W www.hotelpetitchamp.co.uk

The island of Sark is truly unique. Until 2007 it had a feudal constitution dating back to the reign of Elizabeth I, with its own government, no income tax and is home to just 550 residents. It is also a natural, car free and tranquil retreat for people who enjoy beautiful walks, breathtaking scenery and a refreshing break from the modern world. The Hotel Petit Champ is a super reflection of all that with its secluded position and views to the sea. Here, under the expert, friendly supervision of the resident proprietors Chris and Caroline Robins, is a true gem of an hotel with a country house atmosphere and 10 cosy en suite bedrooms, some of which have balconies and all of which have been refurbished to a high standard.There are three sun-lounges as well as a peaceful library lounge. Drinks before dinner are taken in the intimate bar and then guests repair to the candlelit restaurant renowned for its excellent cuisine with local lobster and crab dishes as specialities. A solar heated swimming pool nestles in the natural setting of an old quarry and forms a perfect sun trap. The Hotel Petit Champ, set in the island magic of Sark, is truly enchanting and the spell draws visitors back for holidays year after year.

 10 ✿ ⳋ ⬉ ✓ ⚓

Small privately owned hotel in a secluded position with sweeping sea views

Rates Single room with breakfast & dinner from £61.75; double from £119.50. **Meals** 5-cse tdh dinner £20.75; alc, lunch & spec. diets available; last orders 2030; bfst from 0830.

Leisure Breaks Travel inclusive holiays available. Details on request.

Other Facilities Horse & carriage tours. Sea fishing, tennis, billiards, badminton nearby.

Awards Good Hotel Guide César Award 2007 *Best Island Hotel in British Isles*

Diners, Mastercard, Visa, Switch accepted. Open April-early October.

Directions
From the Methodist Chapel, follow the signposts to the Hotel which lead towards the sea.

Nearby attractions
La Seigneurie Gardens

Distances
Guernsey St Peter Port 8, Herm 5.

Fact File
Illustrated Guide to
Historic Houses and Gardens,
Attractions and Walks

Roundstone, Galway

Ireland

The Emerald Isle has a central plain, surrounded by a rim of mountains and hills. It offers some of the most varied and unspoiled scenery in Europe - quiet sandy beaches, semi-tropical bays warmed by the Gulf Stream, and rugged cliffs that make up 3500 miles of coastline. And all populated by just 3.5 million welcoming friendly souls of great charm, musicality and learning.

Giant's Causeway

Waterford Crystal Shop

Hotels guide

Further information:
Bora Failte (Irish Tourist Board)
Baggot Street Bridge, Dublin 2
Tel: 00353 1 602 4000

www.ireland.ie

Dublin

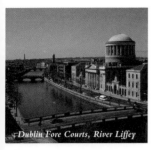

Dublin Fore Courts, River Liffey

James Joyce Tower, Sandycove
Malahide Castle, Malahide
National Botanic Gardens,
  Glasnevin
Newbridge House, Donabate
Phoenix Park
Powerscourt House & Gardens,
  Enniskerry
Powerscourt Townhouse Centre
Rathfarnham Castle
Royal Hospital, Kilmailham
Trinity College Dublin

St Patrick's Cathedral

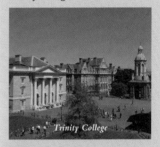

Trinity College

Attractions

Castle State Apartments
Chester Beatty Library
Christ Church Cathedral
City Hall Exhibition
Drimnagh Castle, Drimnagh
Dublin Writers' Museum
Dublin Zoo
Fry Model Railway
Guinness Factory Tour
Irish Museum of Modern Art
James Joyce Centre & Museum
Municipal Art Gallery/
  Hugh Lane Gallery
National Gallery of Ireland
National Museum of Ireland
National Transport Museum
National Wax Museum
Number 29 Geogian Museum
Old Jamieson Distillery
Shaw Birthplace
Skerries Mills, Co Dublin

Dublin is the gateway for most visitors to Ireland and there is much to see. It is a city steeped in history and buzzing with youthful energy. Medieval, Georgian and modern architecture provide a backdrop to a friendly bustling port where the cosmopolitan and charming converge in delightful diversity.

It is a thriving centre for culture and home to a great literary tradition. It is also the cradle of much musical talent, from the Dubliners to the Chieftains to U2. Dublin provides a host of offerings to the visitor of every taste and age group. 'Must Do's' include a trip to the **Guinness Museum** and a pint at The **Gravity Bar**, followed by a visit to **Trinity College** with its magnificent library and Book of Kells. **Temple Bar**, the informal artists' quarter of the city, is a fascinating labyrinth of shops, galleries and theatres.

A trip to **Docklands** should take in the 18th century **Jamieson's Irish Whisky distillery**. One of the most important museums is **The**

Customs House

Dublin Writers Museum, where works of the masters Joyce, Shaw, Yeats and Beckett can be viewed. Other cultural attractions include the house where George Bernard Shaw was born and the **James Joyce Museum.** The **Georgian Doors quarter** contains a museum dedicated to this period of the city's development. Modern architecture *aficionados* can wonder at the rebuilt **Smithfield** area, displaying the best of modern urban architecture whilst retaining traditional features of this colourful area.

A good way of seeing the city is to buy a *Dublin Pass*, offering convenience and savings to those who wish to see several attractions. It is not advisable to take a private car into the city centre. The Dart fast transit system and the Luas red and green lines take you there faster and much can be seen on foot or by bus or taxi.

St. Patrick's Day Parade

TOP 20 Historic Houses Gardens and Parks

Circuit of Ireland

TOP 20 Attractions

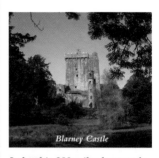

Blarney Castle

Glenveragh Park

Ireland is 300 miles long and about 170 miles wide. **Dublin** and **Belfast** have fine airports. Car ferries run from **Holyhead** (Anglesey) to **Dun Laoghaire**, **Fishguard** and **Pembroke** to **Rosslare**, **Swansea** to **Cork** and **Stranraer** in Scotland to **Larne** in Ulster. As well as established Aer Lingus routes from the UK, Ryanair now flies from nine regional UK airports to the Republic at very low cost.

Ireland, North & **South**, has a huge choice for people of varied interests. Fishing, the **Dublin Horse Show**, racing, splendid golf courses, unpolluted sands, ancient relics and all sorts of magnificent coastal scenery like the spectacular **Cliffs of Moher** on the west coast and **Blarney Castle**, near **Cork**, where you can kiss the stone and supposedly be rewarded with exceptional eloquence.

The Giants' Causeway, easily reached from **Portrush** in **County Antrim** and its thousands of basalt columns are certainly one of the most curious geological formations

in the world. Circling Ireland clockwide from Rosslare you can visit the famous glass factory at **Waterford**; in nearby **Middleton**, the home of Irish Whisky, you can tour a distillery.

Wexford has a famous Opera Festival and Heritage Park. **County Cork** and **County Kerry** provide the finest and most varied scenery. **Cork** is Ireland's second city, home of Murphy's stout and the famous jazz festival. **Killarney** has the highest peaks in Ireland, **MacGillicuddy's Reeks**, at 3414 ft.

Limerick and **Galway** are the main cities of the **West Coast**; the latter famous for its annual Race Meeting and Oyster Festival. In nearby **Connemara** you will find the famous marble and see the wild ponies. Southwest of **Westport** in **County Mayo** the 2510ft high hump of **Croagh Patrick** (near Knock) attracts annual pilgrimages up is stony flanks. **County Donegal** is famed for its Atlantic Drive and has one of the least polluted coasts in Europe.

THIS CARD IS DESIGNED TO HELP ELIMINATE AIDS IN AFRICA

Every time you shop with American Express® RED we will give 1% of your total spend to the Global Fund to help fight AIDS in Africa. Has there ever been a better reason to shop?

APPLY NOW
Call 0800 843 2273 or visit
AmericanExpressRED.co.uk

Maryborough Hotel & Spa

280

Maryborough Hill, Douglas, Cork
T (021) 436 5555 F (021) 436 5662 E info@maryborough.ie
T (International) +353 [0] (21) 436 5555 W www.maryborough.com

The Maryborough is a charming old world mansion at the centre of natural parkland with majestic oaks, rhododendrons and an outstanding collection of shrubs and plants. Every room has views of these outstanding gardens. The 18th century core building has been restored to preserve all the original Georgian features: high stuccoed ceilings, gracious curved staircases with antique furniture to match. The Garden Room connects the old mansion with the new wing and leads to the 21st century amenities - banqueting and conference areas, state-of-the-art leisure club, swimming pool, ESPA Spa and to the contemporary restaurant which serves an exciting mixture of modern flavours and styles, created where possible from fresh local produce. Douglas is a pleasant suburb of Cork, handy for the airport and ferry port, close to the city centre and road network, yet Maryborough provides an oasis of old world elegance, mixed with new world efficiency. A good business or holiday hotel for those embarking on a tour of southwest Ireland.

Georgian mansion with 21st-century extension and facilities

🛏 93 ⅍ ♿ ☉ ⚞ ▾ 🍴 ⬛ ⬇ 🌳 🍸 🚗 🚲 ⚲ 11 x ⣿ 500

Directions From Cork take N71 twds Bandon. Left at rdbt for Douglas, head for Golf Cse, hotel on left.
Nearby attractions
Riverstown House Cork, Dunkathel Hse Cork, Blarney Castle, Kinsale & Charles Fort
Distances
Cork 3, Airport 5, Killarney 51, Dublin 157

Rates Single room with breakfast from €145; double from €190.
Meals Tdh dinner €40; alc, lunch & spec. diets available; last orders 2200.
Leisure Breaks Two nights b & b + one dinner from €175 per person sharing
Other Activities Sat TV, wireless LAN connecton, massage at hotel. Fishing, golf, riding, watersports, sailing nearby

& all major cards accepted. Open all year.

Co. Cork, Douglas

after prices = hotel accepts Advantage Card from Signpost readers - see back of this boo

Ballymaloe House
Shanagarry, Co. Cork
T (021) 465 2531 F (021) 465 2021 E res@ballymaloe.ie
T (International) +353 [0] (21) 465 2531 W www.ballymaloe.ie

281

Ballymaloe is a large family farmhouse, still with its 14th century keep, situated on a 400-acre farm 20 miles east of Cork city. It has become well known throughout the British Isles and the USA for the high standard of its accommodation and cuisine. To stay here is to savour all the charm of Irish country living at its best, as exemplified by the spacious public rooms graced by modern Irish paintings and by the large comfortable drawing room where you can relax in front of a roaring log fire. The bedrooms are full of character and are cosy, traditionally furnished or more modern depending whether they are in the main "home" or in one of the outbuildings. The Craft Shop, Ballymaloe Cookery School in Shanagarry, the restaurant in the Crawford Art Gallery in Cork City are all also run by members of the Allen family. The cuisine in the hotel has won many plaudits. Vegetables are home grown and fish is fresh from Ballycotton nearby.

 33 ⎵ ✓ 🍴 /ᐧ ⇲ P

Comfortable country house of exceptional cuisine and comfort

Rates Double/twin room with breakfast €150-300; single occ'y from €120.
Meals Tdh dinner €65; lunch & spec. diets available; last orders 2130.
Leisure Breaks 3 days, dinner, b & b €486 per pers (Winter)/€540 per pers Summer).
Other Activities Fishing, golf, riding, tennis, watersports, sea bathing nearby.

Directions
From Cork N25 to Midleton, rt to Cloyne, br left twds Shanagarry, hotel on left.
Nearby attractions
Bantry House, Blarney Castle, Cobh the Queenstown Story, Crawford Art Gallery.
Distances
Cork 25, Waterford 64, Dublin 163.

 & major cards accepted. Closed Dec 23-27.

Co. Cork, Shanagarry

Castle Murray House Hotel & Restaurant
St John's Point, Dunkineely, Co. Donegal
T (07497) 37022 F (07497) 37330 E info@castlemurray.com
T (International) +353 [0] (7497) 37022 W www.castlemurray.com

Standing on the coast road to St John's Point on the south west of Donegal overlooking the sparkling waters of Mc Swyne's Bay, this friendly family run hotel offers a luxurious base from which to explore the beautiful and unspoiled county of Donegal. The hotel has ten individually themed and highly appointed bedrooms, most with staggering sea views of Mc Swyne's Bay and Mc Swyne's Castle which is floodlit at night. Rooms have the usual extras including best Irish bed linen in opulent surroundings. The highly renowned French restaurant has dramatic views of the bay and specialises in fresh, locally caught seafood, none of which is fresher than a lobster chosen from the hotel's own tank! Fine wine complements the traditional yet innovative cuisine. The traditional bar with its open fire adds to the charm. Ripples of laughter and warm conversation encourage guests to relax and soak up the atmosphere. There is much to see and do in the area: the fishing port of Killybegs, Donegal Town with the Donegal Bay waterbus and Glenveigh National Park, home to one of the biggest red deer herds in Ireland.

Family run hotel, voted 'One of the top 50 most romantic places to stay'   🛏 10 🍴 🛥 🎣 🚶₁₈ 🐕

Directions From Donegal Town N56 for Dunkineely; 1m after town branch left for St Johns Point - hotel ½ m down on left.

Nearby attractions
Slieve League (highest cliffs in Europe), Glenveigh Nat Pk, Fintra Beach (Blue Flag)

Distances
Donegal 18, Derry 48, Dublin 182.

Rates Single room inc. breafast €80-90; double/twin room €120-140.
Meals 4-cse tdh dinner from €48; Sunday lunch (5-cse) €27; spec. diets available; last orders 2130. Restaurant closed Mons & Tues Oct-April exc. BkHol
Leisure Breaks Please see our website for special offers available.
Other Activities Dean's Open Farm & Equestrian Centre, Portnoo Golf Cse, angling & sightseeing trips by boat can be arranged.

& all major credit cards accepted. 'Hotel' closed mid Jan-mid Feb.

Co. Donegal, Dunkineely

Glenogra Guest House

64 Merrion Road, Ballsbridge, Dublin 4

T (01) 668 3661 F (01) 668 3698 E info@glenogra.com
T (International) +353 [0] (1) 668 3661 W www.glenogra.com

Peter Donohoe has recently taken over and is enhancing this guest house of 12 beautifully appointed rooms. A finely appointed Edwardian residence opposite the Royal Dublin Society (RDS) and Four Seasons Hotel, it is close to the city centre, bus routes and the Sandymount DART station, and only minutes' walk from the US embassy and many fine bars and restaurants. Breakfast has always been regarded as the essential foundation to the day by the hosts. Refurbished bedrooms, all non-smoking and with WIFI broadband Internet connection, have every modern convenince and are smartly decorated in harmony with the period residence. There is a garden to relax in after a hard day's shopping or sightseeing and Sky Digital TV is available in the residents' lounge. There is ample off street parking at the front. Glenogra is a four star Irish Tourist Board Guesthouse and AA/RAC ◊◊◊◊◊ establishment, ideal for business or leisure travellers looking for good value accommodation near the centre of Dublin. High standards and dedication to guests' comfort make Glenogra one of the city's outstanding guesthouses.

🛏 12 ⚙ ☺ (+WIFI) 🅿 12

Townhouse hotel in the Ballsbridge area of central Dublin

Rates Single room inc. breafast from €79; double/twin room fm €109. [Ad]

Other facilities Garden, SKY TV lounge. No restaurant.

Directions From Trinity College, take Mount St/Northumberland Rd to Ballsbridge. Hotel on left after Serpentine Ave.

Nearby attractions National Gallery, Chester Beatty library, City Hall, Nat. History Mus, Royal Hibernian

Distances Central Dublin 3, Airport 11.

 & major credit cards accepted. Open all year.

Co. Dublin, Dublin

Hotel Europe
Killarney, Co. Kerry
T (064) 31900 F (064) 32118 E sales@kih.liebherr.com
T (International) +353 [0] (64) 31900 W www.killarneyhotels.ie

Space, grace and elegance are but a few of the words which would describe this modern hotel set overlooking Killarney's lakes and mountains. All the rooms are bright and airy, beautifully furnished with a perfect blend of antique and modern and the elegance is enhanced by the quiet efficiency of the staff. There are superb views from the restaurant where the most delicious Irish and international cuisine can be enjoyed, with local fish, lobster and smoked salmon as specialities. The hotel is the right choice for an active holiday. Some of Ireland's most beautiful and famous golf courses are within easy reach of the hotel. The spectacular surrounding countryside also provides opportunities for tennis, swimming, pony trekking, cycling and hiking. The hotel itself has an excellent fitness centre and children can entertain themselves in the playroom or ride the hotel's own Hafflinger ponies. Hotel Europe is the ideal place to relax after an invigorating day exploring some of Ireland's finest countryside.

Elegant modern hotel on the shores of Lough Leane

206 (inc 6 suites) 200

Directions
From Limerick/Dublin take N21/N22 to Killarney. Rt in town B562; hotel on left 2m

Nearby attractions
Listowel Literary Museum, Ross Castle, Muckross House, Killagha Abbey.

Distances
Tralee 22, Kenmare 24, Cork 54, Dublin 189

Rates Single/double room with breakfast from €198.
Meals Tdh 4-cse dinner €50; alc, lunch & spec. diets available; last orders 2130
Leisure Breaks Details on application.
Other Activities Fishing, watersports & squash nearby. Shooting by arrangement.

 Diners, Mastercard & Visa accepted. Open March - October.

Hotel Dunloe Castle
Killarney, Co. Kerry
T (064) 44111 **F** (064) 44583 **E** sales@kih.liebherr.com
T (International) +353 [0] (64) 44111 **W** www.killarneyhotels.ie

285

Like its sister hotel, the Europe, Dunloe Castle is a modern hotel set in the most fabulous gardens leading to the ruins of the old castle itself. The park is host to a remarkable award-winning botanical collection of rare flowers and plants as well to grazing Hafflinger horses. Inside the hotel, the furnishings and decor are faultless, inviting and comfortable and, whilst every facility is provided for meetings and conferences, the keynote is an atmosphere in which to relax and unwind. The restaurant serves the most delicious food with the accent on local specialities. The surrounding countryside is famous for walking, fishing and riding, with tennis and swimming on the premises. What could be more rewarding than to dine here after, let us say, a day playing golf opposite the hotel or one of the numerous famous courses nearby, fishing or perhaps walking up the Gap of Dunloe? This is the outdoor sportsman's paradise, the gourmet's heaven and the holiday maker's *Shangri-La*, all packaged into one superb venue.

🛏 110 (inc 1 suite) 🚶 ⚔ 📶 🎣🏊18 🎵 ∪ ⚲ 🎫 50

Rates Single/double room with breakfast from €190.
Meals Tdh 4-cse dinner €50; alc, lunch & spec. diets available; last orders 2130
Other Activities Historical gardens, sailing & squash nearby. Shooting by arrangement.

 Diners, Mastercard & Visa accepted. Open May - October.

Modern hotel next to the old castle ruins on the shores of Lough Leane

Directions
From Limerick/Dublin take N21/N22 to Killarney. Rt in town B562; hotel on left 3m
Nearby attractions
Listowel Literary Museum, Ross Castle, Muckross House, Killagha Abbey.
Distances
Tralee 25, Kenmare 27, Cork 57, Dublin 191

Co. Kerry, Killarney

Hotel Ard Na Sidhe
Caragh Lake, Killorglin, Co. Kerry
T (066) 976 9105 F (066) 976 9282 E sales@kih.liebherr.com
T (International) +353 [0] (66) 976 9105 W www.killarneyhotels.ie

It is a pity to call this an hotel, for at Ard Na Sidhe (*The House of the Fairies*), built by an English lady in 1880, one is a guest in an elegant country house. Warmly furnished, it has that welcoming atmosphere that so many hotels try to emulate but few seem to achieve. With fabulous award-winning gardens and parkland sloping down to the lake, the house offers a tranquillity rarely found today. It has valuable antiques, open fires and a magnificent, mature garden which has twice won first prize in the Irish National Gardens Competition. You can read, go for walks, paint, dream or simply 'switch off' in this idyllic setting. For those seeking a more active holiday, the environs provide more sporting activities than almost any comparable area in Europe; golf (nine courses within a 30-mile radius), fishing and hill trekking to name a few. Whilst Ireland is a relaxing country, even a leisurely tour is tiring. Any visit to the southwest and the Ring of Kerry would be incomplete without staying here for at least a couple of days to recharge the batteries.

Country house in immaculate gardens on the shores of Lake Caragh   19

Directions
From Limerick/Dublin take N21/R561/N70 to Killorglin, then small rd to Lough Caragh.
Nearby attractions
Listowel Literary Museum, Ross Castle, Muckross House, Killagha Abbey.
Distances
Killarney 12, Tralee 16, Cork 64, Dublin 207

Rates Single/double/twin room with breakfast from €185.
Meals Tdh 4-cse dinner €50; spec. diets available; last orders 2100.
Other Activities Leisure facilities available at sister hotels Europe & Dunloe Castle (see preceding pages).

 Diners, Mastercard & Visa accepted. Open May - October.

Manor West Hotel, Spa & Leisure Club
Killarney Road, Tralee, Co. Kerry
T (066) 719 4500 F (066) 712 4545 E info@manorwesthotel.ie
T (International) +353 [0] (66) 719 4500 W www.manorwesthotel.ie

Whether on business or holiday, this contemporary hotel with its comprehensive facilities and high standards of comfort and cuisine is the ideal place to stay. Kerry Airport, with direct flights to the UK and Europe is just 20 minutes away. Shannon and Cork airports are both about 80 miles away. Bedrooms are spacious and well equipped and range from standard to suites, including the penthouse Jacuzzi Suites. Guests may dine either in the Walnut Room Restaurant which offers both an *à la carte* and *table d'hôte* menu or in the informal Mercantile Bar & Bistro. Conference and banqueting suites of varying capacity are also available.
The Harmony Wellness Suites, on the Executive Penthouse level offer an extensive range of Elemis treatments and therapies in an atmosphere of calm and serenity, the ultimate in pampering. Tralee has much to offer the visitor: museum, horse racing, a multiplex cinema, sandy beaches, nearby marina and equestrian centre.

🏨 50 ✂ ♿ 🍴 🛏 🍸 ☺ ♀ 3x 👥 250 P 100

Rates Single with breakfast from €75; double/twin from €100.
Meals 3-cse tdh Walnut Room Restaurant €35 ; alc, lunch & spec. diets available; last orders 2100' bfst fm 0730.
Leisure Breaks Special midweek or weekend breaks - log onto our website for details. Golf, fishing, sailing & spa breaks also available.
Other Activities Fishing, golf, jogging, watersports/beach, sailing, squash, tennis, riding all within ten miles.

& all major credit cards accepted. Open all year exc. Dec 24-26.

Town centre on the Ring of Kerry with Leisure Club
Directions From Dublin N7/N21 to Ballymacthomas rdbt outskts of Tralee, take 2nd exit to Clashlehane rdbt. Take 1st exit fr Manor West Retail Prk, 3rd exit at mini-rdbt.
Nearby attractions Siamsa Tire, Kerry County Museum, Blennerville Windmill & Steam Train.
Distances Killarney 16, Cork 66, Dublin 216

Co. Kerry, Tralee

The Horse and Jockey Inn
N8 Main Road, Nr. Thurles, Co. Tipperary
T (0504) 44192 **F** (0504) 44747 **E** horseandjockeyinn@tinet.ie
T (International) +353 [0] (504) 44192 **W** www.horseandjockeyinn.com

If you are at all interested in equestrian sports, be it racing, hunting or just hacking or if you just appreciate the beauty of horses, then this is the place for you! The Horse & Jockey is located on a great traditional crossroads of Ireland, North/South and East/West. It has been trading for over 250 years. Recently the owners have refurbished the whole building - adding on bedrooms to create a blend of luxury and unspoiled friendliness, and in 2006 a state-of-the-art spa. Our inspector's room was very comfortable, and the bathroom had big brass taps, fluffy white towels and many little luxuries. Equestrian pictures and memorabilia grace the the walls of the public rooms. Well known jockeys and trainers gaze down from the dining room walls - Mick Kinane, Enda Bolger, Charlie Swan, Jamie Spenser and Aidan O'Brien to name just a few. You might even find yourself sitting next to one of them as several of Ireland's leading racecourses, training yards and studs are nearby. There are books and old photographs to look at in the hotel's comfortable sitting rooms. There is even an hotel shop with designer clothes, local pottery and jewellery.

Well known equestrian inn situated at one of Ireland's crossraods   🛏 33 🍴 ♿ 🌐 🛋 🍽 🎿

Directions
Take the N8 Dublin-Cork Rd. Inn at X-roads with N62 south of Thurles.

Nearby attractions
Bolton Library Cashel, Rock of Cashel, Excel Heritage Centre, Tipp'y. Birr Castle.

Distances
Thurles 5, Cashel 9, Limerick 47, Dublin 150

Rates Single room with breakfast from €80; double from €150.
Meals Alc Restaurant; lunch & spec. diets available; last orders 2145.
Other Facilities Hotel shop. Massage.

 & major credit cards accepted. Open all year.

Co. Tipperary, Nr. Thurles

Rathsallagh Country House & Golf Club
Dunlavin, Co. Wicklow

289

T (045) 403112 **F** (045) 403343 **E** info@rathsallagh.com
T (International) +353 [0] (45) 403112 **W** www.rathsallagh.com

The approach to Rathsallagh is a long drive bisecting the golf course. Happily there are cattle grids whose rattle reminds golfers to give way to cars when making their swing! Rathsallagh was converted from a Queen Anne stable block into a comfortable country house with bags of charm and character. It sits in 530 acres of mature parkland, central to Glendalough, the Wicklow mountains and the world famous Curragh. Joe and Kay O'Flynn will make you feel at ease with all home comforts and excellent food prepared from local ingredients, fresh fish from the Wexford coast and local game in season being specialities. Breakfast is also special - there are big enticing silver domes on the sideboard and bread is home made. Indeed Rathsallagh has won the National Breakfast Award four times. The golf course was designed by Peter McEvoy and Irish professional Christy O'Connor and is laid out to 252 acres of lush parkland, with mature trees, natural water hazards, USGA-specification greens and a general rolling landscape, belying its age. Rathsallagh is only an hour's drive from Dublin and makes the perfect spot for a holiday for golfer and non-golfer alike.

Former Queen Anne stable block, now comfortable hotel & golf club

Rates Single room with breakfast from €195; double from €270.
Meals Alc Restaurant; lunch (rs only) & spec. diets available; last orders 2100; bfst fm 0700.
Leisure Breaks 2 nts b & b, 1 evening meal + choice of golf lesson or massage €199 per person sharing. 3rd nt €55. Selected midweek breaks Oct-Mar.
Other Facilities Massage. Airport pickup & car rental by arr't. Fishing 20 miles

Directions
From Dublin take the M7/M9, then N9 Carlow Rd, turn lft @Blackrath Stud-2m

Nearby attractions
The K Club, Glendalough-Wicklow Nat'l Park, Irish National Stud, The Curragh RC

Distances
Dunlavin 2, Naas 14, Kildare 25, Dublin 31

 & major credit cards accepted. Open all year.

Co. Wicklow, Dunlavin

HOTELS WITH SPORTING AND CONFERENCE FACILITIES

Below we list Signpost hotels who can offer Golf, Conference Facilities, Fishing & Shooting, Civil Wedding Licences, Swimming Pools, Spas or Gyms, and those who accept pets.

Hotels with Golf (own course or special

Page arrangements with an adjacent course)

Page	
6	Meudon Hotel, Cornwall
10	Treglos Hotel, Constantine Bay
22	Bovey Castle, Moretonhampstead
27	Palace Hotel, Torquay
29	The Park, Bath
44	Knoll House, Studland Bay, Dorset
51	Chewton Glen, New Milton, Hants
53	Priory Bay Hotel, Isle of Wight
77	Romney Bay House, New Romney
88	Beauport Park, Hastings, E Sussex
103	The Inn at Woburn, Bedfordshire
112	The Brudenell, Aldeburgh
117	Hintlesham Hall, Nr. Ipswich
137	Wind-in-the-Willows, Glossop
150	Stapleford Park, Melton Mowbray
158	Whittlebury Hall, Northamptonshire
201	Rudding Park, Harrogate
227	Trefeddian Hotel, Gwynedd
242	Lake Country House, Nr. Builth Wells
255	Greywalls, Gullane, East Lothian
256	Royal Marine Hotel, Brora
269	La Grande Mare Hotel, Guernsey
281	Ballymaloe House, Co. Cork
284	Hotel Europe, Killarney, Co. Kerry
285	Hotel Dunloe Castle, Co. Kerry
289	Rathsallagh Cntry Hse & Golf Club

Hotels with Conference Facilities

(for 60+ delegates)

Page	
5	Bedruthan Steps Hotel, Cornwall
15	Garrack Hotel, St Ives, Cornwall
18	The Berry Head Hotel, Devon
19	Combe House, Gittisham
21	The Cottage Hotel, Hope Cove
22	Bovey Castle, Moretonhampstead
24	Ilsington Cntry Hse Hotel, Devon
27	Palace Hotel, Torquay
29	The Park, Bath
37	The Great House at Sonning, Berks
38	Sir Christopher Wren's House Hotel
40	Taplow House, Maidenhead
41	Stoke Place, Stoke Poges
46	Springfield Country Hotel, Dorset
49	Careys Manor, Brocklehurst
51	Stanwell House, Lymington
52	Chewton Glen, New Milton, Hants
55	Cotswold Lodge Hotel, Oxford
62	Searcy's Roof Garden R'ms, London SW1
71	New Linden Hotel, London W2
78	Little Silver Cntry Hotel, Tenterden
82	Bingham Hotel, Richmond-upon-Thames
80	Richmond Hill Hotel, Surrey
83	Deans Place Hotel, Alfriston

Page	
84	Powder Mills Hotel, Battle
87	Lansdowne Hotel, Eastbourne
88	Beauport Park, Hastings, Sussex
89	Newick Park, Nr. Lewes
90	Flackley Ash Hotel, Peasmarsh
103	The Inn at Woburn, Bedfordshire
105	Pendley Manor Hotel, Tring
113	Waveney House Hotel, Beccles
114	The Angel, Bury St Edmunds
116	Ravenwood Hall Hotel, Bury St Eds
117	Hintlesham Hall, Nr. Ipswich
120	The Black Lion Hotel, Long Melford
133	Makeney Hall Hotel, Nr Belper
135	Donington Manor Hotel, Derbyshire
138	Santo's Higham Farm, Derbyshire
150	Stapleford Park, Melton Mowbray
151	Barnsdale Lodge, Rutland Water
152	Branston Hall Hotel, Nr. Lincoln
153	Washingborough Hall Hotel, Nr. Lincoln
154	Fawsley Hall, Northanptonshire
155	Rushton Hall, Kettering
157	The New French Partridge, Northampton
158	Whittlebury Hall, Towcester
160	Colwick Park Hotel, Nottingham
161	Country Cottage Hotel, Nr. Nottingham
164	Prince Rupert Hotel, Shrewsbury
166	Peacock Hotel, Kenilworth
169	Colwall Park, Malvern
180	Armathwaite Hall, Cumbria
183	Derwentwater Hotel, Nr. Keswick
184	Lodore Falls Hotel, Nr. Keswick
186	Skiddaw Hotel, Keswick
187	George Hotel, Penrith
201	Rudding Park, Harogate
205	Monk Fryston Hall, Nr. Selby, Yorks
206	Solberge Hall, Northallerton
208	Red Lion Hotel, Skipton
216	Tre-Ysgawen Hall, Anglesey
218	Falcondale Mansion, Lampeter
219	Royal Oak Hotel, Betws-Y-Coed
223	Plas Maenan, Llanwrst
224	The West Arms, Nr. Llangollen
225	Wild Pheasant Hotel, Llangollen
231	Portmeirion Hotel, Gwynedd
232	Allt-Yr-Ynys, Monmouth/Herefords
234	Glen-Yr-Afon House Hotel, Monmouths
239	Caer Beris Manor, Powys
241	Lake Vyrnwy Hotel, Powys
242	Lake Country House & Spa, Builth Wells
251	Banchory Lodge Hotel, Ballater
256	Royal Marine Hotel, Brora
263	Dunalastair Hotel, Kinloch Rannoch
274	Longueville Manor, Jersey
280	Maryborough House, Co Cork
287	Manor West Hotel, Tralee

Hotels with Fishing (✓ = + game shooting)

6	Meudon Hotel, Cornwall
7	Mullion Cove Hotel, Cornwall
8	Trevalsa Court, Cornwall
11	The Old Coastguard, Penzance
13	The Rosevine Hotel, Porthscatho
19	Combe House, Gittisham
26	Tides Reach Hotel, Devon
27	Palace Hotel, Torquay
28	Kitley House Hotel, Yealmpton ✓
41	Stoke Place, Buckinghamshire
47	The Priory, Wareham
73	Walletts Court, Nr, Dover, Kent
79	Cedar House Hotel, Cobham
89	Newick Park, Nr. Lewes ✓
95	Gravetye Manor, East Grinstead
102	Mill House Hotel & Restaurant, Beds
113	Waveney House Hotel, Beccles
115	Clarice House, Bury St Edmunds ✓
130	Izaak Walton Hotel, Derbyshire
137	Wind in the Willows, Glossop
149	Moccas Court, Herefords
150	Stapleford Park, Melton Mowbray ✓
155	Rushton Hall, Nr. Kettering
159	Langar Hall, Nottinghamshire
160	Colwick Hall Hotel, Nottingham
165	Soulton Hall, Shropshire ✓
167	Buckland Manor, Broadway
176	Lovelady Shield, Cumbria
180	Armathwaite Hall, Cumbria ✓
183	Derwentwater Hotel, Nr. Keswick
184	Lodore Falls Hotel, Nr. Keswick
188	Inn on the Lake, Windermere
190	Gilpin Lodge, Cumbria
191	Lindeth Howe Cntry Hse Hotel
192	Linthwaite House, Cumbria
193	Gibbon Bridge Hotel, Lancashire
202	The Sportsman's Arms, Yorkshire ✓
217	Ty'n Rhos Country House, Caernarfon
219	Royal Oak Hotel, Betwys-Y-Coed
224	West Arms Hotel, Nr. Llandudno ✓
228	Sygun Fawr, Beddgelert
229	Penmaenuchaf Hall, Gwynedd
230	Palé Hall, Lake Bala ✓
233	Inn at the Elm Tree, Newport ✓
232	Allt-Yr-Ynys Hotel, Monmouths ✓
239	Caer Beris Manor, Powys ✓
240	Gliffaes Cntry Hse Hotel, Powys ✓
241	Lake Vyrnwy Hotel, Powys ✓
242	Lake Country House & Spa, Powys
251	Banchory Lodge Hotel, Ballater
254	Ardanaseig Hotel, Kilchrenan ✓
260	Pool House, Wester Ross
261	Eddrachilles Hotel, Highland
263	Dunalastair Hotel, Perthshire ✓
264	Loch Tummel Inn, Perthshire
281	Ballymaloe House, Co Cork
282	Castle Murray House, Co Donegal
282	Hotel Europe, Killarney, Co Kerry
283	Hotel Dunloe Castle, Co Kerry

Hotels Licensed for Civil Weddings

6	Bedruthan Steps Hotel, Nr Newquay
14	Rose-in-Vale Hotel, St Agnes
19	Combe House, Gittisham
22	Bovey Castle, Moretonhampstead
28	Kitley House Hotel, Yealmpton
29	The Park, Bath
37	The Great House at Sonning
38	Sir Christopher Wrens's House Hotel
39	Crown Hotel, Amersham
40	Taplow House, Maidenhead
41	Stoke Place, Stoke Poges
48	Montagu Arms, Beaulieu
49	Careys Manor, Brocklehurst
51	Stanwell House, Lymington
52	Chewton Glen, Hampshire
53	Priory Bay Hotel, Isle of Wight
62	Searcys Roof Garden Rooms, London SW1
68	Blakes Hotel, London SW7
78	Little Silver Country Hotel, Tenterden
79	Cedar House, Cobham
80	Richmond Gate Hotel, Surrey
82	The Bingham Hotel, Richmond-u-Thames
83	Deans Place Hotel, Alfriston
84	Powder Mills Hotel, Battle
85	Blanch House, Brighton
89	Newick Park, Nr. Lewes
94	Millstream Hotel & Rest't, Bosham
95	Gravetye Manor, East Grinstead
105	Pendley Manor Hotel, Tring
106	Redcoats Farmhouse Hotel, Herts
108	Kings Head Hotel, Norfolk
111	Broom Hall Cntry Hotel, Norfolk
113	Waveney House Hotel, Beccles
114	The Angel Hotel, Bury St Edmunds
116	Ravenwood Hall Hotel, Bury St Ed's
118	Salthouse Harbour Hotel, Ipswich
119	The Swan Hotel, Lavenham
120	Black Lion Hotel, Long Melford
130	Izaak Walton Hotel, Derbyshire
131	Riverside House Hotel, Derbyshire
132	Dannah Farm Country House, Derbs
133	Makeney Hall Hotel, Nr. Belper
135	Donington Manor, Castle Donington
140	East Lodge Hotel, Derbyshire
144	Burleigh Court, Minchinhampton
145	Three Choirs Vineyard, Newent
146	Grapevine Hotel, Stow-on-the-Wold
149	Moccas Court, Herefordshire
150	Stapleford Park, Melton Mowbray
152	Branston Hall Hotel, Lincolnshire
153	Washingborough Hall, Lincolnshire
154	Fawsley Hall, Northamptonshire
155	Rushton Hall, Nr. Kettering
156	Falcon Hotel, Northamptonshire
157	New French Partridge, Nr. Northampton
158	Whittlebury Hall, Nr. Towcester
159	Langar Hall, Nottinghamshire
160	Colwick Hall Hotel, Nottingham

161	Country Cottage Hotel, Nottingham
176	Lovelady Shield Hotel, Cumbria
182	Borrowdale Gates C'ntry H'se Hotel
186	Skiddaw Hotel, Keswick
187	George Hotel, Penrith
188	Inn on the Lake, Windermere
189	Sharrow Bay Hotel, Cumbria
192	Linthwaite House Hotel, Cumbria
193	Gibbon Bridge Hotel, Lancashire
201	Rudding Park, Harrogate
205	Monk Fryston Hotel, Yorkshire
206	Solberge Hall Hotel, Northallerton
208	Red Lion Hotel, Skipton
217	Ty'n Rhos Country House, Caernarfon
218	Falcondale Mansion, Lampeter
219	Royal Oak Hotel, Betwys-Y-Coed
223	Plas Maenan, Conwy Valley
224	West Arms Hotel, Llanarmon DC
225	Wild Pheasant, Llangollen
229	Penmaenuchaf Hall, Gwynedd
230	Palé Hall, Lake Bala
231	Portmeirion Hotel, Gwynedd
232	Allt-Yr-Ynys Hotel, Monmouthshire
233	Inn at the Elm Tree, Newport
236	Warpool Court Hotel, Pembrokeshire
237	Penally Abbey, Pembrokeshire
240	Gliffaes Country Hse Hotel, Powys
241	Lake Vyrnwy Hotel, Powys
242	Lake Country House & Spa, Powys
251	Banchory Lodge Hotel, Ballater
254	Ardanaseig Hotel, Kilchrenan
256	Royal Marine Hotel, Brora
257	Flodigarry Cntry Hse Hotel, Isle of Skye
262	Tigh an Eilean Hotel, Shieldaig
263	Dunalastair Hotel, Perthshire
264	Loch Tummel Inn, Perthshire
282	Castle Murray Hotel, Co. Donegal
289	Rathsallagh Country House & Golf Club

Hotels with Swimming Pools

(✹ = indoor)

10	Treglos Hotel, Constantine Bay ✹
13	Rosevine Hotel, Porthscatho
14	Rose-in-Vale Hotel, St Agnes
15	Garrack Hotel, St Ives, Cornwall ✹
18	The Berry Head, South Devon ✹
22	Bovey Castle, Moretonhampstead
24	Ilsington Cntry Hse Hotel, Dartmoor
26	Tides Reach Hotel, South Devon
27	Palace Hotel, Torquay + ✹
44	Knoll House Hotel, Dorset
46	Springfield Country Hotel, Dorset
48	Montagu Arms Hotel, Beaulieu
49	Careys Manor Hotel & Senspa ✹
52	Chewton Glen, Hampshire + ✹
53	Priory Bay Hotel, Isle of Wight
73	Walletts Court, Dover, Kent ✹

80/81	Richmond Hill/Gate Hotels, Surrey ✹
83	Deans Place Hotel, Alfriston
84	Powder Mills Hotel, Battle
88	Beauport Park, East Sussex
89	Newick Park, Nr. Lewes
90	Flackley Ash Hotel, East Sussex ✹
91	Rye Lodge, Rye, East Sussex ✹
92	Brickwall Hotel, Sedlescombe
105	Pendley Manor Hotel, Tring ✹
111	Broom Hall Hotel, Norfolk ✹
115	Clarice House, Bury St Edmunds ✹
116	Ravenwood Hall Hotel, Bury St Ed's
117	Hintlesham Hall, Ipswich
148	Corse Lawn House Hotel, Glos ✹
150	Stapleford Park, Melton Mowbray
152	Branston Hall, Lincolnshire ✹
153	Washingborough Hall Hotel, Lincoln
155	Rushton Hall, Nr Kettering
158	Whittlebury Hall, Nr Towcester
164	Prince Rupert Hotel, Shrewsbury ✹
179	Appleby Manor Hotel, Cumbria
180	Armathwaite Hall, Cumbria ✹
190	Gilpin Lodge, Cumbria ✹
194	Chadwick Hotel, Lytham ✹
203	Feversham Arms, Helmsley
216	Tre-Ysgawen Hall, Anglesey ✹
219	Royal Oak Hotel, Betws-Y-Coed ✹
225	Wild Pheasant Hotel, Llangollen
227	Trefeddian Hotel, Gwynedd ✹
231	Portmeirion Hotel, Gwynedd
232	Allt-Yr-Ynys, Monmouthshire ✹
236	Warpool Court, Pembrokeshire ✹
237	Penally Abbey, Pembrokeshire ✹
242	Lake Country House & Spa, Powys ✹
256	Royal Marine Hotel, Brora ✹
269	La Grande Mare Hotel, Guernsey +✹
271	The White House, Herm, C I
272	The Club Hotel & Spa, Jersey
274	Longueville Manor, Jersey
275	Hotel Petit Champ, Sark, C I
280	Maryborough House, Co. Cork ✹
281	Ballymaloe House, Co Cork
284	Hotel Europe, Killarney, Co. Kerry ✹
285	Hotel Dunloe Castle, Co Kerry ✹
287	Manor West Hotel, Spa & Leisure Club ✹
288	Horse & Jockey Inn, Co. Tipperary ✹

Hotels with spas or gyms

15	Garrack Hotel, St Ives, Cornwall
22	Bovey Castle, Moretonhampstead
24	Ilsington Cntry Hse Hotel, Devon
26	Tides Reach Hotel, South Devon
27	Palace Hotel, Torquay
38	Sir Christopher Wren's House Hotel
44	Knoll House Hotel, Dorset
46	Springfield Country Hotel, Dorset
48	Montagu Arms Hotel, Beaulieu
49	Careys Manor Hotel & Senspa, Hants
52	Chewton Glen, Hampshire

64	Walletts Court, Dover, Kent
80	Richmond Hill/Gate Hotels, Surrey
90	Flackley Ash Hotel, East Sussex
105	Pendley Manor Hotel, Tring
115	Clarice House, Bury St Edmunds
117	Hintlesham Hall, Nr. Ipswich
118	Salthouse Harbour Hotel, Ipswich
132	Dannah Farm Country House
150	Stapleford Park, Melton Mowbray
152	Branston Hall, Lincolnshire
154	Fawsley Hall, Northamptonshire
155	Rushton Hall, Nr. Kettering
158	Whittlebury Hall, Northamptonshire
164	Prince Rupert Hotel, Shrewsbury
179	Appleby Manor Hotel, Cumbria
180	Armathwaite Hall, Cumbria
188	Inn on the Lake, Windermere
192	Lindeth Howe Cntry Hse Hotel
193	Gibbon Bridge Hotel, Lamcashire
194	Chadwick Hotel, Lancashire
203	Feversham Arms, Helmsley
216	Tre-Ysgawen Hall, Anglesey
219	Royal Oak Hotel, Betws-Y-Coed
225	Wild Pheasant Hotel, Llangollen
242	Lake Country House & Spa, Powys
256	Royal Marine Hotel, Brora
269	La Grande Mare Hotel, Guernsey
272	The Club Hotel & Spa, Jersey
275	Maryborough House, Co. Cork
284	Hotel Europe, Killarney, Co. Kerry
287	Manor West Hotel, Spa & Leisure Club
288	Horse & Jockey Inn, Co Tipperary

Hotels who accept pets (can be charged)

6	Meudon Hotel, Cornwall
7	Mullion Cove Hotel, Cornwall
10	Treglos Hotel, Constantine Bay
13	Rosevine Hotel, Porthscatho
14	Rose-in-Vale Cntry Hse Hotel, St Agnes
15	Garrack Hotel, Cornwall
16	Gurnards Head, St Ives
17	Blagdon Manor Hotel, Ashwater
19	Combe House, Gittisham
24	Ilsington Cntry Hse Hotel, Devon
25	Collaven Manor, Devon
26	Tides Reach, Salcombe, Devon
31	Luttrell Arms, Dunster
35	The Christopher Hotel, Eton
36	Ye Olde Bell, Hurley
37	The Great House at Sonning
42	Plumber Manor, Dorset
51	Stanwell House Hotel, Lymington
53	Priory Bay Hotel, Isle of Wight
56	The Lamb at Hindon, Wiltshire
74	Hotel Relish, Folkestone
76	Who'd a Thought It, Maidstone
79	Lansdowne Hotel, Eastbourne
84	Powder Mills Hotel, Battle

89	Newick Park, Nr. Lewes
90	Flackley Ash Hotel, East Sussex
96	Chequers Hotel, Pulborough
105	Pendley Manor Hotel, Tring
107	The White Horse, Brancaster Staithe
108	Kings Head Hotel, Gt Bircham
109	Beechwood Hotel, North Walsham
112	Brudenell Hotel, Aldeburgh
116	Ravenwood Hall, Bury St Edmunds
119	The Swan Hotel, Lavenham
120	Black Lion Hotel, Long Melford
130	Izaak Walton Hotel, Derbyshire
134	Biggin Hall, Derbyshire
135	Castle Donington Hotel, Derbyshire
133	Makeney Hall Hotel, Derbyshire
142	Dial House Hotel, Gloucestershire
146	Grapevine Hotel, Stow-on-the-Wold
148	Corse Lawn House Hotel, Glos
150	Stapleford Park, Melton Mowbray
151	Barnsdale Lodge, Nr. Oakham
154	Fawsley Hall, Northamptonshire
156	Falcon Hotel, Northamptonshire
159	Langar Hall, Nottinghamshire
161	Country Cottage Hotel, Nottingham
162	Old Vicarage Hotel, Shropshire
165	Soulton Hall, Shropshire
169	Colwall Park Hotel, Malvern
175	Broxton Hall, Cheshire
176	Lovelady Shield, Cumbria
179	Appleby Manor, Cumbria
181	Rothay Garden, Windermere
184	Lodore Falls Hotel, Nr. Keswick
188	Inn on the Lake, Windermere
200	Waren House, Northumberland
205	Monk Fryston Hall, Yorkshire
206	Solberge Hall Hotel, Northallerton
207	White Swan, Pickering, Yorkshire
208	Red Lion Hotel, Skipton
217	Ty'n Rhos Country House, Caernarfons
218	Falcondale Mansion, Lampeter
221	Sychnant Pass House, Conwy
224	West Arms Hotel, Nr. Llangollen
228	Sygun Fawr, Bedgellert
232	Allt-Yr-Ynys Hotel, Monmouthshire
233	The Inn at the Elm Tree, Newport
238	Felin Fach Griffin, Brecon
241	Lake Vyrnwy Hotel, Powys
242	The Lake Country House & Spa, Powys
252	Abbots Brae, Argyll
253	George Hotel, Inveraray, Argyll
254	Ardanaseig Hotel, Argyll
256	Royal Marine Hotel, Brora
257	Flodigarry C'ntry H'se Hotel, Isle of Skye
258	Greshornish House Hotel, Isle of Skye
262	Tigh an Eilean, Shieldaig
263	Dunalastair Hotel, Kinloch Rannoch
264	Loch Tummel Inn, Perthshire
274	Longueville Manor, Jersey

LOCATION INDEX

Location

ENGLAND

Page

THE WEST COUNTRY

Cornwall

Location	Hotel	Page
Bedruthan	Bedruthan Steps Hotel	5
Falmouth	Meudon Hotel	6
Lizard Peninsula	Mullion Cove Hotel	7
Mevagissey	Trevalsa Court	8
Padstow	Cross House Hotel	9
Padstow	Treglos Hotel	10
Penzance	The Old Coastguard Hotel	11
Porthallow	Talland Bay Hotel	12
Portscatho	The Rosevine Hotel	13
St Agnes	Rose-in-Vale Hotel	14
St Ives	The Garrack Hotel	15
St Ives	The Gurnards Head	16

Devon

Ashwater	Blagdon Manor	17
Brixham	The Berry Head Hotel	18
Nr. Honiton	Combe House Hotel/Rest't	19
Nr. Honiton	Home Farm Hotel	20
Hope Cove	The Cottage Hotel	21
Moretonhampstead	Bovey Castle	22
Moretonhampstead	White Hart Hotel	23
Newton Abbot	Ilsington Country Hse Hotel	24
Okehampton (Sourton)	Collaven Manor Hotel	25
Salcombe	Tides Reach Hotel	26
Torquay	Palace Hotel	27
Yeampton	Kitley House Hotel	28

Somerset

Nr. Bath	The Park Hotel	29
Bath	Windsor Hotel	30
Dunster	The Luttrell Arms	31

CENTRAL SOUTHERN ENGLAND

Berkshire

Eton	The Christopher Hotel	35
Hurley	Ye Olde Bell	36
Sonning	The Great House	37
Windsor	Sir Christopher Wren's House Hotel	38

Buckinghamshire

Amersham	The Crown Hotel	39
Nr. Maidenhead	Taplow House Hotel	40
Stoke Poges	Stoke Place	41

Dorset

Sturminster Newton	Plumber Manor	42
Studland Bay	Manor House Hotel	43
Studland Bay	Knoll House Hotel	44/45
Wareham	Springfield Country Hotel	46
Wareham	The Priory Hotel	47

Hampshire & Isle of Wight

Beaulieu	Montagu Arms Hotel	48
Brockenhurst	Careys Manor Hotel	49
Brockenhurst	Le Poussin at Whitley Ridge	50
Lymington	Stanwell House Hotel	51

THE HEART OF ENGLAND

300

ALPHABETICAL INDEX OF HOTELS

Other Signpost Approved Partners

The Signpost Advantage Card is supplied free of charge to purchasers of the book.

It entitles the bearer to a 10% discount on room rates (only) quoted in this book in those hotels who have an **Ad** printed beside their prices. This is according to availability and at the discretion of the hotelier. It applies only to accommodation - not to meals or extras. Some hotels may offer a room upgrade instead.

Please write to Priory Publications Ltd, PO Box 24, Brackley, Northamptonshire NN13 5BR to receive your free Advantage Card.

NB: Readers who have not yet *purchased* a copy of Signpost should fill in and mail one of the cards on the preceding pages, ticking the box for an Advantage Card.

CONDITIONS OF USE

A. Advantage Cards are not interchangeable, must be signed on the back and only give benefit to the signatory of the card.

B. 10% discount may be granted on presentation of the card on accommodation only.

C. As an alternative to a 10% discount, a hotel may offer a free room upgrade.

D. Cards are valid from the time of purchase of *Signpost/Premier Hotels of Great Britain and Ireland* (the USA title) until 31 December 2007.

E. Readers should state at the time of booking that they are Signpost Advantage Card holders and should check the advantages the establishment is offering.

F. Only Signpost establishments with an **Ad** printed by their room rates in this guide are taking part in the Advantage Card promotion.

G. Benefits may not apply at Christmas, New Year and Bank Holiday periods; also at certain peak periods at individual hotels, e.g. at the time of York or Cheltenham Races in hotels local to such events.

MAP SECTION

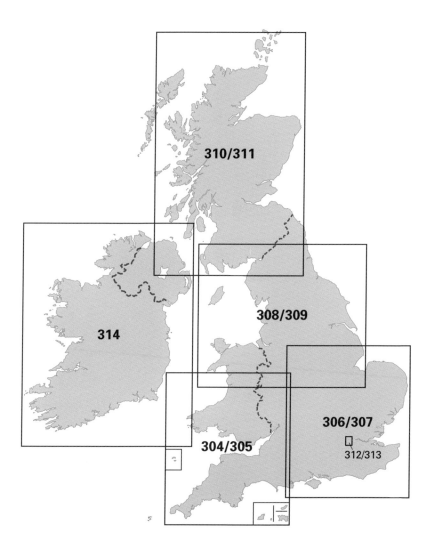

310/311

308/309

314

306/307

304/305

312/313

Numbers in black ovals on the following maps denote page numbers
of Signpost approved hotels. Turn to these pages for full details of
accommodation in the area where you are looking.

Maps designed and produced by GEOprojects (UK) Ltd., Reading. RG1 4QS. © GEOprojects (UK) Ltd.

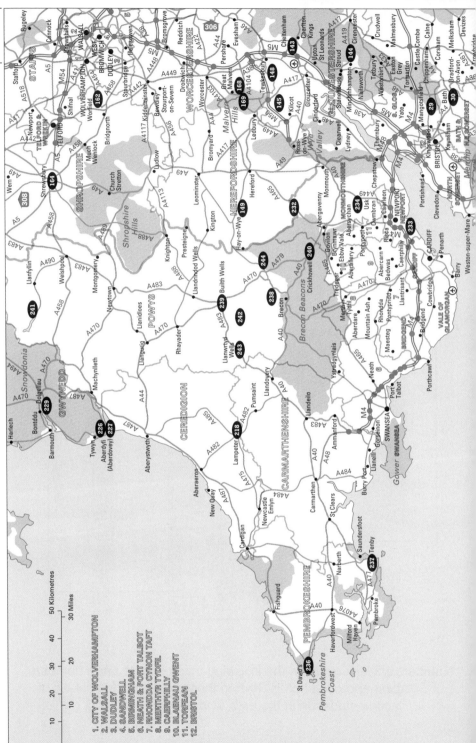

304

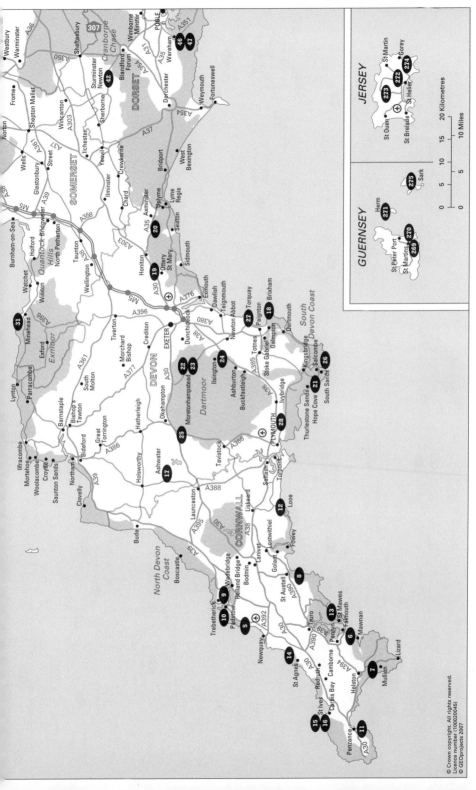

305

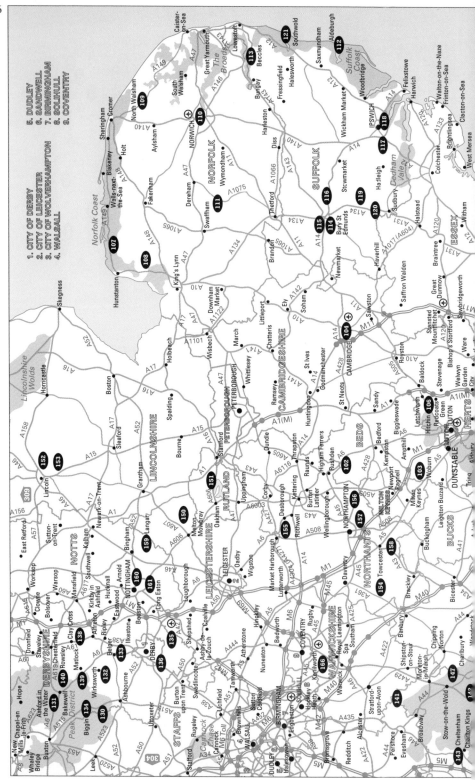

307

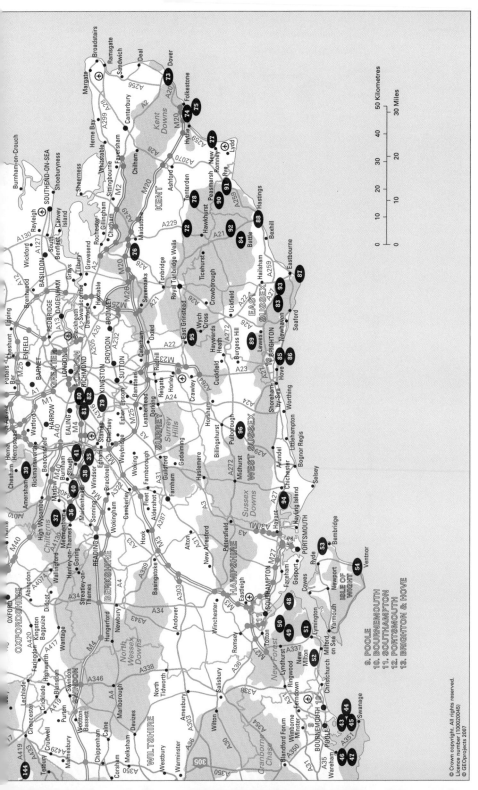

50 Kilometres

30 Miles

| 0 | 10 | 20 | 30 | 40 | 50 |

| 0 | 10 | 20 | 30 |

9. POOLE
10. BOURNEMOUTH
11. SOUTHAMPTON
12. PORTSMOUTH
13. BRIGHTON & HOVE

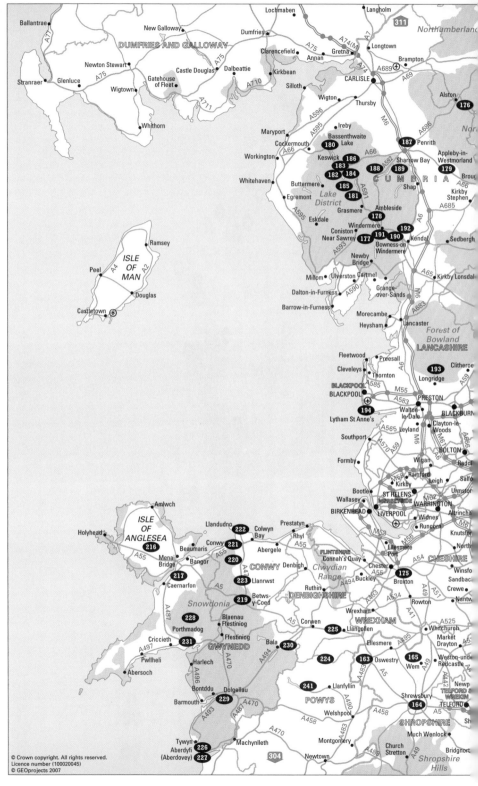

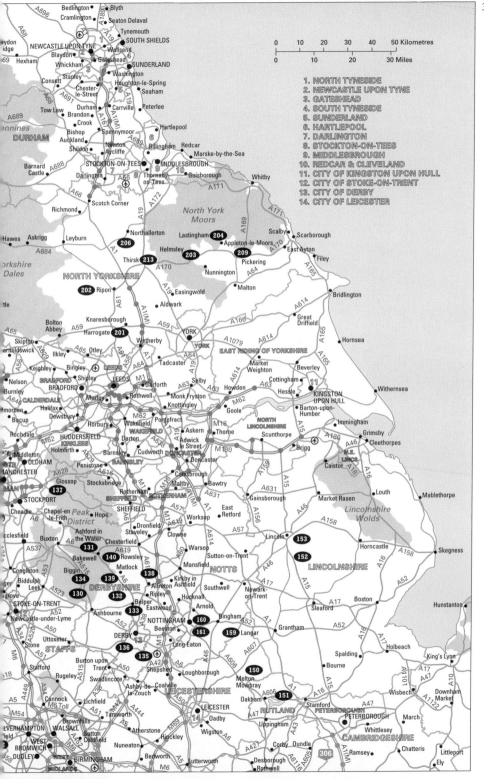

1. NORTH TYNESIDE
2. NEWCASTLE UPON TYNE
3. GATESHEAD
4. SOUTH TYNESIDE
5. SUNDERLAND
6. HARTLEPOOL
7. DARLINGTON
8. STOCKTON-ON-TEES
9. MIDDLESBROUGH
10. REDCAR & CLEVELAND
11. CITY OF KINGSTON UPON HULL
12. CITY OF STOKE-ON-TRENT
13. CITY OF DERBY
14. CITY OF LEICESTER

311

1. CITY OF DUNDEE
2. CLACKMANNANSHIRE
3. CITY OF EDINBURGH
4. WEST DUNBARTONSHIRE
5. EAST DUNBARTONSHIRE
6. NORTH LANARKSHIRE
7. INVERCLYDE
8. RENFREWSHIRE
9. CITY OF GLASGOW
10. EAST RENFREWSHIRE
11. NORTH TYNESIDE
12. NEWCASTLE UPON TYNE
13. GATESHEAD
14. SOUTH TYNESIDE
15. SUNDERLAND
16. HARTLEPOOL

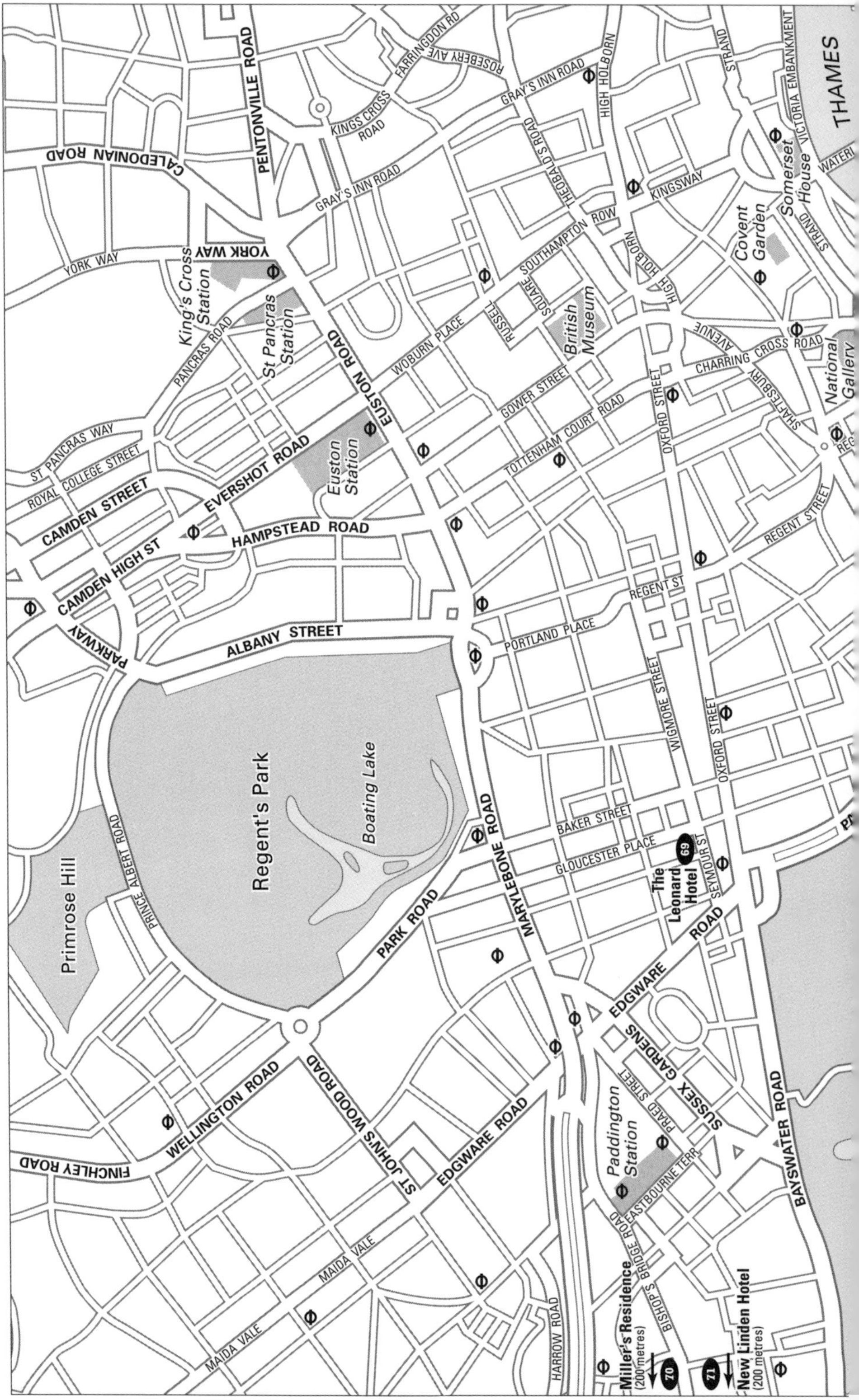

THAMES

STRAND

VICTORIA EMBANKMENT

WATERL

Somerset House

Covent Garden

National Gallery

REC

KINGSWAY

HIGH HOLBORN

SHAFTESBURY AVENUE

CHARING CROSS ROAD

REGENT STREET

OXFORD STREET

HIGH HOLBORN

GRAY'S INN ROAD

FARRINGDON RD

ROSEBERY AVE

PENTONVILLE ROAD

KINGS CROSS ROAD

GRAY'S INN ROAD

THEOBALD'S ROAD

SOUTHAMPTON ROW

RUSSELL SQUARE

British Museum

GOWER STREET

TOTTENHAM COURT ROAD

REGENT ST

PORTLAND PLACE

WIGMORE STREET

OXFORD STREET

BAKER STREET

GLOUCESTER PLACE

SEYMOUR ST

The Leonard Hotel 69

EDGWARE ROAD

CALEDONIAN ROAD

YORK WAY

YORK WAY

King's Cross Station

St Pancras Station

PANCRAS ROAD

EUSTON ROAD

EVERSHOT ROAD

WOBURN PLACE

Euston Station

HAMPSTEAD ROAD

ST PANCRAS WAY

ROYAL COLLEGE STREET

CAMDEN STREET

CAMDEN HIGH ST

PARKWAY

ALBANY STREET

PRINCE ALBERT ROAD

Regent's Park

Boating Lake

Primrose Hill

MARYLEBONE ROAD

PARK ROAD

FINCHLEY ROAD

WELLINGTON ROAD

ST JOHNS WOOD ROAD

EDGWARE ROAD

EDGWARE ROAD

SUSSEX GARDENS

PRAED STREET

Paddington Station

BISHOP'S BRIDGE ROAD

EASTBOURNE TERR.

BAYSWATER ROAD

HARROW ROAD

MAIDA VALE

MAIDA VALE

Miller's Residence (200 metres) 70

New Linden Hotel (200 metres) 71

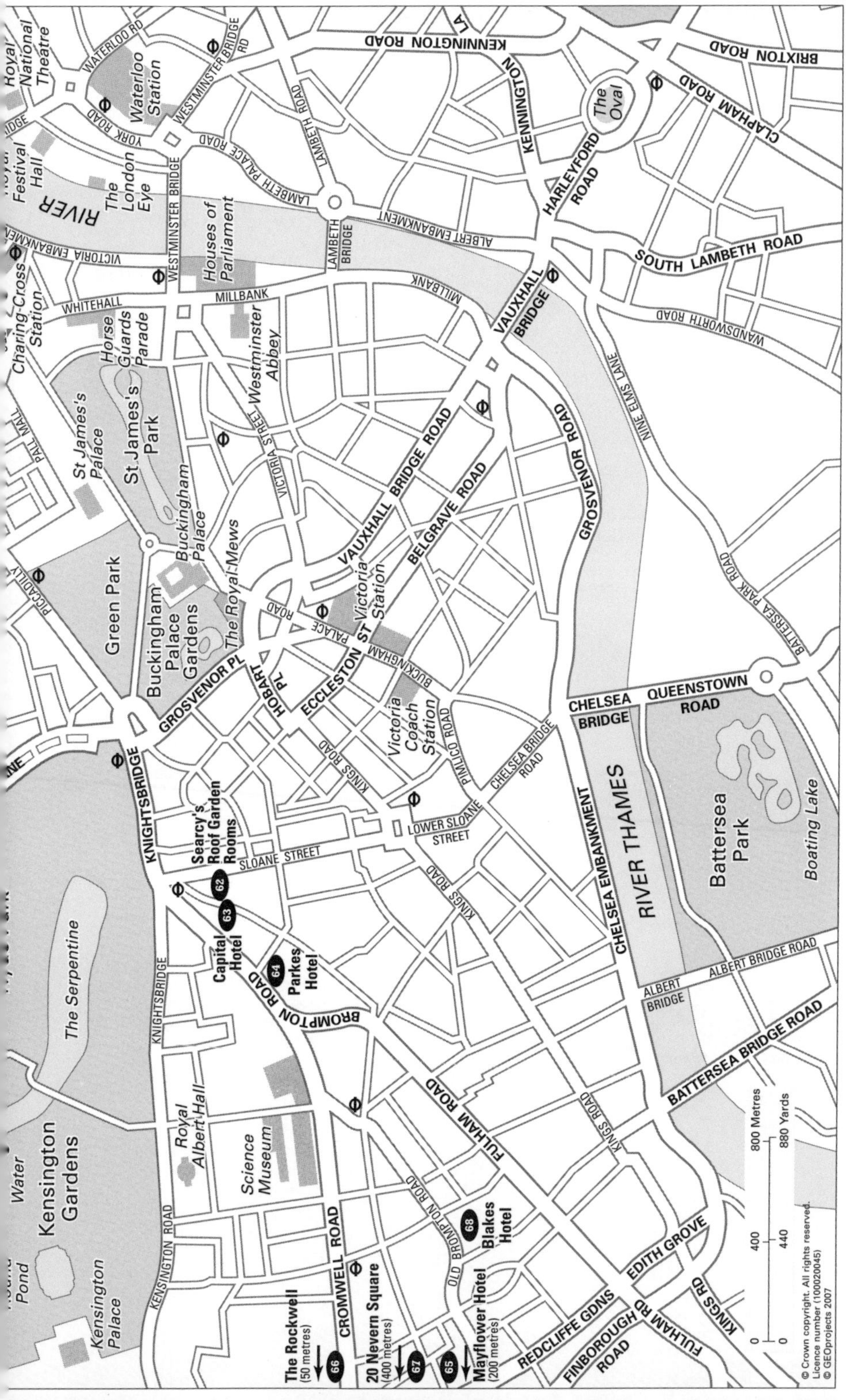

Royal National Theatre
Waterloo Station
WATERLOO RD
WESTMINSTER BRIDGE RD
KENNINGTON ROAD
KENNINGTON LA
BRIXTON ROAD
CLAPHAM ROAD
The Oval
KENNINGTON
HARLEYFORD ROAD
YORK ROAD
Royal Festival Hall
The London Eye
RIVER
WESTMINSTER BRIDGE
LAMBETH PALACE ROAD
LAMBETH ROAD
Houses of Parliament
LAMBETH BRIDGE
ALBERT EMBANKMENT
SOUTH LAMBETH ROAD
VICTORIA EMBANKMENT
Charing Cross Station
WHITEHALL
MILLBANK
Horse Guards Parade
Westminster Abbey
VAUXHALL BRIDGE
WANDSWORTH ROAD
NINE ELMS LANE
PALL MALL
St James's Palace
St James's Park
Buckingham Palace
The Royal Mews
VICTORIA STREET
VAUXHALL BRIDGE ROAD
BELGRAVE ROAD
GROSVENOR ROAD
PICCADILLY
Green Park
Buckingham Palace Gardens
Victoria Station
BUCKINGHAM PALACE ROAD
BATTERSEA PARK ROAD
GROSVENOR PL
HOBART PL
ECCLESTON ST
Victoria Coach Station
PIMLICO ROAD
CHELSEA BRIDGE
CHELSEA BRIDGE ROAD
QUEENSTOWN ROAD
KNIGHTSBRIDGE
Searcy's Roof Garden Rooms
KINGS ROAD
LOWER SLOANE STREET
SLOANE STREET
CHELSEA EMBANKMENT
RIVER THAMES
Battersea Park
Boating Lake
62
63
Capital Hotel
64
Parkes Hotel
BROMPTON ROAD
ALBERT BRIDGE
ALBERT BRIDGE ROAD
BATTERSEA BRIDGE ROAD
The Serpentine
Royal Albert Hall
Science Museum
FULHAM ROAD
Kensington Gardens
Round Pond
Kensington Palace
KENSINGTON ROAD
CROMWELL ROAD
OLD BROMPTON ROAD
68
Blakes Hotel
EDITH GROVE
The Rockwell (50 metres)
66
20 Nevern Square (400 metres)
67
Mayflower Hotel (200 metres)
65
REDCLIFFE GDNS
FINBOROUGH ROAD
FULHAM RD
KINGS RD
0 400 800 Metres
0 440 880 Yards
© Crown copyright. All rights reserved. Licence number (100020045)
© GEOprojects 2007

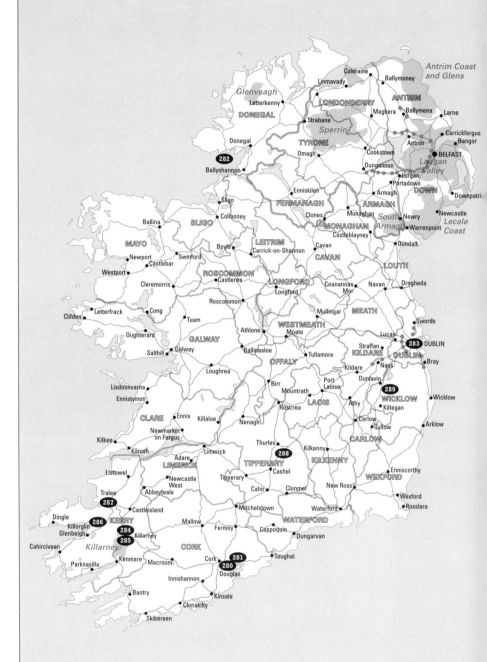

SEND FOR YOUR FREE BROCHURES

TO RECEIVE THE BROCHURE OF ANY HOTEL FEATURED IN THIS 68th
EDITION, SIMPLY PUT THE APPROPRIATE PAGE NUMBERS IN THE
BOXES BELOW AND RETURN THE CARD TO US.
ALTERNATIVELY E-MAIL US ON info@signpost.co.uk UP TO 9 PAGE
NUMBERS AND YOUR NAME AND ADDRESS.

PLEASE LIST IN PAGE ORDER

NAME (Mr/Mrs/Miss...(CAPITALS PLEASE)

ADDRESS...

....

....POSTCODE...

E-MAIL ADDRESS...

SIGNPOST
PRIORY PUBLICATIONS LTD
PO BOX 24
BRACKLEY
NORTHAMPTONSHIRE NN13 5BR

AFFIX
STAMP

SIGNPOST - COLOUR HOTEL GUIDE 2007
ORDER FORM

No. of copies	Price	Total
	£11.95	
For postage per copy to....		
UK and Europe, add £1.55		
Outside Europe Airmail, add £5		
Total (inc. carriage)		
Please include an Advantage Card		

TO SIGNPOST, PRIORY PUBLICATIONS LTD, SYRESHAM, BRACKLEY, NORTHANTS NN13 5HH (Fax: 01280 850576)

I enclose cheque in the sum of £_____
made payable to Priory Publications Ltd, or

I wish to pay by Visa/Master Card/Amex; please charge to my account. My card number is (13 or 16 digits):

Signature   Expiry date

/

Name (on card)

Address

Postcode

Please deliver to:

NAME...

ADDRESS..

....

....POSTAL CODE.......................

SIGNPOST - COLOUR HOTEL GUIDE 2007
ORDER FORM

No. of copies	Price	Total
	£11.95	
For postage per copy to....		
UK and Europe, add £1.55		
Outside Europe Airmail, add £4		
Total (inc. carriage)		
Please include an Advantage Card		

TO SIGNPOST, PRIORY PUBLICATIONS LTD, SYRESHAM, BRACKLEY, NORTHANTS NN13 5HH (Fax: 01280 850576)

I enclose cheque in the sum of £_____
made payable to Priory Publications Ltd, or

I wish to pay by Visa/Master Card/Amex; please charge to my account. My card number is (13 or 16 digits):

Signature   Expiry date

/

Name (on card)

Address

Postcode

Please deliver to:

NAME...

ADDRESS..

....

....POSTAL CODE.......................

CUT ALONG DOTTED LINE

AFFIX
STAMP

SIGNPOST
PRIORY PUBLICATIONS LTD
PO BOX 24
BRACKLEY
NORTHAMPTONSHIRE NN13 5HH

AFFIX
STAMP

SIGNPOST
PRIORY PUBLICATIONS LTD
PO BOX 24
BRACKLEY
NORTHAMPTONSHIRE NN13 5HH